Spatial autocorrelation

A.D.Cliff and J.K.Ord

Pion Limited, 207 Brondesbury Park, London NW2 5JN

Library edition ISBN 0 85086 036 9
Student edition ISBN 0 85086 037 7

Set on IBM 72 Composers by Pion Limited, London.
Printed in Great Britain by J.W.Arrowsmith Limited, Bristol.

Preface

The analysis of spatially located data is one of the basic concerns of the geographer and the ecologist, but it is also assuming increasing importance in many other disciplines, notably economics and geology. The central theme underlying this monograph is that the locations of the points or areas to which data refer can provide some information about the spatial pattern of variation in these data. That is, the data exhibit spatial autocorrelation. This monograph gives some statistical methods for analysing the spatial patterns inherent in geographically located data, and also tries to provide some insights into the underlying (stochastic) processes forming the patterns. Throughout the monograph, therefore, we take the locations of the observation units as given, and focus attention upon the spatial relationship between the variate values of these units. Hence the methods we discuss do not include the various nearest neighbour statistics which describe the spatial pattern formed by the locations of the units themselves relative to each other. Nor, for two reasons, do we consider spectral analysis. First, Rayner (1971), in the same series as this book, and Granger (1969) have reviewed in some detail the applicability of spectral methods to the analysis of spatial data. Second, the method of bivariate spectral analysis described by Rayner for the analysis of spatial data depends critically upon the assumption of stationarity. This is often difficult both to sustain and to interpret for the problems faced in human geography, although the approach has been more successful in oceanography, geology, and meteorology. A more suitable alternative approach is that of Granger, who has developed spectral methods to compare time series collected at different spatial locations. Bassett and Haggett (1971) illustrate some of Granger's ideas in their study of the spatial variation in some time series of levels of unemployment in southwest England.

The layout of the monograph is as follows. In chapter 1, a formal definition of spatial autocorrelation and some basic notation are introduced. Several measures of autocorrelation in the plane are discussed, and testing procedures using these measures are given. The theory underlying these testing procedures is discussed in chapter 2, and a series of geographical applications of the measures are described in chapters 3 and 4. In chapter 5, the theory required to test for autocorrelation in spatially located regression residuals is stated, and a series of examples, which illustrate the points made, are given in chapter 6. Chapter 7 is a discussion of the choice of an appropriate test statistic from the several dealt with in the monograph for analysing a given data set. In chapter 8, the theory of partial correlation in the plane is discussed and illustrated. Finally, in appendix 1, different models for spatial autocorrelation in stochastic processes are considered. Appendix 2 comprises data, while appendix 3 discusses maximum likelihood estimation in autoregressive models.

Since research workers in many disciplines are interested in the theory and practice of spatial analysis, we hope the monograph will find readers in fields as varied as econometrics, ecology, geography, geology, planning, statistics, and regional science. In organising the material covered in the book, we have tried to take into account the great variety in the level of mathematical training of this potential audience. Chapters 2, 5 (except sections 1 and 2), and 7 could be omitted at a first reading by those concerned chiefly with understanding tests for spatial autocorrelation and how to use them, rather than the theoretical bases of the tests. Readers who have had an introductory course in statistical theory should be able to follow all except the named chapters. The named chapters employ more advanced statistical ideas and assume a more rigorous training in statistics. By organising the material in this way, we hope that the monograph will be useful both to research workers and to practitioners. To help the reader, a glossary of notation used in the test appears on p.170 ff. In addition, throughout the book we have used the convention that tables, figures, and equations are numbered consecutively within each chapter, so that 1.2 means chapter one, item two. Sections and subsections have been used, so that 2.3.1 indicates chapter 2, section 3, subsection 1.

Finally, we would add, despite the fact that spatially located data forms the basic material of many disciplines, there is still only a relatively small literature which considers methods of analyzing such data. We hope that this book will help to fill this gap.

A. D. Cliff
J. K. Ord
Bristol, January, 1973

Acknowledgements

The applications given in the monograph use data from several sources. The authors wish to thank the following organisations and journal editors for permission to reproduce material: Economic Geography, Charles Griffin and Company Ltd., Institute of Statisticians, Japanese Journal of Geology and Geography, Regional Studies, Royal Statistical Society, and Weidenfeld and Nicolson. Thanks are also extended to the various authors for their permission to use this material.

Our gratitude is due to several people who have aided in the preparation of the monograph. First, to Professor Clive Granger, University of Nottingham, who has afforded much valuable criticism on a number of occasions. In particular he suggested the addition of the material in appendix 1 and the glossary of notation. Second, to several colleagues at Bristol who have made many constructive comments. Third, to Simon Godden, the cartographer in the Geography Department at Bristol, who drew the diagrams, and fourth, to Mrs. Anne Kempson in the Economics Department at Bristol, who produced a first class typescript from a difficult manuscript. Finally, we record that the findings described in this monograph form part of a four year programme of work entitled 'Contiguity Constraints in Region Building Programs', ongoing in the Department of Geography at Bristol. This work is financed in part by the Social Science Research Council, and our thanks are due to them for their support.

To Margaret (A. D. C.) and Rosemary (J. K. O.)

Contents

List of Figures

List of Tables

Appendix Tables

1

Some measures of autocorrelation in the plane

1.1 Introduction

It is often necessary to consider the geographical distribution of some quality or phenomenon in the counties or states of a country, and one of the questions we may ask is whether the presence of some quality in a county makes its presence in neighbouring counties more or less likely. For example, Cruickshank (1940, 1947) has considered this kind of problem when examining regional variations in England and Wales in the incidence of human cancer of specific organs, such as the liver and lung. Cruickshank computed the relative mortality rate for various cancers in each of the 62 counties of England and Wales. For each cancer, he then divided the range for the mortality rate into seven equal parts, and colour coded each county according to the mortality rate class it occupied. So, for example, all counties with a relative mortality rate from liver cancer of 0–4% might be coded white, those with 5–8% black, and so on. Cruickshank then investigated whether the white, black, etc., counties were grouped together in any particular parts of the country in an attempt to isolate local environmental factors which might increase the incidence of that kind of tumour. As another example, Cox (1969) was interested in whether the percentage Democrat vote by state in various US Presidential elections displayed a high degree of areal contiguity: that is, if one state voted Democrat, did this increase the probability that neighbouring states would also vote Democrat? Cox also wished to determine whether the tendency of the Democrat vote to cluster in certain groups of states at the beginning of the twentieth century had become less pronounced at the present time. For example, the states of the Deep South traditionally voted Democrat up to 1964, but did not group so clearly in 1968.

If the presence of some quality in a county of a country makes its presence in neighbouring counties more or less likely, we say that the phenomenon exhibits *spatial autocorrelation.* While the examples we have given are for area-based data, rather than point-like objects such as plants in a field or meteorological stations, it is also possible to test for spatial autocorrelation among variate values collected at points. Thus we might wish to test for spatial autocorrelation in rainfall values at various meteorological stations in the UK.

It is the purpose of this monograph to define various measures of spatial autocorrelation in areal and point pattern data, and to examine, with applications, the properties of these measures. For simplicity of discussion we shall consider principally the formulation of 'counties' within a 'country' in the monograph, but as noted above, it is important to remember that any lattice of regions or set of points, at which the value of a variate has been obtained, could be considered using the methods to be discussed.

In this chapter the spatial autocorrelation problem is defined formally in section 2, and the various measures of areal association which have been proposed in the literature are reviewed in sections 3 and 4. Use of these measures is illustrated in section 5 by testing for spatial autocorrelation among cell values in a 4 x 4 regular lattice; this work is intended to show how to solve and interpret the equations presented. Use of the measures in the examination of some problems of current geographical interest is discussed in chapters 3 and 4.

1.2 The spatial autocorrelation problem

Consider a study area which is exhaustively partitioned into n nonoverlapping counties. Let the observed value of a variate X, in the typical county i, be x_i. X can describe either (1) a single population from which repeated drawings are made to give the $\{x_i\}$; or (2) a separate population for each county, in which case the populations will usually be assumed to be identically distributed, and the value of X in county i is obtained by sampling from the population for county i. In either case, (1) or (2), the population(s) may be either finite or infinite. If finite, they may be either partially or exhaustively sampled. The choice between population models (1) and (2) for generating the sample county values depends upon the problem in hand. For example, if the researcher is testing for spatial autocorrelation in, say, the size of dairy herds in the English and Welsh counties, it is probably easier to conceptualise the county values as being generated by partitioning up a single finite population of milch cows into the 62 county herds [population model (1)], rather than being generated by model (2). Conversely, if the researcher is testing for spatial autocorrelation in the *per caput* average annual income of the countries of Western Europe, it is probably more reasonable to view the sample country values as being generated by population model (2) rather than by model (1). It is important to note, however, that the choice of population model does not affect the derivation of the measures of spatial autocorrelation, nor the method of analysis.

Having decided upon the appropriate population model, we make the following definition. If for every pair of counties i and j in the study area the drawings which yield x_i and x_j are uncorrelated, then we say that there is no spatial autocorrelation in the county system on X. Conversely, spatial autocorrelation is said to exist if the drawings are not all pairwise uncorrelated. A detailed consideration of various models for spatial autocorrelation in stochastic processes is undertaken in appendix 1.

The problem of determining whether geographical data are spatially autocorrelated is fundamentally different from measuring autocorrelation in stationary time series. This is because the variate in a time series is influenced only by past values, while for a spatial process dependence extends in all directions. Thus Whittle (1954, page 434) has noted

"At any instant in a time series, we have the natural distinction of past and future, and the value of the observation at that instant depends only upon past values. That is, the dependence extends only in one direction: backwards ... (In) the more general two dimensional case of (say) a field, a dab of fertilizer applied at any point in the field will ultimately affect soil fertility in *all* directions".

Stated more formally, a first order autoregressive model for a time series would be

$$x_t = \rho x_{t-1} + \epsilon_t, \qquad t = 1, 2, \ldots, n, \tag{1.1}$$

where x_t is the value of X at time t, ρ is a parameter, and the ϵ_t are random disturbances. In the spatial situation the first order autoregressive model for a regular lattice with R rows and S columns, considering only interactions between cells with a common edge, would be,

$$x_{r,s} = ax_{r-1,s} + bx_{r+1,s} + cx_{r,s-1} + dx_{r,s+1} + \epsilon_{r,s}, \tag{1.2}$$

where $RS = n$, and a, b, c, and d are parameters. Note that model (1.2) holds only for interior cells of the lattice, and a slightly modified form is required when $x_{r,s}$ is one of the border cells of the lattice. See figure 1.1.

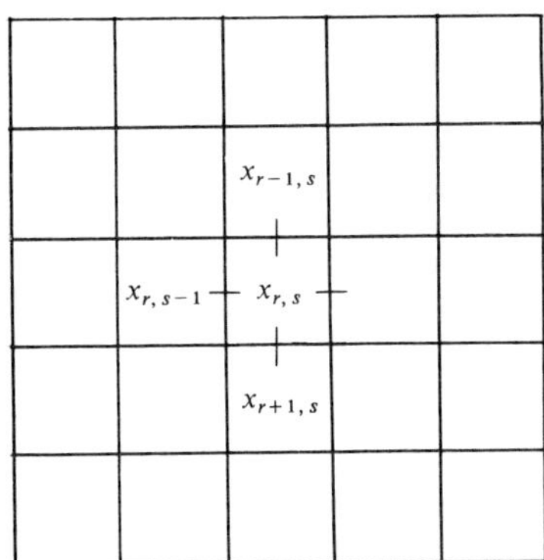

— Represents a join

Figure 1.1. First order autoregressive model for a regular lattice.

1.3 Basic measures of spatial autocorrelation

In the remainder of this chapter we assume that the $\{x_i\}$ are raw data rather than residuals from a calculated regression or trend surface. Testing for spatial autocorrelation among such residuals presents special problems and these are discussed in chapter 5. The tests for spatial autocorrelation which have been proposed in the literature are discussed conveniently according to the kind of data (nominal, ordinal, or interval scaled) to which they may be applied. Fortunately this also coincides with the historical order of development of the tests.

1.3.1 Tests for nominal data

The simplest nominal scale is a binary classification. In each of the n counties we note whether a given event has or has not occurred. If it has, the county is colour coded black B, and if it has not, the county is colour coded white W. If two counties have a boundary of positive nonzero length in common, they are said to be linked by a *join*. A join may link two B counties, two W counties, or a B and a W county. These joins are called BB, WW, and BW joins respectively. To determine whether events in neighbouring counties are spatially autocorrelated or not, we count the numbers of BB, BW, and WW joins which occur in the county system, and compare these numbers with the expected numbers of BB, BW, and WW joins under the null hypothesis, H_0, of no spatial autocorrelation among the counties. Intuitively it can be appreciated that a 'lot' of BB joins, compared with the expected number under H_0, implies clustering of the B counties in the plane, while a 'lot' of BW joins implies some sort of alternating pattern of B and W counties as, for example, along the rows and columns of a chessboard.

Put formally, the method of analysis is as follows (Moran, 1948). Let $\{\delta_{ij}\}$ be a connection matrix in which $\delta_{ij} = 1$ if the ith and jth counties are joined, and $\delta_{ij} = 0$ otherwise. Let $x_i = 1$ if the ith county is B, and $x_i = 0$ if the ith county is W. The observed number of BB joins in the county system is then given by

$$BB = \tfrac{1}{2}\textstyle\sum_{(2)} \delta_{ij}x_i x_j, \tag{1.3}$$

and the observed number of BW joins is given by

$$BW = \tfrac{1}{2}\textstyle\sum_{(2)} \delta_{ij}(x_i - x_j)^2, \tag{1.4}$$

where

$$\textstyle\sum_{(2)} = \sum\limits_{\substack{i=1 \\ i \neq j}}^{n} \sum\limits_{j=1}^{n} .$$

The observed number of WW joins is given by

$$WW = A - (BB + BW), \tag{1.5}$$

where A is the total number of joins in the county system. Denote the number of counties joined to the ith county by L_i. A is then defined as

$$A = \tfrac{1}{2}\sum_{i=1}^{n} L_i . \tag{1.6}$$

The definition of a join given at the beginning of this section implies that $\delta_{ij} = \delta_{ji}$ for all i and j; that is $\{\delta_{ij}\}$ is symmetric. The factor of $\frac{1}{2}$ in equations (1.3), (1.4), and (1.6) eliminates the duplication of information which arises by counting both ij and ji joins when they carry the same information because of the symmetry property.

The usual method employed to determine whether BB, BW, and WW depart significantly from random expectation is to use the fact that these join count statistics are asymptotically normally distributed (see chapter 2), and to assume that these results hold approximately for moderate sized lattices. The first two moments of the coefficients are then used to specify the location (μ_1') and scale (μ_2) parameters of the normal distribution. Using this approach, we note that the moments of the coefficients may be evaluated under either of two assumptions:

(1) free sampling (or sampling with replacement), where we suppose that the individual counties are independently coded B or W with probabilities p and $q = 1-p$ respectively;

(2) nonfree sampling (or sampling without replacement), where we assume that each county has the same probability, *a priori*, of being B or W, but coding is subject to the overall constraint that there are n_1 counties coloured B and n_2 coloured W, and $n_1+n_2 = n$.

The first two moments of the join counts are given by Moran (1948) as follows.

Free sampling

$$\mu_1'(BB) = Ap^2, \tag{1.7}$$

$$\mu_1'(BW) = 2Apq, \tag{1.8}$$

$$\mu_1'(WW) = Aq^2, \tag{1.9}$$

$$\mu_2(BB) = Ap^2+2Dp^3-(A+2D)p^4, \tag{1.10}$$

$$\mu_2(BW) = 2(A+D)pq-4(A+2D)p^2q^2, \tag{1.11}$$

$$\mu_2(WW) = Aq^2+2Dq^3-(A+2D)q^4. \tag{1.12}$$

Nonfree sampling

$$\mu_1'(BB) = \frac{An_1^{(2)}}{n^{(2)}}, \tag{1.13}$$

$$\mu_1'(BW) = \frac{2An_1n_2}{n^{(2)}}, \tag{1.14}$$

$$\mu_1'(WW) = \frac{An_2^{(2)}}{n^{(2)}}, \tag{1.15}$$

$$\mu_2(BB) = \frac{An_1^{(2)}}{n^{(2)}}+\frac{2Dn_1^{(3)}}{n^{(3)}}+\frac{[A(A-1)-2D]n_1^{(4)}}{n^{(4)}}-\left[\frac{An_1^{(2)}}{n^{(2)}}\right]^2, \tag{1.16}$$

$$\mu_2(BW) = \frac{2An_1n_2}{n^{(2)}}+\frac{4[A(A-1)-2D]n_1^{(2)}n_2^{(2)}}{n^{(4)}}+\frac{2Dn_1n_2(n_1+n_2-2)}{n^{(3)}} -4\left[\frac{An_1n_2}{n^{(2)}}\right]^2, \tag{1.17}$$

$$\mu_2(WW) = \frac{An_2^{(2)}}{n^{(2)}} + \frac{2Dn_2^{(3)}}{n^{(3)}} + \frac{[A(A-1)-2D]n_2^{(4)}}{n^{(4)}} - \left[\frac{An_2^{(2)}}{n^{(2)}}\right]^2. \quad (1.18)$$

In these equations,

$$D = \tfrac{1}{2}\sum_{i=1}^{n} L_i(L_i - 1),$$

and $n^{(b)} = n(n-1)\ ...\ (n-b+1)$.

Quite commonly the nominal scale will have classes ($k > 2$) rather than the simple binary classification discussed above. Each class may then be assigned one of k distinct colours, and each county is called after the colour of the class into which it falls. Conventionally, the analysis then proceeds by counting the number of joins between counties of (1) the same colour, (2) two different colours, and (3) all counties of different colours. Each of these distributions is tested for significant departure from randomness in the same way as for $k = 2$. The first two moments of the distributions (1)–(3) under free and nonfree sampling are given by the following expressions.

Free sampling

Definition p_α ($\alpha = r, s, t, u, ...$) is the probability that a county is colour α.

Joins between counties of the same colour

$$\mu_1' = Ap_r^2, \quad (1.19)$$

$$\mu_2 = Ap_r^2 + 2Dp_r^3 - (A + 2D)p_r^4. \quad (1.20)$$

Joins between counties of two different colours

$$\mu_1' = 2Ap_rp_s, \quad (1.21)$$

$$\mu_2 = 2Ap_rp_s + 2Dp_rp_s(p_r + p_s) - 4(A + 2D)p_r^2p_s^2. \quad (1.22)$$

Total number of joins between counties of different colours

$$\mu_1' = 2A\sum_{r=1}^{k-1}\sum_{s=r+1}^{k} p_rp_s, \quad (1.23)$$

$$\mu_2 = 2(A+D)\sum_{r=1}^{k-1}\sum_{s=r+1}^{k} p_rp_s - 2(4A+5D)\sum_{r=1}^{k-2}\sum_{s=r+1}^{k-1}\sum_{t=s+1}^{k} p_rp_sp_t - 4(A+2D)\left(\sum_{r=1}^{k-1}\sum_{s=r+1}^{k} p_r^2p_s^2 - 2\sum_{r=1}^{k-3}\sum_{s=r+1}^{k-2}\sum_{t=s+1}^{k-1}\sum_{u=t+1}^{k} p_rp_sp_tp_u\right). \quad (1.24)$$

Nonfree sampling

Definition n_α($\alpha = r, s, t, u, ...$) is the number of counties of colour α.

Joins between counties of the same colour

$$\mu_1' = \frac{An_r^{(2)}}{n^{(2)}}, \tag{1.25}$$

$$\mu_2 = \frac{An_r^{(2)}}{n^{(2)}} + \frac{2Dn_r^{(3)}}{n^{(3)}} + \frac{[A(A-1)-2D]n_r^{(4)}}{n^{(4)}} - \left[\frac{An_r^{(2)}}{n^{(2)}}\right]^2. \tag{1.26}$$

Joins between counties of two different colours

$$\mu_1' = \frac{2An_rn_s}{n^{(2)}}, \tag{1.27}$$

$$\mu_2 = \frac{2An_rn_s}{n^{(2)}} + \frac{2Dn_rn_s(n_r+n_s-2)}{n^{(3)}} + \frac{4[A(A-1)-2D]n_r^{(2)}n_s^{(2)}}{n^{(4)}} - 4\left[\frac{An_rn_s}{n^{(2)}}\right]^2. \tag{1.28}$$

Total number of joins between counties of different colours

$$\mu_1' = \frac{2A\sum_{r=1}^{k-1}\sum_{s=r+1}^{k} n_rn_s}{n^{(2)}}, \tag{1.29}$$

$$\begin{aligned}\mu_2 = {} & \left\{\frac{2(A+D)}{n^{(2)}} - \frac{4[A(A-1)-2D](n-1)}{n^{(4)}}\right\}\sum_{r=1}^{k-1}\sum_{s=r+1}^{k} n_rn_s - \left\{\frac{2(4A+5D)}{n^{(3)}}\right. \\ & \left. - \frac{12[A(A-1)-2D]}{n^{(4)}} - \frac{8A^2}{n^{(3)}(n-1)}\right\}\sum_{r=1}^{k-2}\sum_{s=r+1}^{k-1}\sum_{t=s+1}^{k} n_rn_sn_t \\ & -4\left[\frac{A+2D}{n^{(4)}} - \frac{2A^2(2n-3)}{n^{(2)}n^{(4)}}\right]\sum_{r=1}^{k-1}\sum_{s=r+1}^{k} n_r^2n_s^2 \\ & -8\left[\frac{2A^2(2n-3)}{n^{(2)}n^{(4)}} - \frac{A+2D}{n^{(4)}}\right]\sum_{r=1}^{k-3}\sum_{s=r+1}^{k-2}\sum_{t=s+1}^{k-1}\sum_{u=t+1}^{k} n_rn_sn_tn_u.\end{aligned} \tag{1.30}$$

If $k = 2$, we obtain, as we should, equations (1.7)–(1.18) as special cases of equations (1.19)–(1.30). In equations (1.19)–(1.30) put $p_r = p$, $p_s = q$, $n_r = n_1$, and $n_s = n_2$. When $k = 2$, $p_r + p_s = 1$, and $n_r + n_s = n$. Then the moments for the distribution of joins between counties of the same colour reduce to those for *BB* joins; while the moments for the distribution of joins between counties of two different colours and for the distribution of the total number of joins between counties of different colours are identical, and reduce to those for *BW* joins.

1.3.2 Tests for ordinal and interval data

If X is ordinal scaled (ranked) or interval scaled, we could group the range of X into k classes, such as quartiles or deciles, and use the colour lattice tests described above; in this case, a loss of information occurs. We now define two further coefficients which assess the degree of spatial autocorrelation between the $\{x_i\}$ in joined counties, where x_i is either the rank of the ith county (ordinal data) or the value of X in the ith county (interval data). Individual county values are therefore retained, and the loss of information which occurs if the join count statistics are employed is avoided.

The first coefficient is due to Moran (1950a) and is given by

$$I = \frac{n}{2A} \frac{\sum_{(2)} \delta_{ij} z_i z_j}{\sum_{i=1}^{n} z_i^2}, \tag{1.31}$$

where $z_i = x_i - \bar{x}$ in addition to previously used notation. The second coefficient has been suggested by Geary (1954). Geary's statistic c is defined as

$$c = \frac{(n-1)\sum_{(2)} \delta_{ij}(x_i - x_j)^2}{4A \sum_{i=1}^{n} z_i^2}. \tag{1.32}$$

Note that both I and c take on the classic form of any autocorrelation coefficient: the numerator term in each is a measure of covariance among the $\{x_i\}$ and the denominator term is a measure of variance. It is also evident that I is based upon the cross-products of the deviations of the x_i from $\bar{x}$ [analogous to the BB join count statistic of equation (1.3)], as opposed to the squared differences between the x_i in Geary's coefficient [analogous to the BW join count statistic of equation (1.4)].

It is shown in the next chapter that both I and c are asymptotically normally distributed as n increases. As with the join count statistics, this result is assumed to hold approximately for small lattices, and I and c are tested for significance as standard normal deviates. The moments of I and c may be evaluated under either of two assumptions:
(1) assumption N, normality. Here we assume that the $\{x_i\}$ are the results of n independent drawings from a normal population (or populations);
(2) assumption R, randomisation. Whatever the underlying distribution of the population(s), we consider the observed value of I or c relative to the set of all possible values which I or c could take on if the $\{x_i\}$ were repeatedly randomly permuted around the county system. There are $n!$ such values.

Using the subscripts N and R to denote the assumptions of normality and randomisation respectively, it can be shown that

$$\mathrm{E_N}(I) = \mathrm{E_R}(I) = -(n-1)^{-1}, \tag{1.33}$$

$$\mathrm{E_N}(I^2) = \frac{4An^2 - 8(A+D)n + 12A^2}{4A^2(n^2-1)}, \tag{1.34}$$

$$\mathrm{E_R}(I^2) = \Big\{n[4A(n^2-3n+3)-8(A+D)n+12A^2] \\ -b_2[4A(n^2-n)-16(A+D)n+24A^2]\Big\}\Big/4A^2(n-1)^{(3)}, \quad (1.35)$$

$$\mathrm{E_N}(c) = \mathrm{E_R}(c) = 1, \quad (1.36)$$

$$\mathrm{var_N}(c) = \frac{(2A+D)(n-1)-2A^2}{(n+1)A^2}, \quad (1.37)$$

$$\mathrm{var_R}(c) = \frac{1}{n(n-2)(n-3)2A^2}\Big\{2A^2[-(n-1)^2b_2+(n^2-3)] \\ +2A(n-1)[-(n-1)b_2+n^2-3n+3] \\ +(D+A)(n-1)[(n^2-n+2)b_2-(n^2+3n-6)]\Big\}, \quad (1.38)$$

where b_2 is the sample kurtosis coefficient m_4/m_2^2, m_j being the jth sample moment of the $\{x_i\}$ about the sample mean.

1.3.3 Choice of test statistic[(1)]

When the researcher wishes to test a real world data set for spatial autocorrelation, he will have to decide which of the coefficients defined in sections 1.3.1 and 1.3.2 to use as his test statistic. The following guidelines are intended to help him make that choice.

(1) With binary (0, 1) data, the join count statistics may be used. Alternatively, I or c could be employed by putting, say, $x_i = 1$ if an event has occurred in the ith county and $x_i = 0$ otherwise. However, with binary data, I and c reduce, apart from constants, almost exactly to the BB and BW statistics respectively. For example, from equations (1.3) and (1.31), it follows that

$$I = \frac{n^2}{An_1(n-n_1)}\left(BB - \frac{n_1}{n}\sum_{i=1}^{n} L_i x_i + \frac{An_1^2}{n}\right) \quad (1.39)$$

when $\delta_{ij} = \delta_{ji}$. Since the join count statistics can be evaluated much more rapidly than I or c (often by hand as opposed to using a computer for I and c), and given the similar results BB and I, and BW and c, yield, there seems little point with binary data in evaluating I or c rather than the join count statistics. Similar arguments cause us to prefer the k colour join counts to I and c when the nominal scale comprises k rather than two classes. If the join counts are used, the researcher has the choice between the free and nonfree sampling models. Free sampling may only be used if the p_α ($\alpha = r, s, t, u, ...$) are known *a priori* (exogenously). If these quantities are estimated from the data by n_α/n ($\alpha = r, s, t, u, ...$) then nonfree sampling must be used.

(1) A full discussion of this topic is deferred until chapter 7.

(2) With ranked or interval scaled data, I and c are preferred to the colour lattice approach. Recall that in order to use the colour lattice approach with these data, the $\{x_i\}$ must be grouped into classes, which results in loss of information. I and c preserve the individual x values, and so avoid this problem. There is little to choose between I and c. However, results given in Cliff and Ord (1969, page 45) suggest that the variance of I is less affected by the distribution of the sample data than is the differences squared form used in Geary's c. This is because the coefficient of the b_2 term in the variance of the Geary statistic is $O(n^{-1})$, whereas for the Moran statistic, the coefficient of the b_2 term is $O(n^{-2})$.

1.3.4 Limitations of measures

The join count statistics, I and c have two important limitations. First, they suffer from what Dacey (1965, page 28) has called the problem of topological invariance. That is, once the connection matrix $\{\delta_{ij}\}$ has been specified, the size and shape of counties in the system, and the relative strength of links between counties (road and rail links, for example) are completely ignored. The measures are, therefore, invariant under certain topological transformations of the underlying county structure. Dacey illustrates this point as follows: Consider a county map P_0, with a connection matrix $\{\delta_{ij}\}$, an assigned set of values $\{x_0\}$, and an index value V_0 (any one of the join count statistics, I or c). Without changing $\{\delta_{ij}\}$ or $\{x_0\}$, it is possible to transform P_0 topologically and to produce a new county map P_1, with $V_1 = V_0$, and for which the measures of spatial autocorrelation are unchanged. For example, P_1 may be constructed from P_0 by the rule that county boundaries are shortened if the counties separated by the boundary have values of opposite sign, and are increased in length if the counties have values of the same sign. Alternatively, the area of counties may be changed so that the area of, say, counties with positive values is increased, and the area of counties with negative values is decreased. All the coefficients described are invariant over such topological transformations because the only element of the underlying county structure which they incorporate is the connection matrix. To reinforce this point, figure 1.2 illustrates three different county systems with the same join structure.

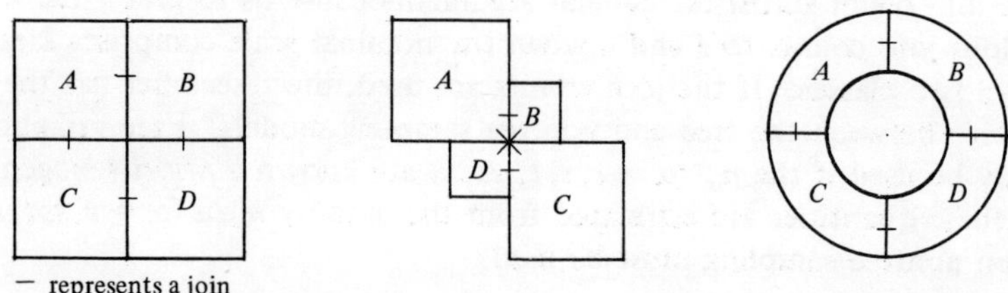

Figure 1.2. Three county systems with the same join structure.

To overcome this difficulty, Dacey (1965) suggested a measure of spatial autocorrelation I', where

$$I' = \frac{n}{2A} \frac{\sum_{(2)} \delta_{ij}\alpha_i\beta_{i(j)}z_iz_j}{\sum_{i=1}^{n} \alpha_i z_i^2}, \tag{1.40}$$

and in which

$$\alpha_i = \frac{a_i}{\sum_{i=1}^{n} a_i}, \qquad \beta_{i(j)} = \frac{b_{ij}}{\sum_{j \in J} b_{ij}}.$$

Here, a_i equals the area of the ith county, b_{ij} denotes the length of the common boundary between the ith and jth counties, and $j \in J$ directs the summation over all j counties joined to i. Unfortunately, as is discussed in chapter 2, it is not possible to express the moments of I' in a usable form, and so no test of significance based on I' is proposed.

The second limitation is one of usage. As defined, joins exist only between physically contiguous counties. With $\{\delta_{ij}\}$ thus specified, the measures search for spatial autocorrelation only between counties which are first nearest neighbours. Thus correlogram analysis, to determine how the autocorrelation function decays over space, has not been attempted with these measures. There is nothing in the structure of the tests which prevents this kind of analysis. For example, we could define 'joins' to exist between counties which are second, rather than first, nearest neighbours. Two counties, i and k, might be called second nearest neighbours if they have no common boundary of positive nonzero length, but there exists a county j such that i and j are contiguous, and j and k are contiguous. Then $\delta_{ik} = 1$ for such pairs of counties, and $\delta_{ij} = 0$ otherwise. Generalisation of the concept of a join to second and higher order neighbours in this fashion has not been attempted in the literature. Even if this were done, however, all joins would still be given equal weight; and in some studies we might wish to give strong links between counties which are not contiguous, and weak links between contiguous counties. Similarly an individual's perception of geographical space is discontinuous (Downs, 1970) and, in perception studies, the researcher might wish to take this into account when defining a connection matrix.

We now give versions of the join count, I, and c statistics which employ general weights to overcome the two limitations discussed above.

1.4 The weighted coefficients

1.4.1 The form of the coefficients

Instead of using binary weights δ_{ij} to operationalise the concept of a join, we now define a generalised weighting matrix, $\boldsymbol{W} \equiv \{w_{ij}\}$, where we denote the effect of county i on county j by the weight w_{ij}. The weighted join count statistics are given by

$$BB = \tfrac{1}{2}\sum_{(2)} w_{ij}x_i x_j, \tag{1.41}$$

$$BW = \tfrac{1}{2}\sum_{(2)} w_{ij}(x_i - x_j)^2, \tag{1.42}$$

and

$$WW = W - (BB + BW), \tag{1.43}$$

where $W = \sum_{(2)} w_{ij}$. The generalisation of Moran's statistic is

$$I = \frac{n \sum_{(2)} w_{ij} z_i z_j}{W \sum\limits_{i=1}^{n} z_i^2}, \tag{1.44}$$

while the generalised Geary coefficient is defined as

$$c = \left(\frac{n-1}{2W}\right) \frac{\sum_{(2)} w_{ij}(x_i - x_j)^2}{\sum z_i^2}. \tag{1.45}$$

1.4.2 Structure of the weights

The use of a generalised weighting matrix $\boldsymbol{W}$, as opposed to a binary connection matrix, allows the investigator to choose a set of weights which he deems appropriate from *prior* considerations. This allows great flexibility in defining the structure of the county system, and permits items such as natural barriers and county size to be taken into account. Further, if different hypotheses are proposed about the degree of contact between neighbouring areas, alternative sets of weights might be used to investigate these hypotheses. It is important to stress that care must be used in the choice of weights if spurious correlations are to be avoided. The factors which are most important will depend upon the study in hand. For example, the amount of interaction between any two counties may depend upon the distance between their geographical or demographic centres, the length of common boundary between the counties, and so on. In urban areas the contact between two zones may depend on the frequency of public transport services.

As a particular example, suppose that it is decided that the relevant variables, which measure the amount of interaction between any pair of counties, are distance between county centres and length of common boundary between counties. Let the distance between the centres of counties i and j be d_{ij}, where distance may be defined by the Euclidean or other appropriate metric [for example, the 'city block' metric in perception studies (Downs, 1970)]. Further, suppose that the proportion of the perimeter of county i which is in contact with j is $\beta_{i(j)}$. We exclude from the perimeter of i those parts which coincide with the boundary of the study area, and note that

$$\sum_{j \in J} \beta_{i(j)} = 1, \tag{1.46}$$

where J is the set of counties contiguous to county i. The weighting system is then defined as some function g of d_{ij} and $\beta_{i(j)}$, that is,

$$w_{ij} = g[d_{ij}, \beta_{i(j)}]. \tag{1.47}$$

Thus we might put

$$w_{ij} = d_{ij}^{-a}[\beta_{i(j)}]^b, \tag{1.48}$$

where a and b are parameters. Positive values of a and b give greater weights to pairs of counties which have shorter distances between their centres, and which have long common boundaries. It should be noted that equation (1.48) gives positive weights only to counties which are contiguous.

Other forms could be used for equation (1.47). For example, an exponential function might replace the Pareto form used for distance in that equation. The choice of functional form for the w_{ij} must lie with the investigator.

It will often happen that $w_{ij} \neq w_{ji}$. The obvious exception to this may occur when the study area is split into regular units such as squares or hexagons. Finally, we observe that there may be some value in first standardising the w_{ij}. For example, they could be scaled so that

$$\sum_{j \in J} w_{ij} = w_{i.} = 1, \qquad i = 1, 2, \ldots, n, \tag{1.49}$$

implying that $W = n$. Under this standardisation the quantity

$$\sum_{j \in J} w_{ij} z_j \tag{1.50}$$

represents a value for z_i 'suggested' by the counties contiguous to i.

Although the example we have given assigns positive weights only to contiguous counties, we could have defined the link between *any* two counties i and k as, say,

$$w_{ik} = d_{ik}^{-a}.$$

This makes clear that we do not restrict the $\{w_{ij}\}$ to defining relationships between contiguous counties as has happened with $\{\delta_{ij}\}$.

1.4.3 Tests of significance

It will be shown in chapter 2 that, when generalised weights are employed, the join count, I, and c statistics are still asymptotically normally distributed as n increases. An approximate test of significance is therefore provided, as with binary weights, by evaluating the coefficients as standard normal deviates. The first two moments of the coefficients are required to carry out this test, and the equations are as follows:

New definitions

$$S_1 = \tfrac{1}{2}\sum_{(2)}(w_{ij}+w_{ji})^2, \tag{1.51}$$

$$S_2 = \sum_{i=1}^{n}(w_{i.}+w_{.i})^2, \tag{1.52}$$

$$w_{i.} = \sum_{j=1}^{n} w_{ij}, \qquad w_{.j} = \sum_{i=1}^{n} w_{ij}. \tag{1.53}$$

Join counts, $k \geqslant 2$

Free sampling

Joins between counties of the same colour (equivalent to BB joins for $k = 2$)

$$\mu_1' = \tfrac{1}{2}Wp_r^2, \tag{1.54}$$

$$\mu_2 = \tfrac{1}{4}[S_1p_r^2 + (S_2-2S_1)p_r^3 + (S_1-S_2)p_r^4]. \tag{1.55}$$

Joins between counties of two different colours (equivalent to BW joins for $k = 2$)

$$\mu_1' = Wp_rp_s, \tag{1.56}$$

$$\mu_2 = \tfrac{1}{4}[2S_1p_rp_s + (S_2-2S_1)p_rp_s(p_r+p_s) + 4(S_1-S_2)p_r^2p_s^2]. \tag{1.57}$$

Total number of joins between counties of different colours ($k \geqslant 3$; when $k = 2$, this case is equivalent to BW joins)

$$\mu_1' = W\sum_{r=1}^{k-1}\sum_{s=r+1}^{k} p_rp_s, \tag{1.58}$$

$$\mu_2 = \tfrac{1}{4}\Bigg[S_2\sum_{r=1}^{k-1}\sum_{s=r+1}^{k} p_rp_s(2S_1-5S_2)\sum_{r=1}^{k-2}\sum_{s=r+1}^{k-1}\sum_{t=s+1}^{k} p_rp_sp_t + 4(S_1-S_2)\Bigg(\sum_{r=1}^{k-1}\sum_{s=r+1}^{k} p_r^2p_s^2 - 2\sum_{r=1}^{k-3}\sum_{s=r+1}^{k-2}\sum_{t=s+1}^{k-1}\sum_{u=t+1}^{k} p_rp_sp_tp_u\Bigg)\Bigg]. \tag{1.59}$$

Nonfree sampling

Joins between counties of the same colour

$$\mu_1' = \frac{Wn_r^{(2)}}{2n^{(2)}}, \tag{1.60}$$

$$\mu_2 = \tfrac{1}{4}\left[\frac{S_1n_r^{(2)}}{n^{(2)}} + \frac{(S_2-2S_1)n_r^{(3)}}{n^{(3)}} + \frac{(W^2+S_1-S_2)n_r^{(4)}}{n^{(4)}} - W^2\left(\frac{n_r^{(2)}}{n^{(2)}}\right)^2\right]. \tag{1.61}$$

Joins between counties of two different colours

$$\mu_1' = \frac{Wn_r n_s}{n^{(2)}}, \tag{1.62}$$

$$\mu_2 = \tfrac{1}{4}\left[\frac{2S_1 n_r n_s}{n^{(2)}} + \frac{(S_2 - 2S_1)n_r n_s(n_r + n_s - 2)}{n^{(3)}} + \frac{4(W^2 + S_1 - S_2)n_r^{(2)} n_s^{(2)}}{n^{(4)}} - 4W^2\left(\frac{n_r n_s}{n^{(2)}}\right)^2\right]. \tag{1.63}$$

Total number of joins between counties of different colours

$$\mu_1' = W\sum_{r=1}^{k-1}\sum_{s=r+1}^{k}\frac{n_r n_s}{n^{(2)}}, \tag{1.64}$$

$$\begin{aligned}\mu_2 = \tfrac{1}{4}\Bigg\{&\left[\frac{S_2}{n^{(2)}} - \frac{4(W^2 + S_1 - S_2)(n-1)}{n^{(4)}}\right]\sum_{r=1}^{k-1}\sum_{s=r+1}^{k} n_r n_s \\ &+ \left[\frac{2S_1 - 5S_2}{n^{(3)}} + \frac{12(W^2 + S_1 - S_2)}{n^{(4)}} + \frac{8W^2}{n^{(3)}(n-1)}\right]\sum_{r=1}^{k-2}\sum_{s=r+1}^{k-1}\sum_{t=s+1}^{k} n_r n_s n_t \\ &+ 4\left[\frac{(S_1 - S_2)}{n^{(4)}} + \frac{2W^2(2n-3)}{n^{(2)}n^{(4)}}\right]\sum_{r=1}^{k-1}\sum_{s=r+1}^{k} n_r^2 n_s^2 \\ &- 8\left[\frac{(S_1 - S_2)}{n^{(4)}} + \frac{2W^2(2n-3)}{n^{(2)}n^{(4)}}\right]\sum_{r=1}^{k-3}\sum_{s=r+1}^{k-2}\sum_{t=s+1}^{k-1}\sum_{u=t+1}^{k} n_r n_s n_t n_u\Bigg\}.\end{aligned} \tag{1.65}$$

The coefficient I

$$\mathrm{E_N}(I) = \mathrm{E_R}(I) = -(n-1)^{-1}, \tag{1.66}$$

$$\mathrm{E_N}(I^2) = \frac{n^2 S_1 - nS_2 + 3W^2}{W^2(n^2 - 1)}, \tag{1.67}$$

$$\mathrm{E_R}(I^2) = \frac{n[(n^2 - 3n + 3)S_1 - nS_2 + 3W^2] - b_2[(n^2 - n)S_1 - 2nS_2 + 6W^2]}{(n-1)^{(3)}W^2}. \tag{1.68}$$

The coefficient c

$$\mathrm{E_N}(c) = \mathrm{E_R}(c) = 1, \tag{1.69}$$

$$\mathrm{var_N}(c) = \frac{(2S_1 + S_2)(n-1) - 4W^2}{2(n+1)W^2}, \tag{1.70}$$

$$\operatorname{var}_{\mathrm{R}}(c) = \Big\{(n-1)S_1[n^2-3n+3-(n-1)b_2]$$
$$-\tfrac{1}{4}(n-1)S_2[n^2+3n-6-(n^2-n+2)b_2]$$
$$+W^2[n^2-3-(n-1)^2b_2]\Big\}\Big/ n(n-2)^{(2)}W^2. \qquad (1.71)$$

If W comprises symmetric binary weights, $W = 2A$, $S_1 = 4A$, and $S_2 = 8(A+D)$. If these equalities in A and D are substituted into equations (1.54)–(1.71), the expectations and variances reduce, as they should, to those for binary weights given in equations (1.19)–(1.30) and (1.33)–(1.38).

1.5 Examples

The method of analysis using the join count, I, and c statistics is now illustrated for two lattices.

1.5.1 Join counts

The study lattice is shown in figure 1.3 in which $k = 2$. We assume that the shaded cells are coloured B and that the remainder are coloured W. Denote the number of B cells by n_1, and the number of W cells by n_2. Then $n_1 = n_2 = 8$ and $n = 16$. We wish to test for spatial autocorrelation in the study lattice using three different forms for $\{\delta_{ij}\}$:

1. $\delta_{ij} = 1$ if the ith and jth cells have a common edge, and $\delta_{ij} = 0$ otherwise. By analogy with chess moves, this is the so-called *rook's case*;
2. $\delta_{ij} = 1$ if the ith and jth cells have a common vertex, and $\delta_{ij} = 0$ otherwise (the *bishop's case*);
3. $\delta_{ij} = 1$ if the ith and jth cells have a common edge or vertex, and $\delta_{ij} = 0$ otherwise (the *queen's case*).

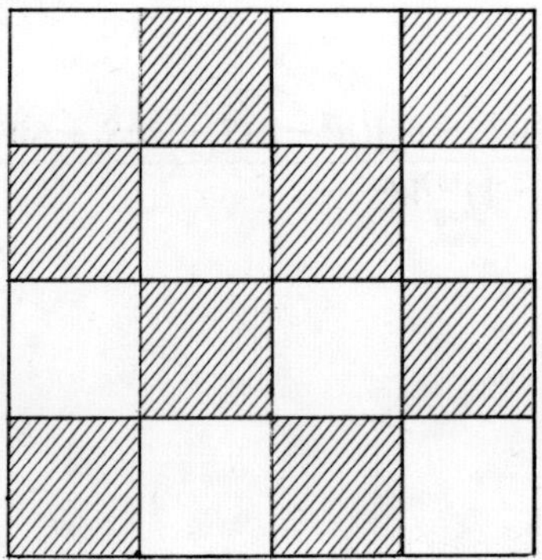

Figure 1.3. Lattice used as an example in section 1.5.1.

From equation (1.6) and the expression for D given after equation (1.18), the values of A and D are as follows.

	A	D	
Rook's case	24	52	
Bishop's case	18	32	
Queen's case	42	204	(1.72)

Note that the sum of A (rook's)$+A$ (bishop's) $= A$ (queen's), as it should. The analysis proceeds as follows.

(1) *Specification of hypotheses.* Null hypothesis H_0: the probability, p, that a cell is a particular colour, say B, is the same for each cell in the lattice, and the colour of a given cell is fixed independently of the colour of all other cells. Alternatively hypothesis H_1: p is not the same for each cell and/or the colours of the cells are not fixed independently.

(2) *Statistical test.* Join counts. If we assume that we know *a priori* that, say, $p = q = 0{\cdot}5$, the free sampling model should be used. If, however, we estimate p and q from the data by n_1/n and n_2/n respectively, then the nonfree sampling equations should be used.

(3) *Significance level.* Let us examine H_0 at various conventional significance levels, say $\alpha = 0{\cdot}1$, $0{\cdot}05$, $0{\cdot}02$, and $0{\cdot}01$.

(4) *Sampling distribution.* We assume that the asymptotic normality of the join count statistics holds for $n = 16$, and that tables of the normal curve can be used.

(5) *Region of rejection.* Since H_1 does not specify direction, two-tailed tests for the distributions of BB, WW, and BW joins are appropriate. Suppose, however, we had postulated that if a given cell is B (with probability p), then cells joined to the given cell will also be B with a probability *greater* than p (positive spatial autocorrelation). Then one-tailed tests would be required; the regions of rejection would be in the positive tail of the normal curve for the distribution of BB and WW joins, and in the negative tail for the distribution of BW joins. Conversely, should we postulate that if a given cell is B (with probability p), then cells joined to the given cell will also be B with a probability *less* than p (negative spatial autocorrelation), the tests will again be one-tailed; the regions of rejection will be in the negative tail of the normal curve for BB and WW joins, and in the positive tail for BW joins.

(6) *Decision.* Apply equations (1.3)–(1.5) to figure 1.3. Since $BB+BW = A-WW$, only two of the three counts contain independent information, but all three are included for purposes of demonstration. If we put $p = q = 0{\cdot}5$ (free sampling), $n_1 = n_2 = 8$ (nonfree sampling), and

substitute these values and those given by result (1.72) into equations (1.7)–(1.18), the set of figures given in table 1.1 is obtained. On the basis of these results, we reject H_0 in favour of H_1 in the rook's and bishop's cases, but accept H_0 in the queen's case. This holds for both free and nonfree sampling.

In the rook's case, the structure of $\{\delta_{ij}\}$ means that we are searching for spatial autocorrelation on the rows and columns of the lattice. It is evident visually from figure 1.3 that the spacing of the *B* and *W* cells is uniform on the rows and columns. This impression is confirmed by the negative values for the standard deviates for the distributions of *BB* and *WW* joins and by the positive value for the standard deviate for the distribution of *BW* joins. A negative deviate for *BB* (or *WW*) joins means that fewer *BB* (or *WW*) joins occur in the lattice than would be expected under H_0. This implies that there are, therefore, fewer *B* (or *W*) cells contiguous to each other in the lattice than would be expected under H_0. A positive deviate for *BW* joins means that more *BW* joins occur in the lattice than would be expected under H_0. This implies that more *B* and *W* cells are contiguous to each other in the lattice than would be expected under H_0. In other words, given that a cell is *B*, there is more chance that cells contiguous to it will be *W* than would be expected under H_0, and less chance that they will be *B*. Negative spatial autocorrelation is therefore said to exist.

Table 1.1. The results of tests for spatial autocorrelation in the join counts example.

$\{\delta_{ij}\}$	Statistic	*BB* joins		*WW* joins		*BW* joins	
		free sampling	nonfree sampling	free sampling	nonfree sampling	free sampling	nonfree sampling
Rook's case	observed	0	0	0	0	24	24
	μ_1'	6·00	5·60	6·00	5·60	12·00	12·80
	σ	3·32	1·37	3·32	1·37	2·45	2·31
	s.n.d.[a]	−1·81	−4·09	−1·81	−4·09	4·90	4·84
		*	****	*	****	****	****
Bishop's case	observed	9	9	9	9	0	0
	μ_1'	4·50	4·20	4·50	4·20	9·00	9·60
	σ	2·72	1·51	2·72	1·51	2·12	2·00
	s.n.d.[a]	1·66	3·19	1·66	3·19	−4·24	−4·80
		*	****	*	****	****	****
Queen's case	observed	9	9	9	9	24	24
	μ_1'	10·50	8·80	10·50	9·80	21·00	22·40
	σ	5·78	2·26	5·78	2·26	3·24	2·61
	s.n.d.[a]	−0·26	−0·35	−0·26	−0·35	0·93	0·61

[a] s.n.d. is the standard normal deviate.
* Significant at $\alpha = 0{\cdot}1$; ** significant at $\alpha = 0{\cdot}05$; *** significant at $\alpha = 0{\cdot}02$; **** significant at $\alpha = 0{\cdot}01$. This asterisk convention for significance levels is used throughout the book.

In the bishop's case, the structure of $\{\delta_{ij}\}$ implies that we are searching for spatial autocorrelation on the diagonals of the lattice. The signs of the standard deviates indicate more *BB* and *WW* joins in the lattice than would be expected under H_0, and fewer *BW* joins. This is interpreted as clustering or positive spatial autocorrelation in the *B* and *W* cells along the diagonals of the lattice, as is evident from figure 1.3.

In the queen's case, the structure of $\{\delta_{ij}\}$ means that we are searching for spatial autocorrelation along the rows, columns, and diagonals of the lattice simultaneously. The result is that the basic patterns given by the rook's and bishop's cases cancel each other out and the overall pattern is interpreted as being random.

An important conclusion may be drawn from this example. The detection of spatial autocorrelation in a lattice depends critically upon the form of $\{\delta_{ij}\}$. The researcher must decide *a priori* whether he wishes to search for spatial autocorrelation generally in a lattice (the queen's case, which has no directional bias), or whether he wishes to detect patterning in particular directions. Thus Cliff (1968) attempted to determine whether the spatial growth pattern of numbers of adopters of an innovation in the Asby district of Sweden was basically oriented north–south as opposed to east–west. This was suggested by the fact that the physical grain of the country, and the pattern of communications responsible for the spread of information about the innovation, trended north–south. The join count statistics were evaluated for a regular lattice like figure 1.3 for two forms of $\{\delta_{ij}\}$:

1. $\delta_{ij} = 1$ if the *i*th and *j*th cells had a common edge on a column of the lattice, and $\delta_{ij} = 0$ otherwise (a N.–S. spread model);
2. $\delta_{ij} = 1$ if the *i*th and *j*th cells had a common edge on a row of the lattice, and $\delta_{ij} = 0$ otherwise (an E.–W. spread model).

Cells were coded *B* if they had an adopter of the innovation in them, and *W* if they did not. For the map analysed, the standard normal deviate for *BB* joins was 2·40 with $\{\delta_{ij}\}$ of form '1', and 1·65 with $\{\delta_{ij}\}$ of form '2', implying, as hypothesised, somewhat greater clustering of *B* cells (adopters) in a north–south direction than east–west. This illustration serves to reinforce the point that the structure of $\{\delta_{ij}\}$ or *W* must be chosen in advance of the analysis, and the structure selected should reflect the form of spatial autocorrelation one is trying to detect.

1.5.2 *I* and *c*

The study lattice is shown in figure 1.4. The lattice represents an imaginary city, with each cell representing a ward. The $\{x_i\}$ are the percentage changes in population, 1961–1971. The four central wards are, therefore, the core portion of the city which has suffered depopulation, while the peripheral wards represent the growing suburbs. We wish to determine whether negative spatial autocorrelation exists between the core wards and the suburban wards. Accordingly $\{\delta_{ij}\}$ is defined so that, as shown in figure 1.4, joins exist only between central and suburban wards. From figure 1.4, $A = 20$, $D = 48$, $\overline{x} = 3\cdot0$, and $b_2 = 2\cdot38$. The analysis follows the same lines as in section 1.5.1.

(1) *Specification of hypotheses.* Null hypothesis H_0: the probability that a ward receives a particular x_i value is the same for each ward in the city, and the level of X_i observed in a given ward is fixed independently of the levels in all other wards. Alternative hypothesis H_1: the level of X_i observed in a central ward is negatively correlated with the level observed in neighbouring suburban wards.

(2) *Statistical tests. I* and *c*. Since b_2 is considerably less than the normal curve value of 3, we evaluate I and c using randomisation (that is, making no assumptions about the distributions of the X_i) and under normality (that is, assuming the X_i are identically normally distributed) to see if failure to meet the normality assumption significantly alters the results obtained.

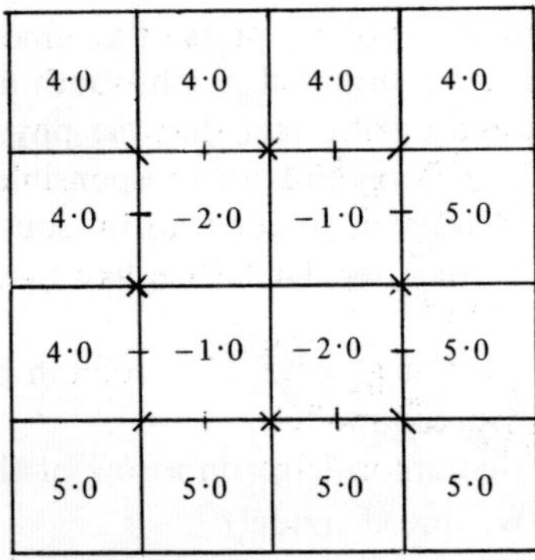

Figure 1.4. Lattice used as an example in section 1.5.2.

Table 1.2. The results for I and c in the change in city population example.

Coefficient	Statistic	Randomisation	Normality
I	observed	−0·98	−0·98
	E(I)	−0·67	−0·67
	σ(I)	0·19	0·19
	standard normal deviate	−4·73 ****	−4·78 ****
c	observed	2·44	2·44
	E(c)	1·00	1·00
	σ(c)	0·26	0·28
	standard normal deviate	−5·47 ****	−5·22 ****

**** Significant at $\alpha = 0\cdot01$.

(3) *Significance level.* We examine H_0 at $\alpha = 0 \cdot 05$ and $0 \cdot 01$.

(4) *Sampling distribution.* We assume that the asymptotic normality of I and c holds for $n = 16$, and that tables of the normal curve can be used.

(5) *Region of rejection.* Direction is indicated by H_1. A one-tailed test is appropriate and, since negative spatial autocorrelation is hypothesised, the region of rejection will be in the negative tail for both I and c. Note that in the case of I, the standard normal deviate is evaluated in the usual way,

$$\frac{I - \mathrm{E}(I)}{\sigma(I)},$$

whereas for Geary's c, we compute

$$\frac{\mathrm{E}(c) - c}{\sigma(c)}.$$

The Geary coefficient is structured so that under H_0, $c = 1$; values of $c < 1$ indicate positive spatial autocorrelation; and values of $c > 1$ indicate negative spatial autocorrelation. We therefore compute $[\mathrm{E}(c) - c]$ rather than $[c - \mathrm{E}(c)]$ so that positive values of the standard deviate correspond to positive spatial autocorrelation, and negative values to negative spatial autocorrelation.

(6) *Decision.* If we solve equations (1.31)–(1.38) for figure 1.4, we obtain the results shown in table 1.2. In all cases, we reject H_0 in favour of H_1. Note that the normality assumption does not seriously affect the results.

2

Distribution theory for the join count, I, and c statistics

2.1 Introduction

In chapter 1 we proposed that the join count, I, and c statistics should be tested for significance as standard normal deviates. Computational formulae for the first two moments of the various coefficients were given, which we suggested should be used to specify the location, μ, and scale, σ^2, parameters of the normal curve. In this chapter we show how the moments given in chapter 1, were derived. Colour lattices are considered in section 2, and the Moran and Geary statistics are examined in section 3. Some higher order moments for the various coefficients are also outlined. In section 4, we prove that the join count, I, and c statistics are all asymptotically normally distributed under the null hypothesis of no spatial autocorrelation, which provides the basis for the test procedure suggested in chapter 1. However, in sections 5–7 we show that the sampling distributions may be badly non-normal in small lattices, and alternative approximations are therefore explored.

2.2 The join count statistics

Following the method of section 1.3.1, we consider a lattice, regular or irregular, of n cells, and allow the ith cell to be coloured black, B, or white, W. The binary variate, X_i for cell i, is defined as

$$\left.\begin{aligned} X_i &= 1, \quad \text{if the } i\text{th cell is } B, \\ &= 0, \quad \text{if the } i\text{th cell is } W \end{aligned}\right\}. \qquad (2.1)$$

Consider the null hypothesis, H_0, that the colour for cell j is selected independently of that for cell i, $i \neq j$, or

$$\text{prob}(X_i = 1, X_j = 1) \quad = \quad \text{prob}(X_i = 1)\text{prob}(X_j = 1), \qquad (2.2)$$

with similar statements for X_i and/or X_j equal to zero. The process of choosing a particular colour is equivalent to success/failure sampling from a population. If the additional assumption is made that

$$\text{prob}(X_i = 1) = p_i = p, \qquad i = 1, 2, ..., n,$$

we have either

1. binomial sampling, if there is no restriction on the sampling process (known as the free sampling model); or
2. hypergeometric sampling, if the total numbers of black and white cells are specified *a priori* (nonfree sampling).

Free sampling corresponds to the situation where p is known and so sampling can take place as if from an infinite population. More commonly, however, p has to be estimated from the data as, say,

$$\hat{p} = \frac{\text{number of black cells}}{\text{total number of cells}} = \frac{n_1}{n}. \qquad (2.3)$$

The sampling process is then conditional upon the observed numbers of black and white cells in the lattice, and the nonfree model is appropriate. Thus the two models are not competitors but depend upon whether or not p is known.

The test statistic based on black–black (BB) joins is written as (see section 1.4.1)

$$BB = \tfrac{1}{2}\textstyle\sum_{(2)} w_{ij} x_i x_j, \tag{2.4}$$

while for black–white (BW) joins we have

$$BW = \tfrac{1}{2}\textstyle\sum_{(2)} w_{ij}(x_i - x_j)^2, \tag{2.5}$$

where x_i is the value observed for variate X_i. We do not consider white–white (WW) joins separately since

$$WW = \tfrac{1}{2}\textstyle\sum_{(2)} w_{ij}(1-x_i)(1-x_j),$$

where $1-x_i = 1$ if cell i is W, and

$$\begin{aligned} BB+BW+WW &= \tfrac{1}{2}\textstyle\sum_{(2)} w_{ij}[x_i x_j + (x_i - x_j)^2 + (1-x_i)(1-x_j)] \\ &= \tfrac{1}{2}\textstyle\sum_{(2)} w_{ij}, \end{aligned} \tag{2.6}$$

a constant. Result (2.6) follows because

$$x_i^r = x_i, \tag{2.7}$$

for all integers $r \geqslant 1$, since x_i can only be zero or one. Thus WW is a linear function of BB and BW and does not supply any additional information.

The first stage in the evaluation of the moments of BB and BW is to calculate the expectations of terms in the x_i. Since equation (2.7) holds, all the terms reduce to one of the forms $x_i, x_i x_j, x_i x_j x_k$, etc. The expectation operator E is defined by the relation $\mathrm{E}[h(X)] = \sum h(x)\mathrm{prob}(X = x)$, where h is some function of x and the summation is over the range of X.

(1) *The free sampling model.* Each observation is an independent drawing with $\mathrm{prob}(X_i = 1) = p$ for all i, so that

$$\mathrm{E}(X_i) = 0 \times (1-p) + 1 \times p = p, \tag{2.8}$$

and $\mathrm{E}(X_i^r) = p$ also. Because each drawing is an independent drawing, $\mathrm{E}(X_i X_j) = \mathrm{E}(X_i)\mathrm{E}(X_j)$ and it follows that $\mathrm{E}(X_i X_j) = p^2$, and so on.

(2) *The nonfree sampling model.* The observations are no longer independent since they are constrained by equation (2.3),

$$\sum_{i=1}^{n} X_i = n_1.$$

Expressions with 1, 2, 3, ... different subscripts correspond to samples of size 1, 2, 3, ... without replacement from a population of size n containing n_1 successes (B cells). The probability of obtaining one cell which is B is

n_1/n. Given this success, the probability of obtaining a second B is reduced to $(n_1-1)/(n-1)$. If we are successful in finding two B cells, the probability of a third is $(n_1-2)/(n-2)$ and so on. Thus

$$\mathrm{E}(X_i) = n_1/n, \tag{2.9a}$$

$$\mathrm{E}(X_i X_j) = \frac{n_1(n_1-1)}{n(n-1)}, \tag{2.9b}$$

$$\mathrm{E}(X_i X_j X_k) = \frac{n_1^{(3)}}{n^{(3)}}, \tag{2.9c}$$

where $n^{(b)} = n(n-1) \dots (n-b+1)$, and

$$\mathrm{E}(X_i X_j \dots X_m) = \frac{n_1^{(b)}}{n^{(b)}}, \tag{2.9d}$$

where b distinct subscripts are represented.

2.2.1 Mean and variance of *BB* and *BW*

From equation (2.4) it follows that

$$\begin{aligned}\mathrm{E}(BB) &= \mathrm{E}[\tfrac{1}{2}\textstyle\sum_{(2)} w_{ij} X_i X_j] \\ &= \tfrac{1}{2}\textstyle\sum_{(2)} w_{ij}\, \mathrm{E}(X_i X_j)\end{aligned} \tag{2.10}$$

$$= \begin{cases} \tfrac{1}{2}Wp^2 & \text{(free)}, \qquad (2.11a) \\[4pt] \dfrac{\tfrac{1}{2}Wn_1^{(2)}}{n^{(2)}} & \text{(nonfree)}, \qquad (2.11b) \end{cases}$$

using equations (2.8) and (2.9b).

To evaluate the variance of BB we start by considering the second crude moment. From equations (2.4) and (2.7)

$$\begin{aligned}\mathrm{E}[(BB)^2] = \tfrac{1}{4}[&\textstyle\sum_{(2)} w_{ij}(w_{ij}+w_{ji})\,\mathrm{E}(X_i X_j) \\ &+ \textstyle\sum_{(3)} (w_{ij}+w_{ji})(w_{ik}+w_{ki})\,\mathrm{E}(X_i X_j X_k) \\ &+ \textstyle\sum_{(4)} w_{ij}\, w_{kl}\, \mathrm{E}(X_i X_j X_k X_l)].\end{aligned} \tag{2.12}$$

The summation signs are to be interpreted as follows:

$\sum_{(2)}$ is equivalent to $\sum_{i=1}^{n} \sum_{\substack{j=1 \\ i \neq j}}^{n}$, $\qquad \sum_{(3)}$ is equivalent to $\sum_{i=1}^{n} \sum_{j=1}^{n} \sum_{\substack{k=1 \\ i \neq j \neq k}}^{n}$,

and

$\sum_{(4)}$ is equivalent to $\sum_{i=1}^{n} \sum_{j=1}^{n} \sum_{k=1}^{n} \sum_{\substack{l=1 \\ i \neq j \neq k \neq l}}^{n}$.

Since $w_{ii} = 0$ for all i, there are $\frac{1}{2}n(n-1)$ terms in the expansion of BB (and BW) as defined by equations (2.4) and (2.5), although many of these will vanish because $w_{ij} = 0$. Hence there are $[\frac{1}{2}n(n-1)]^2$ possible terms in the expansion on the right hand side of equation (2.12). The types of terms and their frequencies are shown in figure 2.1 and it may be verified that the total number of terms is indeed $[\frac{1}{2}n(n-1)]^2$.

The weights given in figure 2.1 are by way of example only; thus the first pattern also has weights $w_{ij}w_{ji}$, while the second has $w_{ij}w_{ki}$, $w_{ji}w_{ki}$, and $w_{ji}w_{ik}$ in addition to the one given. These permutations of the indices are reflected in expansion (2.12).

Given expansion (2.12), and since

$$\mathrm{var}(BB) = \mathrm{E}[(BB)^2] - [\mathrm{E}(BB)]^2, \tag{2.13}$$

it follows from factorizing equation (2.10) that

$$\begin{aligned}4\,\mathrm{var}(BB) = {} & \textstyle\sum_{(2)} w_{ij}(w_{ij}+w_{ji})\{\mathrm{E}(X_i X_j) - [\mathrm{E}(X_i X_j)]^2\} \\ & + \textstyle\sum_{(3)} (w_{ij}+w_{ji})(w_{ik}+w_{ki})[\mathrm{E}(X_i X_j X_k) - \mathrm{E}(X_i X_j)\,\mathrm{E}(X_i X_k)] \\ & + \textstyle\sum_{(4)} w_{ij}w_{kl}[\mathrm{E}(X_i X_j X_k X_l) - \mathrm{E}(X_i X_j)\,\mathrm{E}(X_k X_l)].\end{aligned} \tag{2.14}$$

	i — j (double join)	j — i — k	i — j k — l
Weight	w_{ij}^2	$w_{ij}w_{ik}$	$w_{ij}w_{kl}$
Number of terms	$\frac{1}{2}n(n-1)$	$n(n-1)(n-2)$	$\frac{1}{4}n(n-1)(n-2)(n-3)$

Figure 2.1. Join patterns for the second moment.

(1) *Free sampling.* Since each drawing is independent

$$\mathrm{E}(X_i X_j) = p^2, \qquad \mathrm{E}(X_i X_j X_k) = p^3,$$

and

$$\mathrm{E}(X_i X_j X_k X_l) = p^4 = \mathrm{E}(X_i X_j)\,\mathrm{E}(X_k X_l),$$

so that equation (2.14) reduces to

$$4\,\mathrm{var}(BB) = \textstyle\sum_{(2)} w_{ij}(w_{ij}+w_{ji})(p^2-p^4) + \sum_{(3)} (w_{ij}+w_{ji})(w_{ik}+w_{ki})(p^3-p^4). \tag{2.15}$$

Putting $w_{i.} = \sum_j w_{ij}$ and $w_{.j} = \sum_i w_{ij}$, we find

$$\begin{aligned}\textstyle\sum_{(3)} (w_{ij}+w_{ji})(w_{ik}+w_{ki}) &= \textstyle\sum_{(2)} (w_{ij}+w_{ji})(w_{i.}+w_{.j}-2w_{ij}) \\ &= \textstyle\sum_i (w_{i.}+w_{.i})^2 - \sum_{(2)} (w_{ij}+w_{ji})^2 \\ &= S_2 - 2S_1,\end{aligned} \tag{2.16}$$

where

$$S_1 = \sum_{(2)} w_{ij}(w_{ij}+w_{ji}) = \tfrac{1}{2}\sum_{(2)}(w_{ij}+w_{ji})^2,$$

and

$$S_2 = \sum_i (w_{i.}+w_{.i})^2.$$

Finally, substituting S_1 and S_2 into equation (2.15), we obtain

$$\begin{aligned}\text{var}(BB) &= \tfrac{1}{4}[S_1p^2(1-p^2)+(S_2-2S_1)p^3(1-p)] \\ &= \tfrac{1}{4}p^2(1-p)[S_1(1-p)+S_2p]. \end{aligned} \tag{2.17}$$

A similar argument holds for BW, yielding equation (1.57). Putting $S_1 = 4A$, $W = 2A$, and $S_2 = 8(A+D)$ yields the formulae for the binary *weights* case [see equations (1.10) and (1.11)].

(2) *Nonfree sampling.* Because of constraint (2.3), the expectations become

$$\text{E}(X_i X_j) = \frac{n_1^{(2)}}{n^{(2)}}, \qquad \text{E}(X_i X_j X_k) = \frac{n_1^{(3)}}{n^{(3)}}, \qquad \text{and } \text{E}(X_i X_j X_k X_l) = \frac{n_1^{(4)}}{n^{(4)}}.$$

We define the following identity

$$\begin{aligned}\sum_{(4)} w_{ij}w_{kl} &= W^2 - \sum_i (w_{i.}+w_{.i})^2 + \sum_{(2)} w_{ij}(w_{ij}+w_{ji}) \\ &= W^2 - S_2 + S_1. \end{aligned} \tag{2.18}$$

Substituting the expectations, which do not depend upon the subscripts, and the identities (2.16) and (2.18) into equation (2.13), we obtain

$$4\,\text{var}(BB) = S_1\left[\frac{n_1^{(2)}}{n^{(2)}} - \frac{2n_1^{(3)}}{n^{(3)}} + \frac{n_1^{(4)}}{n^{(4)}}\right] + S_2\left[\frac{n_1^{(3)}}{n^{(3)}} - \frac{n_1^{(4)}}{n^{(4)}}\right] + \frac{W^2n_1^{(4)}}{n^{(4)}} - \left[\frac{Wn_1^{(2)}}{n^{(2)}}\right]^2. \tag{2.19}$$

$$\text{As } n \to \infty, \qquad \frac{n_1^{(j)}}{n^{(j)}} \to p^j;$$

but result (2.19) does *not* approach that given in equation (2.17) because the last two terms do not vanish. Instead, they approach

$$-\frac{4W^2p^2(1-p)}{n}.$$

Thus, in the limit, for the nonfree sampling case, we have

$$4\,\text{var}(BB) = p^2(1-p)\left[S_1(1-p)+S_2p-\frac{4W^2}{n}\right].$$

Var(BW), given in equation (1.63), can be found by similar methods.

As with BB, var(BW) for nonfree sampling does not approach var(BW) for free sampling as $n \to \infty$. Rather, the limiting form is

$$\operatorname{var}(BW) = S_1pq + \tfrac{1}{4}pq(1-4pq)\left(\frac{S_2 - 4W^2}{n}\right) .$$

Finally we note that insertion of terms in A and D for S_1, S_2, and W^2 in equation (2.19) and the corresponding expression for var(BW) gives the binary weights results of equations (1.16) and (1.17).

2.2.2 Higher moments

Derivation of the third and higher order moments follows exactly the same lines as for the first two moments. The third and fourth moments for the two and k-colour join counts are given in the literature as follows:

(1) *Free sampling.*
$k = 2$, rook's case (Moran, 1948; Krishna Iyer, 1949),
queen's case (BB only, Dacey, 1965),
queen's, bishop's, row-only, and column-only cases (Cliff, 1969).
$k > 2$, all cases (Cliff, 1969);

(2) *Nonfree sampling*
all cases (Cliff, 1969).

The types of terms which occur in the third moments, and their weights, are shown in figure 2.2, while those for the fourth moment appear in figure 2.3. Terms marked with an asterisk have two or more separate links, and, in the free sampling case, do not appear in the final forms of the moments.

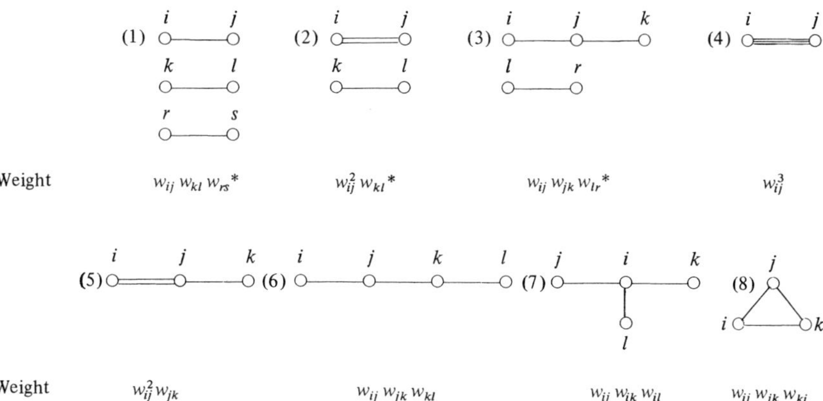

Figure 2.2. Join patterns for the third moment. [The numbers are as allocated by Moran (1948)].

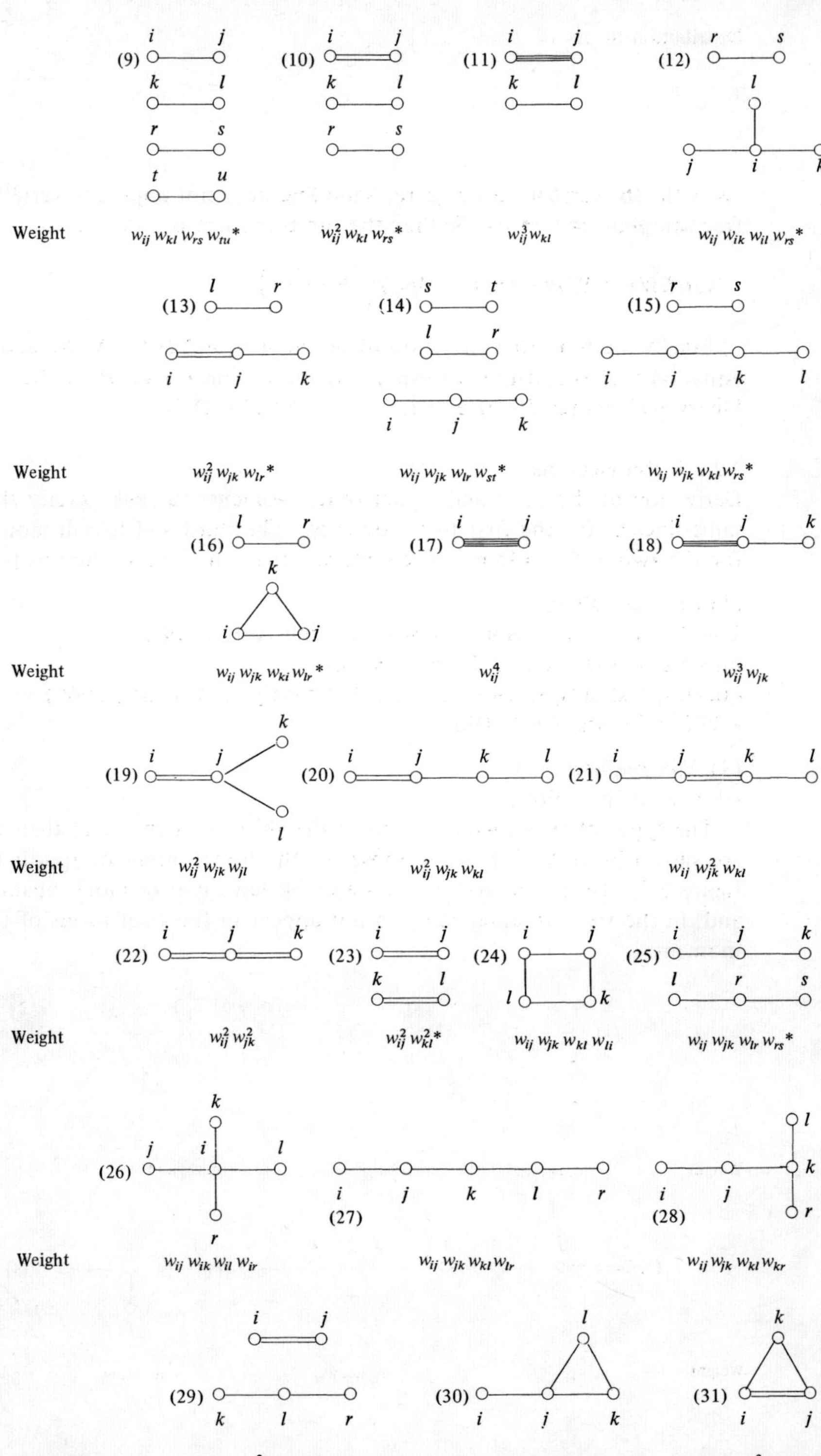

Figure 2.3. Join patterns for the fourth moment.

2.3 The Moran and Geary statistics

The method by which we obtain the moments of the Moran and Geary coefficients is the same as for the join count statistics, but the expectation terms are somewhat more complicated. As indicated in section 1.3.2, the moments may be evaluated under the null hypothesis either by assuming that: 1. the observations are random independent drawings from one (or separate identical) normal population(s)—assumption N; or by assuming that: 2. the observations are random independent drawings from one (or separate identical) population(s) with unknown distribution function(s), so that the set of all random permutations may be considered—assumption R. In the remainder of this section we evaluate only the moments for I. Those for c are obtained by comparable operations.

2.3.1 The moments of I, given assumption N

If X is a normal variate $N(\mu, \sigma^2)$, then $E(X) = \mu$, $E[(X-\mu)^2] = \sigma^2$, $E[(X-\mu)^3] = 0$, and $E[(X-\mu)^4] = 3\sigma^4$. Thus, for a sample of size n with observed values $x_1, x_2, \ldots, x_n$, and

$$\bar{x} = \frac{1}{n}\sum_{i=1}^{n} x_i,$$

the variates Z_i corresponding to the observed values $z_i = x_i - \bar{x}$ have expectations

$$\left.\begin{aligned} &E(Z_i) = 0, \qquad E(Z_i^2) = \left(1-\frac{1}{n}\right)\sigma^2, \qquad E(Z_i\, Z_j) = -\frac{\sigma^2}{n}, \\ &E(Z_i^2 Z_j^2) = \frac{(n^2-2n+3)\sigma^4}{n^2}, \qquad E(Z_i^2 Z_j\, Z_k) = -\frac{(n-3)\sigma^4}{n^2}, \\ &\text{and} \\ &E(Z_i\, Z_j\, Z_k\, Z_l) = \frac{3\sigma^4}{n^2}. \end{aligned}\right\} \tag{2.20}$$

The key theorem which allows us to evaluate the moments of I under assumption N is due to Pitman (1937) and Koopmans (1942).

Theorem: If $X_1, \ldots, X_m$ are independent identically distributed normal variates, say $N(0, 1)$, then any scale-free function of them, $h(X_1, \ldots, X_m)$, is distributed independently of $Q = \sum_{i=1}^{m} X_i^2$.

Proof: Consider the moment generating function

$$M(t_1, t_2) = E[\exp(t_1 h + t_2 Q)].$$

Then

$$M(t_1, t_2) \propto \int_{(m)} \exp(t_1 h)\exp[-\tfrac{1}{2}(1-2t_2)x_i^2]\prod_{i=1}^{m} dx_i,$$

and therefore

$$M(t_1, t_2) = (1 - 2t_2)^{-m/2}\, \mathrm{E}[\exp(t_1 h)],$$

so that h and Q are independent, and Q is distributed as chi-square with m degrees of freedom.

In the present context, if all the x_i (and thus z_i) are replaced by λx_i in I (or c), the value of the statistic is unchanged. Thus I is truly a scale-free function of the x_i. Apart from a constant, the denominator of I is $\sum_{i=1}^{n} z_i^2$. Although the Z_i are not independent, they can be transformed into $(n-1)$ independent identical normal variates, so that, by Cochran's theorem, $\sum Z_i^2$ is distributed as chi-square with $(n-1)$ degrees of freedom.

Thus, from the Pitman–Koopmans theorem, I and Q $(=\sum Z_i^2)$ are independent so that

$$\mathrm{E}(I^p Q^p) = \mathrm{E}(I^p)\,\mathrm{E}(Q^p), \quad \text{for any positive } p. \tag{2.21}$$

In Dacey's coefficient, I', given in equation (1.40), the denominator term is $\sum \alpha_i z_i^2$, which cannot be transformed into the form of Q, as is required by the theorem, except when the mean of X_i is known; a case which is not of practical interest.

If we return now to I we find that, since

$$IQ = \frac{n}{W} \sum_{(2)} w_{ij} z_i z_j,$$

it follows that

$$\mathrm{E}(I^p) = \frac{\mathrm{E}(I^p Q^p)}{\mathrm{E}(Q^p)} = \left(\frac{n}{W}\right)^p \frac{\mathrm{E}[(\sum_{(2)} w_{ij} Z_i Z_j)^p]}{\mathrm{E}(Q^p)}\,. \tag{2.22}$$

Equation (2.22) allows us to evaluate the crude moments of I. Thus

$$\mathrm{E}(I) = \frac{n}{W} \frac{\mathrm{E}(\sum_{(2)} w_{ij} Z_i Z_j)}{\mathrm{E}(\sum Z_i^2)}. \tag{2.23}$$

From equation (2.20), the denominator term has expectation $(n-1)\sigma^2$, which also follows directly from the fact that Q is distributed as chi-square with $(n-1)$ degrees of freedom. For the numerator,

$$\begin{aligned} \mathrm{E}\left[\sum_{(2)} w_{ij} Z_i Z_j\right] &= \sum_{(2)} w_{ij}\, \mathrm{E}(Z_i Z_j) \\ &= -\frac{\sigma^2 W}{n}. \end{aligned}$$

Finally,

$$\begin{aligned} \mathrm{E}(I) &= \frac{n}{W}\left(-\frac{\sigma^2 W}{n}\right) \Big/ (n-1)\sigma^2 \\ &= -\frac{1}{n-1}. \end{aligned} \tag{2.24}$$

Evaluation of the second crude moment proceeds in the same way, with

$$\mathrm{E}(I^2) = \frac{n^2\mathrm{E}[(\sum_{(2)} w_{ij} Z_i Z_j)^2]}{W^2\mathrm{E}[\sum Z_i^2)^2]}. \tag{2.25}$$

From the chi-square distribution the denominator term in equation (2.25) has expectation $(n-1)(n+1)\sigma^4$. The numerator term becomes

$$\begin{aligned}(\textstyle\sum_{(2)} w_{ij} Z_i Z_j)^2 = {} & \textstyle\sum_{(2)} w_{ij}(w_{ij}+w_{ji})Z_i^2 Z_j^2 \\ & + \textstyle\sum_{(3)} (w_{ij}+w_{ji})(w_{ik}+w_{ki})Z_i^2 Z_j Z_k \\ & + \textstyle\sum_{(4)} w_{ij} w_{kl} Z_i Z_j Z_k Z_l.\end{aligned} \tag{2.26}$$

If we substitute the expectations (2.20) into equation (2.26), we obtain, for the expected value of (2.26), the expression

$$\begin{aligned}&\frac{\sigma^4}{n^2}[(n_2 - 2n+3) \textstyle\sum_{(2)} w_{ij}(w_{ij}+w_{ji}) - (n-3)\sum_{(3)} (w_{ij}+w_{ji})(w_{ik}+w_{ki}) \\ &\quad + 3 \textstyle\sum_{(4)} w_{ij} w_{kl}].\end{aligned} \tag{2.27}$$

The identities (2.16) and (2.18), and the definitions of S_1 and S_2, then enable us to write expression (2.27) as

$$\frac{\sigma^4}{n^2}[(n^2 - 2n+3)S_1 - (n-3)(S_2 - 2S_1) + 3(W^2 + S_1 - S_2)],$$

which reduces to

$$\frac{\sigma^4}{n^2}(n^2 S_1 - nS_2 + 3W^2).$$

Finally

$$\mathrm{E}(I^2) = \frac{1}{(n-1)(n+1)W^2}(n^2 S_1 - nS_2 + 3W^2). \tag{2.28}$$

Higher order moments may be evaluated in the same way. However, the results increase rapidly in complexity as the following equation for $\mathrm{E}(I^3)$ shows:

$$\mathrm{E}(I^3) = -\frac{3(n-1)(n-5)S_1 + 2n^3 S_3 - 3n^2(WS_1 + S_4) + 3W(3nS_2 - 5W^2)}{2(n-1)(n+1)(n+3)W^3}, \tag{2.29}$$

where

$$S_3 = \textstyle\sum_{(3)} (w_{ij}+w_{ji})(w_{ik}+w_{ki})(w_{jk}+w_{kj}),$$

and

$$S_4 = \textstyle\sum_{(2)} (w_{ij}+w_{ji})(w_{i.}+w_{.i})(w_{j.}+w_{.j}).$$

The third and fourth moments for c, under assumption N, are given in Geary (1954).

2.3.2 The moments of I under assumption R

If the set of $n!$ equally likely random permutations of the county sample values is considered, the moments of I and c may be evaluated under the null hypothesis of no spatial autocorrelation, *conditional* upon the n sample values observed. Thus

$$\text{prob(county } k \text{ has observation } z_i) = \frac{1}{n},$$

for all i and k, so that, for each county, the average Z observed is

$$\frac{1}{n}z_1 + \frac{1}{n}z_2 + \ldots + \frac{1}{n}z_n = \frac{1}{n}\sum z_i = \bar{z},$$

which is zero by definition. We write this as $E(Z_i) = 0$, with the understanding that the expectation is being taken over the $n!$ random permutations.

Likewise

$$E(Z_i^2) = \frac{1}{n}\sum z_i^2 = m_2, \quad \text{say.}$$

Given that a particular cell has value z_i, a neighbouring cell can take any z_j, other than z_i, with probability $1/(n-1)$ so that

$$\begin{aligned} E(Z_i Z_j) &= \frac{1}{n-1}E[Z_i(Z_1 + \ldots + Z_{i-1} + Z_{i+1} + \ldots + Z_n)] \\ &= \frac{1}{n-1}E\left[Z_i\left(\sum_{j=1}^{n} z_j - Z_i\right)\right] \\ &= \frac{1}{n-1}E(Z_i^2) = -\frac{m_2}{n-1}, \end{aligned} \tag{2.30}$$

since $\sum_{i=1}^{n} z_i = 0$ by definition. Using expectation (2.30), we obtain

$$E\left(\sum_{(2)} w_{ij} Z_i Z_j\right) = \sum_{(2)} w_{ij} E(Z_i Z_j) = -\frac{m_2 W}{n-1},$$

and it follows that

$$E(I) = \frac{n}{W}\left(-\frac{m_2 W}{n-1}\right)\Big/ nm_2 = -\frac{1}{n-1}, \tag{2.31}$$

the same value as under assumption N. Higher moments of Z may be evaluated in the same way, and we find that

$$\left.\begin{aligned} E(Z_i^2 Z_j^2) &= \frac{nm_2^2 - m_4}{n-1}, \\ E(Z_i^2 Z_j Z_k) &= \frac{2m_4 - nm_2^2}{(n-1)^{(2)}}, \\ E(Z_i Z_j Z_k Z_l) &= \frac{3nm_2^2 - 6m_4}{(n-1)^{(3)}}, \end{aligned}\right\} \tag{2.32}$$

where

$$n^{(b)} = n(n-1)\ \dots\ (n-b+1), \text{ and } nm_4 = \sum_{i=1}^{n} z_i^4 .$$

Working from expression (2.26) we find, upon substitution of the expectations (2.32) into (2.26), that

$$\mathrm{E}[(\textstyle\sum_{(2)} w_{ij} Z_i Z_j)^2] = \frac{\sum_{(2)} w_{ij}(w_{ij}+w_{ji})(nm_2^2-m_4)}{n-1} + \frac{\sum_{(3)}(w_{ij}+w_{ji})(w_{ik}+w_{ki})(2m_4-nm_2^2)}{(n-1)^{(2)}} + \frac{\sum_{(4)} w_{ij}\, w_{kl}(3nm_2^2-6m_4)}{(n-1)^{(3)}} . \qquad (2.33)$$

The identities (2.16) and (2.18), and rearrangement of the terms, enable us to reduce equation (2.33) to

$$\frac{m_2^2}{(n-1)^{(3)}}\{n[(n^2-3n+3)S_1-nS_2+3W^2]-b_2[(n^2-n)S_1-2nS_2+6W^2]\},$$

where $b_2 = m_4/m_2^2$

The denominator term of I, $(\sum z_i^2)^2$, is invariant under random permutations and is identically equal to $(nm_2)^2$, so that finally we obtain

$$\mathrm{E}(I^2) = \frac{n[(n^2-3n+3)S_1-nS_2+3W^2]-b_2[(n^2-n)S_1-2nS_2+6W^2]}{(n-1)^{(3)}W^2} . \qquad (2.34)$$

Again, if we consider the Dacey coefficient I', we note that the denominator term $\sum \alpha_i z_i$ is not invariant under random permutations, so that the moments of I' cannot be expressed in a usable form.

The higher moments of I under assumption R are much more complicated than under assumption N because $\mathrm{E}(Z_i^3) \neq 0$. For the third moment of I, see Cliff and Ord (1969, pages 37 and 38).

When the Z_i are 0 or 1, and n_1/n is near to $\frac{1}{2}$, I corresponds approximately to the BW join count statistic under nonfree sampling, since

$$I = -\frac{2nBW}{Wn_2} + \frac{2n(n_2-n_1)BB}{Wn_1n_2} + \frac{Wn_1}{n_2} .$$

2.4 The distributions of the test statistics

If we are to use the statistics discussed above as test statistics, we need to know the form of the sampling distribution under H_0. Except for very small lattices exact evaluation of the distribution function is impractical, and approximations must be found. The main result proved in this section is that, as n increases, the distribution of I (or c) approaches normality under fairly mild conditions. To obtain this result in general terms, which allow ready extension to the regression residuals case (see chapter 5), we use a matrix formulation. If the reader is willing to accept the proof, he should move on to section 2.5.

Let $\boldsymbol{x}' = (x_1, ..., x_n)$, $\boldsymbol{z}' = (z_1, ..., z_n)$. Then

$$\boldsymbol{z} = \boldsymbol{M}\boldsymbol{x}, \quad \text{where} \quad \boldsymbol{M} = \boldsymbol{I}_n - \frac{1}{n}\boldsymbol{1}\boldsymbol{1}'. \tag{2.35}$$

$\boldsymbol{I}_n$ is the identity matrix of order n, and $\boldsymbol{1}' = (1, 1, ..., 1)$, a $(1 \times n)$ row vector. The test statistic I may be written as

$$I = \frac{\boldsymbol{z}'\boldsymbol{W}\boldsymbol{z}}{\boldsymbol{z}'\boldsymbol{z}}, \tag{2.36}$$

where $\boldsymbol{W} = \{w_{ij}\}$, the matrix of weights, and the weights have been scaled so that $\sum_{(2)} w_{ij} = n$. Using equation (2.35), (2.36) may be transformed into

$$I = \frac{\boldsymbol{x}'\boldsymbol{T}\boldsymbol{x}}{\boldsymbol{x}'\boldsymbol{M}\boldsymbol{x}}, \tag{2.37}$$

where $\boldsymbol{T} = \boldsymbol{M}'\boldsymbol{W}\boldsymbol{M}$, and $\boldsymbol{M}'\boldsymbol{M} = \boldsymbol{M}^2 = \boldsymbol{M}$, since $\boldsymbol{M}$ is idempotent. We assume, without loss of generality, that the X variates have zero means and unit variances. Then, under assumption N, the moment generating function of $\boldsymbol{x}'\boldsymbol{T}\boldsymbol{x}$ is

$$\begin{aligned} \mathrm{E}[\exp(\theta \boldsymbol{x}'\boldsymbol{T}\boldsymbol{x})] &= (2\pi)^{-n/2} \int_{(n)} \exp(\theta \boldsymbol{x}'\boldsymbol{T}\boldsymbol{x} - \tfrac{1}{2}\boldsymbol{x}'\boldsymbol{x}) \mathrm{d}x_1, ..., \mathrm{d}x_n \\ &= |\boldsymbol{I}_n - 2\theta \boldsymbol{T}|^{-1/2}. \end{aligned} \tag{2.38}$$

The moments of the numerator of equation (2.37) may be evaluated from equation (2.38), and cumulants of $\boldsymbol{x}'\boldsymbol{T}\boldsymbol{x}$ are

$$\kappa_j = 2^{j-1}(j-1)! \sum_{i=1}^{n} \nu_i^j, \tag{2.39}$$

where $\nu_1, ..., \nu_n$ are the eigenvalues (latent roots) of the matrix $\boldsymbol{T}$. For a more detailed discussion see Durbin and Watson (1950, pages 418–21). From equations (2.22) and (2.39), the cumulants of I are

$$\mathrm{E}(I) = \frac{n\bar{\nu}}{n-1}, \qquad n\bar{\nu} = \sum_{i=1}^{n} \nu_i, \tag{2.40}$$

$$\kappa_2(I) = \mathrm{var}(I) = \mu_2(I) = \frac{2}{n^2-1} \sum_{i=1}^{n} (\nu_i - \bar{\nu})^2 = \frac{2n}{n^2-1}\sigma_\nu^2, \tag{2.41}$$

$$\kappa_3(I) = \mu_3(I) = \frac{8\sum(\nu_i - \bar{\nu})^3}{(n-1)(n+1)(n+3)}, \tag{2.42}$$

and

$$\begin{aligned} \kappa_4(I) &= \mu_4(I) - 3[\mu_2(I)]^2 \\ &= \frac{48\sum(\nu_i - \bar{\nu})^4}{(n-1)(n+1)(n+3)(n+5)} + \frac{96(n+2)\left[\sum(\nu_i - \bar{\nu})^2\right]^2}{(n^2-1)^2(n+3)(n+5)}. \end{aligned} \tag{2.43}$$

The dominant term in the jth cumulant is

$$\sum_{i=1}^{n} (\nu_i - \bar{\nu})^j .$$

The set of necessary and sufficient conditions for the distribution of I to approach normality is that, for $j \geqslant 3$,

$$\phi_j(\nu) = \sum_{i=1}^{n} (\nu_i - \bar{\nu})^j \Bigg/ \left[\sum_{i=1}^{n} (\nu_i - \bar{\nu})^2 \right]^{j/2} \tag{2.44}$$

be o(1), where o means 'of smaller order than'. That is, $\phi_j(\nu)$, should be of order $n^{-\epsilon}$ (where $\epsilon > 0$). The purpose of the set of conditions (2.44) is to ensure that the higher order cumulants of $[I - E(I)]/[\mu_2(I)]^{1/2}$ vanish as n increases. The conditions will be met provided that the extreme ν_i are not too large relative to the others. A sufficient, but not necessary, condition which formalises the concept of 'not too large' is that

$$\frac{\max\limits_i |\nu_i - \bar{\nu}|}{\sigma_\nu} \text{ be } O(n^{-1/2}), \tag{2.45}$$

where O means 'of the same order as' and σ_ν is defined by equation (2.41). Equations (2.44) and (2.45) can be transferred back to the original matrix, $\boldsymbol{W}$. Denote the eigenvalues of $\boldsymbol{W}$ by $\lambda_1, \ldots, \lambda_n$. Then conditions (2.44) and (2.45) apply to $\phi_j(\lambda)$ and $\max\limits_i |\lambda_i - \bar{\lambda}|/\sigma_\lambda$.

To show that the conditions are not always satisfied, we present a simple counter-example.

Example. Consider the star lattice with a single articulation point, as shown in figure 2.4.

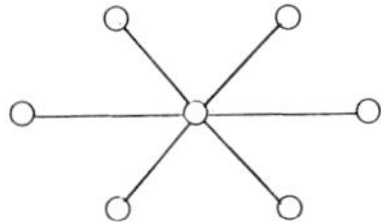

Figure 2.4. A simple star lattice.

Label the centre 1 and the other points 2, 3, ..., n. Assign binary weights to each link so that the matrix of weights is

$$\boldsymbol{W} = \left[\begin{array}{c|c} 0 & 1 \; . \; . \; . \; 1 \\ \hline 1 & \\ \vdots & \boldsymbol{O} \\ 1 & \end{array} \right] .$$

The eigenvalues of $\boldsymbol{W}$ are $(n-1)$ zeros and $-2(1-n^{-1})$. Thus

$$\bar{\lambda} = -\frac{2(n-1)}{n^2}, \qquad n\sigma_\lambda^2 = 4\left(1 - \frac{1}{n}\right)^3$$

and

$$\sum_{i=1}^{n} (\lambda_i - \bar{\lambda})^3 = -8\left(1 - \frac{1}{n}\right)^4 \left(1 - \frac{2}{n}\right),$$

so that,

$$\phi_3(\lambda) = -\left(1 - \frac{2}{n}\right)\left(1 - \frac{1}{n}\right)^{-\frac{1}{2}} \rightarrow -1$$

as $n \rightarrow \infty$. It can also be seen that

$$\max_i |\lambda_i - \bar{\lambda}| / \sigma_\lambda = (n-1)^{\frac{1}{2}}.$$

Hence the distribution of I is not asymptotically normal for this lattice. Cliff and Ord (1972) show that a beta distribution is appropriate for this lattice.

The proof of asymptotic normality for BB and BW under free sampling follows from a theorem of Noether (1970), which may be stated as follows:

Theorem 1: Consider the statistic $T = \sum_{(2)} w_{ij} t_{ij}$, where t_{ij} is a uniformly bounded function of the observed values x_i and x_j, and t_{ij} and t_{kl} are independent unless they have at least one common subscript. Also, put $W = \sum_{(2)} w_{ij}$. Then as the sample size, n, tends to infinity, T will be asymptotically normally distributed if $W^{-2}\text{var}(T)$ is exactly of order n^{-1}.

Proof. Carried out by showing that the moments of T approach those of the normal distribution as $n \rightarrow \infty$. For details, the reader should consult Noether (1970).

To see how this theorem can be applied to the statistics given in chapter 1, consider the BW join count and let

$$t_{ij} = 1, \text{ if the join is } BW,$$
$$= 0, \text{ otherwise.}$$

For regular lattices it follows that S_1/W^2 and S_2/W^2 are both of order n^{-1}.

Provided that $0 < p < 1$, it follows that $W^{-2}\text{var}(T)$ is exactly of order n^{-1}, and the statistic is asymptotically normally distributed for any regular lattice; var(T) is given by equation (1.57).

As a counter-example, consider the star lattice described earlier. Here, $W = 2(n-1)$, $S_1 = 4(n-1)$, and $S_2 = 4n(n-1)$, so that S_1/W^2 is of order n^{-1}. However, S_2/W^2 is of order 1, so that W^{-2} var(T) is of order 1 and the theorem does not hold. As the theorem expresses only a sufficient condition, this does not demonstrate that the asymptotic distribution *is* non-normal, but warns that this may well be the case (non-normality may be established by showing that the Pearson β_1 coefficient does not approach zero as $n \rightarrow \infty$).

Asymptotic normality for these statistics may also be demonstrated directly, as in Moran (1948), for example.

In order to establish the asymptotic normality of statistics under assumption R we use the following theorem of Hoeffding (1952):

Theorem 2: Let $F(y)$ be a distribution function uniquely determined by its moments, μ_k, and let $\{F_n(y)\}$, $n = 1, 2, ...$, be a sequence of random distribution functions with moments μ_{nk}.

If $\mu_{nk} \to \mu_k$ in probability as $n \to \infty$ for $k = 1, 2, ...$, then $F_n(y) \to F(y)$ in probability at every continuity point of $F(y)$.

In the present context, let $F_n(y)$ correspond to the distribution of any statistic, under assumption R, for n observations, and let $F(y)$ correspond to the normal distribution. Then the statistic will have a normal distribution if its moments converge in probability to those of the normal. In practice, it is often convenient to show that the moments of the statistic under assumption R converge to those under assumption N, and then to use the asymptotic normality of the statistic under assumption N.

In general, provided that S_1/W^2 and S_2/W^2 are both of order n^{-1}, and some of the observations are different [that is, prob$(x_i \neq x_j) > 0$ for some pairs], the theorem will hold. For binary data, the requirement is readily expressed as

$$0 < \lim_{n \to \infty} \frac{n_1}{n} < 1.$$

With regard to the conditions on the weights, the underlying requirement is that no definite subset of counties should dominate the lattice, as does the articulation point in the star lattice. A useful check, deriving from the requirement that S_2/W^2 be $O(n^{-1})$ is that

$$\max_i \left\{ \frac{(w_{i.} + w_{.i})}{W} \right\} \text{be of order } n^{-1}. \tag{2.46}$$

This is not a formal condition that can be incorporated into a theorem, but it can be checked and gives a guide as to whether the application of a normal approximation is reasonable.

2.5 Evaluation of the distribution functions

The proof of normality given above is asymptotic only, and may not provide a reasonable approximation for the small lattices met in applications (typically n is less than 50). Empirical investigations (Cliff and Ord, 1971) suggest that this is indeed the case, and alternative approximations to the distribution functions (DF's) of the coefficients are required in such cases if we are to test sensibly the calculated value of the coefficients. One way of refining results would be to use the third (and possibly fourth) moments of the statistics to define a Gram–Charlier expansion. This has not been pursued to date because of the practical difficulties of evaluating the higher order moments numerically, even when the theoretical forms are known. However, for regular lattices and under assumption N, this approach deserves further consideration. We recall that the third and fourth moments are available as listed in sections 2.2.2 and 2.3.2.

A second approach is to use Monte Carlo methods to examine the form of the DF's of the coefficients. There are four factors which will affect the shape of the DF's. These are:

1. the shape of the county system and the average number of joins per county (defined as A/n);
2. the weights used $\{w_{ij}\}$;
3. the distribution of the variate, X;
4. the size of the county system, n.

The authors have recently completed an extensive simulation study of the DF's of all the measures of autocorrelation described in chapter 1. The findings for the I coefficient have been published in Cliff and Ord (1971), so we review the results only briefly in section 2.5.1. We then go on, in sections 2.5.2 and 2.6, to report the findings obtained for the join count and c statistics.

2.5.1 Simulation study for I

In the case of the I coefficient, various data sets were taken and the sampling frame comprised the $n!$ possible arrangements of the data values among the n counties in a given county system. In any one set of runs of the simulation programme, three of the four factors '1'–'4' above were held constant, and the fourth was allowed to vary, so that its effect on the DF of I could be explored. Since, for testing purposes, we only wish to evaluate the DF of I in the tails, the centre of the distribution was largely ignored, and interest was focussed on the tail regions for conventional probability levels of up to 10% in a one-tailed test.

Each simulation run consisted of generating m random permutations of the data set. In each run, m was usually 300, and anything from one to six such runs were carried out for a particular combination of the factors. I was computed for each permutation. The empirical distribution of I was constructed, and the observed percentage points of this distribution were compared with the cutoff points obtained from various theoretical approximations. The 100α percentage point of I, I_α, in these approximations was usually of the form,

$$y_\alpha = \frac{I_\alpha + k_\alpha (n-1)^{-1}}{\sigma(I)}$$

or

$$I_\alpha = y_\alpha \sigma(I) - k_\alpha (n-1)^{-1}, \qquad (2.47)$$

where y_α is treated as a standardised normal deviate. $\sigma(I)$ is the standard deviation of I, and k_α is a constant depending only on α. The straightforward use of the normal distribution corresponds to taking $k_\alpha = 1$ for all α. It is clear that, whatever k_α is chosen, equation (2.47) approaches the normal approximation as n increases.

A total of 36 different factor combinations was considered. Binary weights were most commonly used, as it soon became evident that the main effect of general weights was exerted through increases in the standard deviation.

As a result of this study, the following procedure was proposed for evaluating the percentage points of I. First, for any given lattice of size n, consider a notional regular lattice of size $t \times t = n$. We define A/n ratios as

$$R = \frac{2(t-1)}{t} < 2, \tag{2.48}$$

in the rook's case, and

$$Q = \frac{2(t-1)(2t-1)}{t^2} < 4 \tag{2.49}$$

in the queen's case. The upper limits occur only if the lattice is mapped onto a torus. The choice of approximation is then made as follows.

Step 1
Calculate A/n for the lattice under consideration (a necessary step anyway).

Step 2
If $R < A/n \leqslant Q$, use equation (2.47) with $k_\alpha = (10\alpha)^{1/2}$. If $A/n \leqslant R$ or $A/n > Q$, use equation (2.47) with $k_\alpha = 1$ for all α. As previously stated, these approximations apply only to the tail regions. Note that α is taken as the one tail probability. For a two-tailed test of size $\alpha*$, put $\alpha = \alpha*/2$ in k_α.

Example. Consider a 25 county system with $A = 55$. Take $t = n^{1/2} = 5$. Then $R = 1{\cdot}6$ and $Q = 2{\cdot}88$. As $A/n = 2{\cdot}2$, the approximation should be used with $k_\alpha = (10\alpha)^{1/2}$. Thus, when $\alpha = 0{\cdot}05$, $k_\alpha = 0{\cdot}7071$ and when $\alpha = 0{\cdot}025$, $k_\alpha = 0{\cdot}5$.

The justification for the proposed rules is that, in a wide variety of situations, the resulting value for I_α did not generally differ significantly from the conventional empirical cutoff levels when tested using chi-square. For fuller details see Cliff and Ord (1971).

The approximations are not satisfactory when:

(1) binary data are used, except when the underlying population is roughly symmetric and the lattice size is fairly large; see section 2.5.3 for further discussion.

(2) one county, or a small group of counties, in the system figures in a high percentage of joins (see the conditions for asymptotic normality in section 2.4).

(3) when n is small ($\leqslant 10$, say). A complete enumeration of the distribution function is often feasible in such cases, particularly when the lattice is regular and binary weights are used.

The rules suggested are clearly '*ad hoc*' and should not be applied blindly; for example, if R is near A/n, look at both approximations. However, used with care, we believe that the resulting inference will not be seriously in error. Finally we stress again that the suggested transformations do not seek to approximate the entire distribution of I by the normal, but only the tail regions.

2.5.2 Simulation study for *c*

In view of the extended discussion of the form of the sampling distribution of I in section 2.5.1 and in Cliff and Ord (1971), the discussion for c can be fairly brief.

Eight distinct simulation runs were performed as shown in table 2.1. The 100α percentage points for the tail areas of the distribution of c using the normal approximation are given by

$$c_\alpha = y_\alpha \sigma(c) - 1, \tag{2.50}$$

where y_α is the standard normal deviate, $\sigma(c)$ is the standard deviation of c, and $\mathrm{E}(c) = 1$. This approximation works well for the lower tail of c (corresponding to positive spatial autocorrelation), but not so well for the upper tail (negative spatial autocorrelation), where the approximation is markedly conservative; that is, the nominal probability that $c > c_\alpha$ in the upper tail may be considerably greater than the true probability. For the

Table 2.1. Details of simulation runs for c.

County system	Weights used	Data set	m
Eire (excluding County Dublin)	binary [(a)]	milch cows [(b)]	200
		ranks	500
		normal scores	500
	county centre/ common boundary [(c)]	milch cows	400
5 x 5 regular lattice, queen's case	binary	ranks	600
		normal scores	600
12 x 2 regular lattice, queen's case, with a 25th county on one end joining 2 other counties	binary	ranks	300
		normal scores	300

(a) $\delta_{ij} = 1$ if the ith and jth counties have a common edge or vertex, and $\delta_{ij} = 0$ otherwise.
(b) Results are taken from Geary (1954), table 2, data set (4).
(c) Defined in Cliff and Ord (1969, pages 32–33 and table A1).

upper tail, the revised formula,

$$c_\alpha = 1 - y_\alpha\, \sigma(c) - k_\alpha(n-1)^{-1}, \tag{2.51}$$

is recommended, where $k_\alpha = (10\alpha)^{1/2}$, as for I.

2.6 Simulation studies for the join count statistics, $k = 2$

The binary form of the data means that the progress to normality of the join count statistics can be very slow, since the probability measure is concentrated at a few points in an irregular manner. We refer to such distributions as being 'lumpy'. Because of the difficulties created by this lumpiness, we have judged it worthwhile to give a fairly full account of the simulation work done on these distributions, so that the extent of the empirical backing for the approximations suggested can be assessed.

2.6.1 The experimental procedure

As in the simulation studies of the sampling distributions of the I and c statistics, a variety of lattices was used together with different proportions (nonfree sampling) or probabilities (free sampling) for black and white cells. Since nonbinary weights make the distribution less lumpy and somewhat easier to approximate, we stoically used binary weights throughout the study. However, the final results may reasonably be applied to the nonbinary weighted forms of the statistics.

To indicate the scope of the sampling experiments, we shall give details for the study of the BB join count under nonfree sampling. The lattices used were as follows:

(1) regular lattices, queen's case ($\delta_{ij} = 1$ if, and only if, two cells had a common edge or vertex) for squares of side 5(1)10. The square of side 6 was also mapped onto a torus, so that all counties had eight joins;

(2) the circle comprising 156 cells (equivalent to a circular time series of this length);

(3) the county systems of England and Wales, and of Eire, excluding County Dublin.

In cases (2) and (3), $\delta_{ij} = 1$ if, and only if, the ith and jth counties had a common boundary. The total number of counties, n, and the total number of joins, A, and A/n, are given in table 2.2. For each lattice, the number of black cells, n_1, was taken as the nearest integer to np, $p = 0{\cdot}1(0{\cdot}1)0{\cdot}9$. For each lattice and value of p, m (= 600) random permutations were generated.

The normal and chi-squared distributions were considered to be plausible approximations to the sampling distribution of BB. Both approximations are fitted using the first two moments of BB given in equations (1.13) and (1.16). Let μ and σ represent, respectively, the mean and standard deviation of the statistic BB. Then, for the normal approximation, N, the

100α percentage point for BB, BB_α say, is given by

$$BB_\alpha = y_\alpha \sigma + \mu, \tag{2.52}$$

where y_α is the 100α percentage point of the standard normal curve. For the χ^2 approximation,

$$BB_\alpha = \gamma x_\alpha, \tag{2.53}$$

where $\gamma = \sigma^2/2\mu$ and x_α is the 100α percentage point of chi-squared with $\nu = 2\mu^2/\sigma^2$ degrees of freedom.

For a given lattice and value of n_1, the upper and lower 10, 5, 2·5, 1, and 0·5 percentage points of N and χ^2 were evaluated and used to partition the generated sampling distribution of BB into eleven classes with boundaries,

$$\begin{gathered} BB < L(0{\cdot}005),\ L(0{\cdot}005) \leqslant BB < L(0{\cdot}01),\ \ldots,\ L(0{\cdot}05) \leqslant BB < L(0{\cdot}10), \\ L(0{\cdot}10) \leqslant BB < U(0{\cdot}10),\ U(0{\cdot}10) \leqslant BB < U(0{\cdot}05),\ \ldots,\ U(0{\cdot}005) < BB. \end{gathered} \tag{2.54}$$

Here $L(\alpha)$ and $U(\alpha)$ represent, respectively, the lower and upper 100α percentage points, and BB represents the number of the m permutations in each class. Thus if $L(\cdot 005) = 4{\cdot}43$, the permutations which yielded 0, 1, 2, 3, or 4 BB joins were recorded in the first class. The goodness-of-fit between the observed frequencies so obtained and the corresponding expected frequencies was examined using the X^2 test with 10 degrees of freedom (for the 11 classes). This was done for every lattice and value of n_1. The results of the X^2 test for all cases are given in table 2.2, while the detailed results which arise from applying equation (2.54) to the 9 x 9 regular lattice, queen's case, are given in the first eight columns of table 2.3.

2.6.2 Analysis of the results

In table 2.2, some X^2 values have been omitted because the lumpy nature of the tail areas made it impossible sensibly to fit any approximation. Greater lumpiness tends to occur in the negative tail, and is even more marked with the BB distributions under free sampling. So, for example, in the 5 x 5 regular lattice, queen's case, with $p = 0{\cdot}1$, the 600 random permutations yielded 0, 1, 2, ... BB joins with the following frequencies,

Number of *BB* joins	Frequency		Number of *BB* joins	Frequency	
	nonfree sampling	free sampling		nonfree sampling	free sampling
0	239	350	5	0	5
1	293	146	6	0	3
2	50	58	7	0	2
3	18	25	8	0	0
4	0	8	9	0	3

Table 2.2. Results of X^2 test of significance for *BB* joins, nonfree sampling.

Lattice	n	A	$\frac{A}{n}$	p 0·1 approximation		0·2		0·3		0·4		0·5		0·6		0·7		0·8		0·9	
				N	χ^2	N	χ^2	N	χ^2	N	χ^2	N	χ^2	N	χ^2	N	χ^2	N	χ^2	N	χ^2
10 × 10 queen's case	100	342	3·42	-		12·6	18·8 **	18·0 **	11·7	10·0	11·7	9·9	14·8	6·1	8·2	9·2	9·2	12·1	12·1	10·3	10·3
9 × 9 queen's case	81	272	3·36	-		15·3	58·1 ****	19·4 **	7·5	20·2 **	8·3	7·7	9·7	11·3	11·3	12·5	12·5	13·2	7·1	7·8	6·4
8 × 8 queen's case	64	210	3·28	-		-		19·0 **	10·6	18·7 **	12·7	16·3 *	7·4	6·0	10·0	11·0	12·3	14·8	14·4	10·2	10·2
7 × 7 queen's case	49	156	3·18	-		-		11·8	22·0 **	15·3	6·9	21·7 **	13·8	18·1 *	13·4	20·3 **	15·7	25·4 ****	13·2	+	
156 cell circle	156	156	1·00	-		-		12·3	27·8 ****	10·2	9·6	9·9	19·7 **	14·6	14·6	14·3	14·3	+		+	
English and Welsh counties	53	119	2·25	-		-		-		19·1 **	12·9	37·2 ****	7·4	20·5 **	9·0	16·1 *	5·5	9·3	7·2	13·5	12·2
6 × 6 queen's case	36	110	3·06	-		-		-		-		8·3	30·5 ****	23·1 **	11·1	21·2 **	6·5	27·5 ****	14·6	+	
5 × 5 queen's case	25	72	2·88	-		-		-		-		17·0 *	9·4	13·9	12·1	7·9	3·9	17·4 *	9·4	+	
Eire (excluding County Dublin)	25	55	2·20	-		-		-		-		-		-		7·6	20·5 **	11·0	11·0	+	
6 × 6 queen's case on a torus	36	144	4·00	-		-		-		15·0	31·9 ****	6·0	7·3	+		+		+		+	

Significance levels (one-tail) * = 10%, ** = 5%, **** = 1%.
- indicates that the distribution is too lumpy in the negative tail to make two-tailed test for spatial autocorrelation sensible.
+ indicates that the distribution is too lumpy in the positive tail to make two-tailed test for spatial autocorrelation sensible.

The following conclusions may be drawn from these facts and table 2.2.
1. Both approximations are fairly successful, provided that $\min(p, 1-p)$ is not too small, say less than or equal to $0 \cdot 2$ for lattice sizes commonly encountered in practice. However, the χ^2 form appears to have the edge.
2. For values of p at equivalent distances from $p = 0 \cdot 0$ and $p = 1 \cdot 0$, the approximations perform much better for the larger value of p. Thus the approximations are better for $p = 0 \cdot 7$ and $0 \cdot 8$ than for $p = 0 \cdot 3$ and $0 \cdot 2$ respectively. *Therefore the join count(s) for the more common colours(s) should be used.* Nothing is lost by using one colour rather than another provided the BW count is also examined; see equation (2.6).
3. From asymptotic power considerations (see chapter 7), counties should be coloured so that the probability of a county being B is near $0 \cdot 5$.

Before making a final recommendation about the form of approximation, it is instructive to look at a singularly ill-behaved case, the 9×9 regular lattice, queen's case, with $p = 0 \cdot 2$ (in fact $n_1 = 16$). The results appear in table 2.3, and give the observed frequencies for the normal and chi-square approximations, along with the expected frequencies required to achieve exactly the probability levels specified in the first column. The X^2 test values are given at the foot of each column.

If the results of table 2.3 are taken at their face value, the case for using the normal approximation appears overwhelming. However, if the cumulative figures in table 2.4 are taken into account, the chi-squared approximation would seem to give a somewhat better indication of 'where to draw the line'. The reason for this seemingly paradoxical behaviour is to be found by looking again at table 2.3, where the cutoff points for the N and χ^2 approximations are given. The lumpy nature of the distribution means that a slight difference between the approximations can empty a whole class, as happens with the 26 observations for $\alpha = 0 \cdot 10/0 \cdot 05$ in the lower tail. This reinforces the conclusion that the join count(s) for the more common colour(s) should be used.

The 'square root' (SR) transformation referred to in tables 2.3 and 2.4 is the transformation commonly used to approximate the chi-squared by the normal when the number of degrees of freedom ν is large. Typically in using the χ^2 approximation we found that the value for ν was large, so that little is lost by using the square root transformation. The 100α percentage point of BB is given by

$$BB_\alpha = \sigma^2 \left[y_\alpha + \left(\frac{4\mu^2 - \sigma^2}{\sigma^2} \right)^{1/2} \right]^2 \Big/ 4\mu, \tag{2.55}$$

where y_α is the 100α percentage point of the normal distribution.

The results are analysed in a different way in table 2.5. If the approximations are correct, then for $m = 600$, we would expect 15 observations to fall below the lower $2\frac{1}{2}$ percentage points, and 15 observations to fall above the upper $2\frac{1}{2}$ percentage points. Consider the 52 data/lattice combinations in table 2.1 for which X^2 values are recorded.

Table 2.3. Comparison of approximations for *BB* statistic, nonfree sampling ($n_1 = 16$), for 9 x 9 regular lattice, queen's case.

Nominal probability level		Expected frequency	Approximate cutoff·points and observed frequencies								
			normal (N)			chi-squared (χ^2)			square root (SR)		
			cutoff	values of *BB* statistic in class	frequency	cutoff	values of *BB* statistic in class	frequency	cutoff	values of *BB* statistic in class	frequency
Upper tail	0·10	30	13·57	14	39	13·69	14	39	13·64	14	39
	0·05	15	14·56	15	16	14·93	15, 16	27	14·83	15	16
	0·025	9	15·42	16	11	16·07	17	6	15·89	16, 17	17
	0·01	3	16·41	17	6	17·47	18	2	17·16	18	2
	0·005	3	17·09	18 or more	5	18·46	19 or more	3	18·06	19 or more	3
Lower tail	0·10	30	6·58	6	26	6·78	empty class	0	6·73	6	26
	0·05	15	5·59	5	11	6·05	6	26	5·94	empty class	0
	0·025	9	4·73	4	5	5·46	5	11	5·30	5	11
	0·01	3	3·74	empty class	0	4·83	empty class	0	4·60	empty class	0
	0·005	3	3·06	3 or less	1	4·43	4 or less	6	4·15	4 or less	6
Remainder		480			480			480			480
Total		600			600			600			600
Value of X^2 statistic					15·3			58·1			32·2

Of the 90 combinations examined, these 52 were the ones for which the N and χ^2 approximations could sensibly be used to provide a two-tailed test for spatial autocorrelation. For these 52, the average numbers of observations which in fact fell above and below the upper and lower $2\frac{1}{2}$ percentage points, and the standard deviations are given for each approximation. In addition the number of times that each approximation was liberal (observed number of *BB* joins exceeded required number) is given. From table 2.5, we can see that the chi-squared approximation, although a little conservative, is fairly well balanced in both tails. By

Table 2.4. An analysis of cumulative frequencies for *BB* statistic, nonfree sampling ($n_1 = 16$), for 9 x 9 regular lattice, queen's case.

Nominal probability levels		Cumulative expected frequencies	Cumulative observed frequencies using approximation		
			normal (N)	chi-squared (χ^2)	square root (SR)
Upper tail	0·10	60	77	77	77
	0·05	30	38	38	38
	0·025	15	22	11	22
	0·01	6	11	5	5
	0·005	3	5	3	3
Lower tail	0·10	60	43	43	43
	0·05	30	17	43	17
	0·025	15	6	17	17
	0·01	6	1	6	6
	0·005	3	1	6	6
X^2			15·3	58·1	33·1

Table 2.5. An analysis of the number of observations for the *BB* 5% points (two tails).

Item	Approximation			
	normal (N)		chi-squared (χ^2)	
	upper tail	lower tail	upper tail	lower tail
Required number of observations (out of 600)	15	15	15	15
Average observed number (52 runs)	15·9	11·0	12·9	13·0
Standard deviation	5·2	3·5	3·8	3·9
Range	5–30	4–21	5–21	4–23
Number of times observed > required	27	4	10	13

contrast the normal approximation is slightly 'heavy' in the upper tail, and decidedly 'light' in the lower tail.

In table 2.6, the same analysis is performed for the 0·5% points in each tail. Here the heaviness in the upper tail, and lightness in the lower tail, of the normal approximation is more marked. The number of times no *BB* joins were observed is a measure of the number of times that the approximation is 'grossly conservative'.

Finally, on the basis of the results presented in this section, we conclude that the normal approximation is not bad, but that the chi-squared (or square root, which is virtually the same thing) is somewhat better. Either equation (2.53) or (2.55) can be readily applied.

2.6.3 The other join count statistics

Similar extensive analyses have been carried out for *BB* joins under free sampling, and for *BW* joins under both free and nonfree sampling. As a result of these studies the following approximations are recommended:

1. *BB* joins (free sampling). The third central moment for *BB*, $\mu_3(BB)$, may be evaluated without too much difficulty using the following equation,

$$\mu_3(BB) = j_4\, p^2(1-p)(1-2p+16p^2-26p^3) + 3j_5\, p^3(1-p)(1-12p+18p^2) + 6j_6\, p^4(1-p)^2 + 6j_7\, p^4(1-p)(1-2p) + 6j_8\, p^3(1-p)^2(1+p), \qquad (2.56)$$

where j_4–j_8 are given by (see figure 2.2)

$$j_4 = \sum{}_{(2)} w_{ij}^3, \qquad j_5 = \sum{}_{(2)} w_{ij}^2\, w_{i.},$$

$$j_6 = \sum{}_{(2)} w_{ij}\, w_{i.}\, w_{j.}, \qquad j_7 = \sum{}_{(1)} w_{i.}^3\,.$$

Table 2.6. An analysis of the number of observations for the *BB* 1% points (two tails).

Item	Approximation			
	normal (N)		chi-squared (χ^2)	
	upper tail	lower tail	upper tail	lower tail
Required number of observations (out of 600)	3	3	3	3
Average observed number (52 runs)	3·77	1·81	2·54	2·83
Standard deviation	1·66	1·47	1·47	1·29
Range	1–8	0–6	0–5	0–6
Number of times observed > required	26	6	16	15
Number of times no observed *BB* > required	0	11	3	2

The best approximation is then the beta distribution, β, with variable $x = BB/R$, range [0, 1], and a and b are parameters, where

$$a = \frac{\mu(2\mu_3\mu+\mu^2\sigma^2-\sigma^4)}{2\sigma^4\mu-\mu_3\mu^2+\mu_3\sigma^2}, \tag{2.57}$$

$$b = \frac{a(a+1)\sigma^2}{\mu^2-a\sigma^2}, \tag{2.58}$$

and

$$R = \frac{\mu(a+b)}{a}. \tag{2.59}$$

See Ord (1972). The test is most easily carried out using Snedecor's F. For the upper tail, put $F = x/(1-x)$ with $2a$ and $2b$ degrees of freedom in the standard tables. For the lower tail, use $F^* = (1-x)/x$ with $2b$ and $2a$ degrees of freedom.

99 data set/lattice combinations were studied. The results of the X^2 test of significance obtained by applying equation (2.54) for the beta, normal, and chi-squared approximations to these combinations are given in table 2.7. Because of lumpiness in either the positive or the negative tail of BB, a two-tailed test for spatial autocorrelation could sensibly be carried out using any of the approximations in only 54 of the cases examined. However, for these 54 cases, β was the preferred approximation on 43 occasions, χ^2 on 6, N on 4, and β and χ^2 were equal on one occasion. If the beta approximation is not used, the square root or chi-squared approximation suggested in the previous section is somewhat better than the normal. Again it is recommended that the more common colours be used, noting that the negative tail is very lumpy when $p \leqslant 0{\cdot}3$ in small lattices ($n \leqslant 50$).

2. BW joins. The results for BW joins proved to be rather similar to those for the c statistic. Let μ and σ denote, respectively, the mean and variance of the BW statistic. Then the cutoff point for the 100α percentage tail area for BW, BW_α say, is given by

$$BW_\alpha = y_\alpha\sigma+\mu-k_\alpha, \tag{2.60}$$

where, in the upper tail, $k_\alpha = 1-(10\alpha)^{1/2}$ for both free and nonfree sampling; and, in the lower tail, $k_\alpha = 2[1-(10\alpha)^{1/2}]$ for nonfree sampling, and $k_\alpha = 3[1-(10\alpha)^{1/2}]$ for free sampling.

The excessive lumpiness noted in the *lower* tail for BB joins under free sampling also occurs in the *upper* tail for BW joins under free sampling, although not for nonfree sampling. Thus when $m = 600$, whereas we would expect 15 observations to fall above the upper $2\frac{1}{2}$ percentage point, on the basis of 57 data set/lattice combinations, the actual numbers observed ranged from 4 to 30 inclusive, and for 51 of these combinations lay in the range 6 to 24 inclusive. Fortunately, we are usually interested in testing for the presence of positive spatial autocorrelation, and these

Table 2.7. The results of the X^2 test of significance for *BB* joins, free sampling.

Lattice	n	A	$\frac{A}{n}$	p 0·1 approximation			0·2			0·3			0·4			0·5			0·6			0·7			0·8			0·9		
				N	χ^2	β	N	χ^2	β	N	χ^2	β	N	χ^2	β	N	χ^2	β	N	χ^2	β	N	χ^2	β	N	χ^2	β	N	χ^2	β
10 x 10 queen's case	100	342	3·42		–		35·5 **	23·0 **	10·8	32·6 ****	7·3	7·3	22·8 **	5·4	12·4	20·6 **	7·5	12·8	17·7 *	11·5	18·6 **	19·9 **	10·9	13·6	20·1 **	21·5 **	14·7	10·8	10·6	13·6
156 cell circle	156	156	1·00		–			–		20·5 **	20·6 **	7·9	11·9	22·6 **	14·1	13·4	10·0	9·0	8·6	16·6 *	7·6	15·2	17·1 *	13·0	21·7 **	18·2 *	3·6	19·0 **	34·0 ****	11·9
6 x 6 queen's case	36	110	3·06		–			–		81·2 ****	35·9 ****	14·0	26·8 ****	22·7 **	8·5	26·4 ****	11·8	12·3	21·0 **	12·9	9·3	17·8 *	20·5 **	11·0	10·4	24·1 ****	10·7	16·4 *	31·4 ****	9·9
English and Welsh counties	53	119	2·25		–			–			–		32·2 ****	38·4 ****	9·1	22·5 **	7·2	15·6	14·4	15·1	9·9	9·6	11·4	6·0	7·2	20·5 **	11·0	17·7 *	24·6 ****	11·3
6 x 6 queen's case on a torus	36	144	4·00		–			–			–		29·9 ****	17·2 *	9·8	22·6 **	10·8	8·4	12·8	14·4	8·0	14·8	5·1	8·6	29·9 ****	27·4 ****	13·4		+	
5 x 5 queen's case	25	72	2·88		–			–			–		42·3 ****	25·8 ****	9·2	64·7 ****	32·0 ****	9·4	19·9 **	16·3 *	9·2	13·2	15·9	8·6	15·4	34·7 ****	12·9		+	
(12 x 2)+1 queen's case	25	58	2·32		–			–			–		44·7 ****	57·5 ****	15·5	26·1 ****	29·6 ****	2·6	22·3 **	35·3 ****	12·5	9·5	28·2 ****	10·0	7·6	52·8 ****	5·7		+	
Eire (excl. Co. Dublin)	25	55	2·20		–			–			–			–		30·2 ****	39·0 ****	10·5	19·0 **	18·9 **	4·2	21·8 **	23·3 ****	9·9	6·1	23·6 ****	4·5		+	
5 x 5 rook's case	25	40	1·60		–			–			–			–			–		43·0 ****	13·8	12·2	8·8	29·0 ****	7·2	23·7 ****	48·9 ****	11·0		+	
(12 x 2)+1 rook's case	25	36	1·44		–			–			–			–			–		23·2 **	14·7	11·9	20·5 **	14·4	9·2	10·8	60·9 ****	7·6		+	
25 cell circle	25	25	1·00		–			–			–			–			–		24·0 ****	24·4 ****	9·9		+			+			+	

Significance levels (one-tail) * = 10%, ** = 5%, **** = 1%.
– indicates that the distribution is too lumpy in the negative tail to make two-tailed test for spatial autocorrelation sensible.
+ indicates that the distribution is too lumpy in the positive tail to make two-tailed test for spatial autocorrelation sensible.

lumpy tails correspond to negative spatial autocorrelation. Where we do wish to test for negative spatial autocorrelation with BW joins, the approximation suggested in equation (2.60) works tolerably well. It is unlikely that any worthwhile improvement can be made except by complete enumeration of the probabilities in the tail area.

2.7 Permutations tests

When the exact distribution function is intractable, and approximations to it are of doubtful accuracy, a procedure due to Barnard and developed by Hope (1968) may be used.

If m values of the statistic concerned are generated under H_0, we should reject H_0 at the $100[(j+1)/(m+1)]$ percent level if the observed value of the statistic exceeded at least the $(m-j)$ smallest generated values (assuming the critical region to be the upper tail).

As an example we take data on the percentage change in population, 1951–1961, in the counties of Wales, including Monmouth. These data are drawn from the Preliminary Census Report (General Register Office, 1961), and are reproduced here in table 2.8. Against the null hypothesis of no spatial autocorrelation in population changes by county we range the alternative of positive spatial autocorrelation, looking for a drift from the rural northern counties of Wales to the more industrialised south. Ranks were used instead of the raw data so that comparisons between the Hope features of the data (the use of ranks is a reasonably efficient procedure, as shown in section 7.3.5). The coefficient I was evaluated using binary weights: $\delta_{ij} = 1$ if the counties i and j had a common boundary and $\delta_{ij} = 0$ otherwise.

Under H_0, using randomisation, $E(I) = -0{\cdot}0833$ and $\sigma(I) = 0{\cdot}1808$. The observed value of I for the rank data is $I_{obs} = 0{\cdot}1106$, yielding the standard deviate $z = 1{\cdot}07$. From tables of the normal distribution (that is using the normal approximation) $\text{prob}(I > I_{obs}) = 0{\cdot}1423$, and there is not sufficient evidence to reject H_0. Inspection of more detailed data reveals a more complex pattern of migration to the towns and city suburbs, away from the rural and mining areas, rather than the simple southward shift suggested by H_1.

We now examine the value of I using the Hope procedure. We generate 19 dummy values of I and reject H_0 at the 5% level if I_{obs} exceeds all these, or at the 10% level if I_{obs} is largest or next to largest. The same procedure has been carried out for 49 and 99 dummy values of I. The results appear in table 2.9 and show the findings for 31 replications of the 19 dummy test, and 12 and 6 replications respectively for the 49 and 99 dummy tests. Using only 19 dummy values, it can be seen that the results vary considerably. For the 49 dummy test the null hypothesis would be rejected (just) only once in twelve at the 10% level. By the time 99 dummy values are used, the probability of a wrong inference for these data is negligible, even at the 10% level.

Table 2.8. Welsh counties: the percentage changes in population, 1961 over 1951.

County	Code	% change	Rank	Contiguous counties
Anglesey	A	2·05	5	C
Brecon	B	−1·7	8	D, E, H, J, M
Carnaervon	C	−2·4	9	A, F, I
Cardigan	D	0·5	7	B, E, I, K, L, M
Carmarthen	E	−2·5	10	B, D, H, L
Denbigh	F	1·8	6	C, E, G, I
Flint	G	3·2	3	F
Glamorgan	H	2·1	4	B, E, J
Merioneth	I	−5·9	12	C, D, F, K
Monmouth	J	4·4	1	B, H
Montgomery	K	−3·8	11	D, F, I, M
Pembroke	L	3·4	2	D, E
Radnor	M	−7·8	13	B, D, K

$n = 13, A = 21, D = 62.$

Table 2.9. The results of repeated permutations tests.

Number (m) of generated values of I used in the test	Number of $I > I_{obs}$	Frequency	prob($I > I_{obs}$)
$m = 19$	0	1	0·05
	1	6	0·10
	2	8	0·15
	3	7	0·20
	4	4	0·25
	5	5	0·30
		31	
$m = 49$	4	1	0·10
	5	1	0·12
	6	4	0·14
	7	1	0·16
	8	2	0·18
	9	1	0·20
	10	2	0·22
		12	
$m = 99$	13	2	0·14
	14	1	0·15
	15	2	0·16
	16	0	0·17
	17	1	0·18
		6	

On the basis of this and other experiments (Cliff and Ord, 1971), we conclude that the permutations test procedure is adequate provided that $m = 49$ or 99 rather than 19. Of course, other values of m are feasible.

Finally, we compare the results of the straightforward normal approximation and the Hope procedure (with $m = 599$) with the transformation suggested in section 2.5.1. By the Hope procedure, the $\alpha = 0 \cdot 05$ and $\alpha = 0 \cdot 10$ percentage points of I (upper tail only) are $I(0 \cdot 05) = 0 \cdot 2415$ and $I(0 \cdot 10) = 0 \cdot 1735$. The value of R given by equation (2.48) is $1 \cdot 44$ ($t = \sqrt{13} \simeq 3 \cdot 60$), while $Q = 2 \cdot 49$. Since $A/n = 1 \cdot 62$, the $c_\alpha = (10\alpha)^{1/2}$ approximation should be used. The results are compared in table 2.10. The improvement rendered by the revised approximation is clear; the original approximation tends to overstate the significance of the results.

Table 2.10. Approximations to the percentage points of I for the Welsh rank data [(a)].

	Hope procedure ($m = 599$)	Normal approximations with	
		$c_\alpha = 1$	$c_\alpha = (10\alpha)^{1/2}$
$I(\cdot 05)$	0·2415 (0·05)	0·2140 (0·07)	0·2557 (0·05)
$I(\cdot 10)$	0·1735 (0·10)	0·1483 (0·12)	0·1674 (0·105)

[(a)] The numbers below the approximate values for I indicate the proportion of I values out of 600 (599+1 observed) which exceed the approximate percentage point.

Applications of the spatial autocorrelation measures to Geary's Irish data and in quadrat count analysis

3.1 Introduction

In this and the next chapter we describe several applications of the measures of spatial autocorrelation outlined in chapter 1. In this chapter we first examine some data given in Geary (1954), and then look at the use of the spatial autocorrelation measures when analysing quadrat count data.

3.2 Geary's Irish data

As a first application of the methods outlined in chapter 1, we shall consider an example originally presented in Geary (1954). Geary used his c statistic to test for spatial autocorrelation between contiguous counties on twelve variables measured in each of the counties of Eire. Geary's

Table 3.1. Data on the counties of Eire.

Serial letter	County (including county boroughs)	Number of milch cows per 1 000 acres of crop and pasture in 1952	Town and village population as percentage of total population in 1951
A	Carlow	67	40·2
B	Cavan	99	17·3
C	Clare	110	24·4
D	Cork	146	52·6
E	Donegal	102	18·9
F	Dublin	108	94·8
G	Galway	69	28·1
H	Kerry	194	26·7
I	Kildare	52	29·2
J	Kilkenny	91	31·1
K	Laoighis	69	26·7
L	Leitrim	102	13·7
M	Limerick	181	48·2
N	Longford	74	21·3
O	Louth	69	63·0
P	Mayo	97	18·5
Q	Meath	55	17·5
R	Monaghan	85	24·6
S	Offaly	55	35·6
T	Roscommon	66	13·2
U	Sligo	92	29·7
V	Tipperary	107	36·5
W	Waterford	122	56·4
X	Westmeath	43	35·8
Y	Wexford	64	34·6
Z	Wicklow	79	49·8

analysis is discussed in Cliff and Ord (1969). By way of example, we look here at two of the variables considered by Geary, namely the numbers of milch cows per 1000 acres of crop and pasture land for each county in 1952, and the percentage of the county population in towns and villages in 1951. These data are reproduced in columns 3 and 4 of table 3.1. As suggested by Geary, County Dublin was omitted from the analysis because of its highly urbanised character compared with the other counties of the Republic. This omission does not materially alter the results for the milch

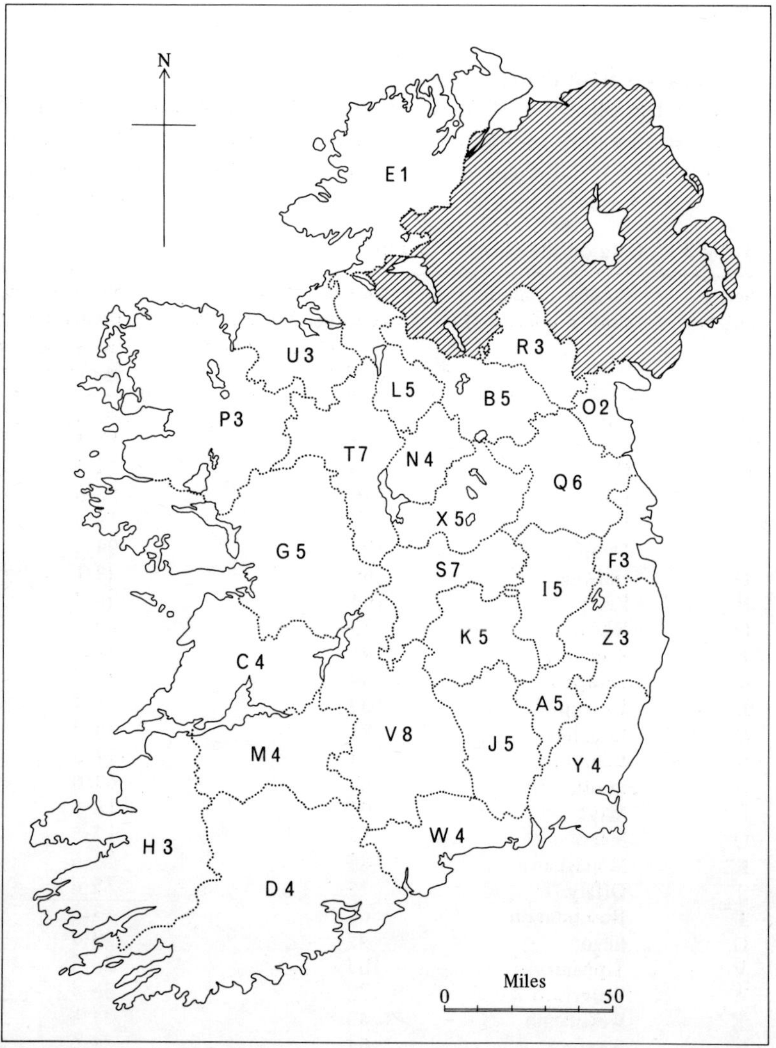

Figure 3.1. The Eire county system showing serial letters and numbers of contiguous counties.

cows data, but it does have a profound effect upon the population variable, as is to be expected. The county map of Eire appears in figure 3.1. The serial letters, A–Z, correspond with those in table 3.1, while the numerals give the number of counties contiguous to each county. The concept of the region in geography leads us to expect both variables to have similar values in contiguous counties, and so the alternative hypothesis is one of positive spatial autocorrelation.

The statistics, I and c (equations 1.44 and 1.45), were evaluated for the two variables. Their moments were obtained under randomisation (assumption R) and under assumption N, that is, assuming the data to be sampled from normal populations. Equations (1.66)–(1.71) were used. To check the validity of assumption N, the sample skewness, b_1, and kurtosis, b_2, coefficients of the two variables were calculated. These coefficients are defined as $b_1 = m_3^2/m_2^3$ and $b_2 = m_4/m_2^2$, where m_j is the jth sample moment about the sample mean. The values of b_1 and b_2 appear in table 3.2. The milch cows data exhibited strong positive skewness, and as the variable is non-negative, a logarithmic transformation brought the data much nearer to normality. The population data, expressed as percentages, must lie in the range 0–100, and might be expected to exhibit the characteristics of a beta distribution with a relatively low value of b_2. This was indeed so, but it was not felt that a transformation was necessary in this case.

In solving equations (1.44)–(1.45) and (1.66)–(1.71), the following weights were used:

(1) For Geary's c, binary weights with $w_{ij} = 1$ if two counties had a common border, and $w_{ij} = 0$ otherwise.

(2) For I, (a) binary weights, and (b) unstandardised and standardised general weights. The unstandardised general weights took the form

$$w_{ij} = d_{ij}^{-1}\,\beta_{i(j)}\,, \tag{3.1}$$

where d_{ij} denotes the distance between the geographic centres of counties i and j, and $\beta_{i(j)}$ denotes the proportion of the perimeter of county i which is in contact with county j. We exclude from the perimeter of county i those parts which coincide with the boundary of the study area. Thus

$$\sum_{j \in J} \beta_{i(j)} = 1,$$

Table 3.2. Values of b_1 and b_2 for the Eire data.

Variable	b_1	b_2	Transformation	b_1	b_2
Milch cows	1·682	4·294	ln	0·179	2·779
Town and village population	0·473	2·619			

where j denotes the set of counties contiguous to county i. The standardised weights are given by

$$w_{ij}^* = \frac{w_{ij}}{c_i}, \tag{3.2}$$

where $c_i = \sum_j w_{ij}$, so that $\sum_j w_{ij}^* = 1$ for all counties. The properties of these generalised weights are discussed in section 1.4.2, while the numerical values of the weights for the Eire county system are given in appendix 2. The standardised weights are particularly relevant in regression analysis (see section 5.2.3). W, S_1, and S_2 are given in table 3.3 for the different sets of weights.

Table 3.3. Values of W, S_1, and S_2 for the Eire county system.

Weights	W(or $2A$)	S_1(or $4A$)	S_2(or $8A+8D$)
Binary	110	220	2176
Unstandardised general	0·8468	0·0187	0·1227
Standardised general	25	15·8493	103·6204

3.2.1 Interpretation of results

The results of the analysis appear in table 3.4. They are almost identical under assumptions N and R for the milch cows transformed data, and for the population data. Even for the raw data on milch cows, the non-normality of the data does not produce seriously different results under assumptions N and R. For the milch cows data, raw or transformed, the unmistakeable conclusion is that there is a very high degree of spatial autocorrelation. This is a not unexpected conclusion since Eire does have several traditional dairying areas, such as the southwest.

The population data produce rather mixed results. The tests based on binary weights indicate a significant degree of positive spatial autocorrelation, but this is not supported by the tests based on general weights. Cliff and Ord (1969) suggested that the reason for this was the low values of w_{ij} assigned under the general weights to the larger counties in the south and southwest of the Republic. This arose because, for those particular counties, the d_{ij} values in equation (3.1) were large, and hence the values of d_{ij}^{-1} were small. The county variate values are very similar in this part of the country, and the lower weights do not emphasise this pattern as strongly as the binary weights. The standardised general weights represent an intermediate weighting system between the binary and unstandardised general weights, and this is reflected in the intermediate value of the standard deviate. In this example the proper conclusion would seem to be that there is some positive spatial autocorrelation throughout the county

Table 3.4. An analysis of the Eire data using the I and c statistics.

Item	Geary's c using binary weights		$I^{(a)}$ using					
			binary weights		unstandardised general weights		standardised general weights	
	N	R	N	R	N	R	N	R
Expected value under H_0	1·0	1·0	−0·0417	−0·0417	−0·0417	−0·0417	−0·0417	−0·0417
Milch cows raw data								
Observed value	0·3418	0·3418	0·5750	0·5750	0·5762	0·5762	0·6566	0·6566
Standard deviation	0·1512	0·1745	0·1186	0·1144	0·1494	0·1438	0·1477	0·1421
Standard deviate	4·35 ****	3·77 ****	5·20 ****	5·39 ****	4·14 ****	4·30 ****	4·67 ****	4·91 ****
Milch cows transformed data								
Observed value	0·4071	0·4071	0·5803	0·5803	0·5854	0·5854	0·6454	0·6454
Standard deviation	0·1512	0·1517	0·1186	0·1186	0·1494	0·1493	0·1477	0·1476
Standard deviate	3·92 ****	3·91 ****	5·24 ****	5·24 ****	4·20 ****	4·20 ****	4·65 ****	4·65 ****
Town and village population data								
Observed value	0·6148	0·6148	0·2284	0·2284	0·1397	0·1397	0·1987	0·1987
Standard deviation	0·1512	0·1487	0·1186	0·1190	0·1494	0·1500	0·1477	0·1483
Standard deviate	2·55 ****	2·59 ****	2·28 **	2·27 **	1·22	1·21	1·61	1·62

** Significant at $\alpha = 0{\cdot}05$ level (one-tailed test)
**** Significant at $\alpha = 0{\cdot}01$ level (one-tailed test)
(a) The testing procedure for I uses the approximation given in equation (2.47).

system, but that this is stronger in the south and southwest than in the rest of the country.

3.3 The method of quadrat counts

The method of quadrat counts is used to reduce the areal distribution of objects displayed on a map to a frequency distribution. This method of data reduction has been discussed in detail by Greig-Smith (1964) and by Kershaw (1964). It has been applied to geographical problems by, among others, Birch (1967), Dacey (1964, 1966a, 1966b, 1968, 1969), Getis (1964), Harvey (1966), Hudson (1967), McConnell (1966), Malm *et al.* (1966), Olsson (1966), and Rogers (1965). The method involves first, dividing a map area into small subareas or quadrats, and then constructing a frequency distribution of the number of quadrats with 0, 1, 2, 3, ... objects of a specified kind within them.

One convenient way of analysing this observed frequency distribution is to compare it with a theoretical distribution derived from some hypothetical spatial process. An important set of theoretical distributions used by geographers for this purpose is the group of Poisson distributions such as the simple Poisson, Neyman type A, and negative binomial models. For example, Matsui (1932) selected two regions in the Tonami Plain, Japan, one in Hukuno Town and the other in Demati Town. He partitioned the former into 1200 quadrats, each side of 100 metres, by superimposing over the area a regular 30 x 40 lattice. Demati Town was partitioned into 750 equal sized quadrats, each of side 130 metres, by a 25 x 30 lattice. For each lattice, Matsui then counted the number of quadrats with 0, 1, 2, ... isolated houses in them, and fitted a simple Poisson distribution to the two resulting frequency arrays. Dacey (1968) repeated this sort of analysis for 21 maps showing the location of isolated houses in Puerto Rico, with the exception that he fitted a negative binomial, rather than a simple Poisson, to the resulting frequency arrays. The results obtained by Matsui and Dacey are compared in Dacey (1969), whose conclusions are consistent with those given later in this chapter.

The spatial process generating the Poisson-type distributions may take one of two forms.

(1) The first form is true contagion or generalised Poisson. Suppose that clusters of objects have been observed, such as plants in a field or houses in a study area. Then we envisage a Poisson distribution of such clusters in the study area, with each cluster containing one or more objects. The number of objects in each cluster follows a generalising distribution. If the generalising distribution is logarithmic, the generalised distribution is written as Poisson $\vee$ logarithmic, which is equivalent to the negative binomial, while Poisson $\vee$ Poisson yields the Neyman type A. Insofar as the existence of a cluster means that an object is 'more likely' to have other similar objects nearby, we say that these processes represent 'true contagion'.

(2) The second form is apparent contagion or compound Poisson. We consider the objects to be generated by a Poisson process as in form (1), but instead of identifying clusters and looking at the number of objects in each cluster, we assume that the number of objects in the ith quadrat is given by a simple Poisson process with mean λ_i, where λ_i may vary from quadrat to quadrat. That is, we assume that λ is itself a random variable and that its distribution may be specified. Thus the final distribution of the random variable R is the Poisson compounded with some other distribution. If λ follows a gamma distribution, the compound distribution is Poisson $\wedge$ gamma, which is the negative binomial. Likewise, Poisson $\wedge$ Poisson yields the Neyman type A.

If no contagion exists, or if $\lambda_i = \lambda$ for all i, the resulting distribution is the simple Poisson.

It is important to note that both the true and apparent contagion processes can yield the same final distribution, as is shown by the examples of the negative binomial and Neyman type A given above. When we obtain a 'good fit' of one of these distributions to an observed frequency array, we are faced with the problem of determining whether the generating process was of the true or apparent contagion form. Ord (1972, sections 6.6 and 7.8) has shown that, in the case of the negative binomial, if quadrat count data are available for two or more time periods, the index of the real contagion model will increase linearly with time, while for the apparent contagion model it remains constant. Often, however, we have an observed frequency array for one time period only, and so we shall now describe an approximate procedure for the negative binomial which can be used in such a situation to distinguish the real and apparent contagion models.

Suppose that the study area has been partitioned into quadrats of a certain size, and that a 'good fit' of the negative binomial to the frequency array of objects in the quadrats has been obtained. Write the negative binomial density as

$$f_r = \text{prob}(R = r) = \binom{k+r-1}{r} p^k(1-p)^r, \tag{3.3}$$

with parameters p and k. Consider a Poisson distribution with parameter λ, and a logarithmic distribution with parameter α. Then the Poisson $\vee$ logarithmic model (the 'true contagion' negative binomial) has parameters

$$k = -\frac{\lambda}{\ln(1-\alpha)}, \tag{3.4}$$

and

$$p = \alpha. \tag{3.5}$$

If s of the original quadrats are combined so that the Poisson parameter becomes $s\lambda$, it follows that k becomes

$$k = -\frac{s\lambda}{\ln(1-\alpha)} \tag{3.6}$$

but p remains

$$p = \alpha \; . \tag{3.7}$$

For the Poisson $\wedge$ gamma model (the 'apparent contagion' negative binomial), with gamma density,

$$g(\lambda) = \frac{\lambda^{b-1} a^b \mathrm{e}^{-a\lambda}}{\Gamma(b)}, \tag{3.8}$$

the negative binomial has parameters

$$k = b, \tag{3.9}$$

and

$$p = \frac{a}{a+1} \; . \tag{3.10}$$

In this case, if s of the original quadrats are combined, the parameters are

$$k = b, \tag{3.11}$$

as before, while p becomes

$$p = \frac{a}{a+s} \; . \tag{3.12}$$

Thus by calculating estimates for p and k for different sized lattices, we can see which of the models appears to be nearer the truth. This is only an approximate method of analysis because we cannot be certain that the quadrats combined to form larger quadrats have the same value of λ initially in the compound Poisson model. However, the procedure would seem to provide a reasonable check.

An alternative approach is to use the spatial autocorrelation measures. If the generalised Poisson model holds, each quadrat will be an independent realisation of the negative binomial, provided that it is large enough to contain the entire cluster. Therefore we should find little or no spatial autocorrelation between adjacent quadrats. On the other hand, if the compound Poisson model is true and we postulate that λ varies from quadrat to quadrat *and* that neighbouring quadrats have similar λ values, then we would expect to detect positive spatial autocorrelation between adjacent quadrats. Although we have used the negative binomial as a specific example to show how the spatial autocorrelation measures may be used to distinguish between the real and apparent contagion models, the same arguments enable us to determine whether the real or apparent contagion form of *any* Poisson model, or the simple Poisson itself, is the most valid representation of the spatial process. The possible decisions are summarised in table 3.5.

A recurring problem in studies of this kind is the choice of quadrat size, which is often rather arbitrary. Changing the quadrat size will usually affect the degree of spatial dependence between quadrats, and the larger the quadrat, the weaker the dependence will be. Thus by starting with very small quadrats and aggregating, as is done later in this section, we can monitor changes in the parameters of the selected Poisson distribution and examine the plausibility of the true or apparent contagion models.

We can now illustrate these various ideas by reexamining Matsui's (1932, page 254) Hukuno Town data set, reproduced here in figure 3.2. From

Table 3.5. Selection of an appropriate theoretical Poisson model.

Item		Poisson model	
		simple	generalised/compound
Spatial autocorrelation	not detected	simple Poisson	true contagion
	detected	apparent contagion?	apparent contagion

2	2	2	1	0	1	0	0	1	2	0	0	0	0	1	2	0	1	0	1	2	2	0	1	1	2	0	1	1	1	1	2	1	1	2	0	1	2	0	2
0	2	0	1	2	0	1	1	1	2	2	0	1	1	0	0	0	1	0	1	0	2	2	0	1	2	2	1	2	1	0	0	1	0	1	0	2	0	1	2
1	0	1	1	0	0	1	0	1	1	1	0	1	0	1	1	0	1	2	0	2	0	0	1	3	0	1	2	1	0	2	1	1	2	0	0	1	0	2	2
0	1	1	1	0	2	0	1	2	0	0	0	2	2	0	0	0	1	0	0	1	2	0	0	0	1	0	0	0	1	0	9	0	0	0	1	1	1	1	1
1	2	0	0	0	0	0	0	0	0	1	0	2	0	2	2	0	1	2	1	0	1	1	1	0	3	0	1	2	0	1	1	1	1	0	0	1	0	3	1
1	3	1	0	1	0	1	0	0	0	0	0	2	2	0	2	0	0	1	0	0	1	0	0	0	0	1	2	1	1	1	2	1	0	2	1	3	1	1	1
0	1	0	0	0	1	0	1	0	1	2	0	1	3	1	1	4	1	3	1	0	1	1	0	0	0	0	0	0	0	2	2	2	0	1	2	0	3	0	1
0	0	1	0	1	0	0	1	0	0	1	3	0	0	1	0	0	1	0	0	1	0	2	2	0	2	0	0	1	2	1	2	2	0	0	1	1	0	0	1
0	1	1	0	1	1	0	1	1	3	1	1	3	0	1	0	2	0	1	0	0	0	1	3	3	2	0	0	0	0	1	0	1	0	1	0	0	0	1	0
0	0	0	0	0	1	1	2	0	0	1	5	2	0	0	0	0	2	0	0	2	1	0	1	0	0	2	0	0	0	1	0	0	1	0	0	0	1	2	0
0	2	0	0	1	1	1	0	1	1	1	0	2	1	4	2	1	0	1	2	2	0	1	1	2	1	0	0	0	0	1	2	2	0	0	0	0	0	0	0
0	0	0	1	1	0	1	0	0	0	0	1	2	2	2	0	0	0	1	0	1	3	1	2	0	0	0	0	0	2	1	2	0	0	0	2	0	1	1	1
0	1	0	0	1	2	0	0	0	0	0	0	0	1	1	0	1	1	1	1	2	1	1	1	3	0	1	0	1	1	0	1	4	1	1	2	0	1	0	2
0	0	0	1	1	1	1	0	1	1	0	0	0	0	1	2	0	1	1	1	1	3	0	2	1	0	0	0	0	2	0	0	0	3	0	2	0	1	1	2
0	1	1	0	0	0	1	1	2	0	0	1	0	0	1	0	0	2	0	0	0	1	1	0	0	0	1	1	1	0	0	0	0	2	0	0	2	1	0	0
3	4	1	1	0	3	1	0	0	0	2	0	0	0	1	0	1	2	1	0	0	1	4	1	0	0	2	2	0	0	0	1	0	1	1	1	0	4	4	0
0	0	1	0	0	1	1	1	1	1	1	0	0	1	0	2	0	3	2	0	2	2	3	1	0	0	1	1	0	1	3	0	0	1	1	0	1	1	1	0
1	1	0	1	0	1	0	0	2	1	0	0	2	2	0	0	2	1	5	2	0	0	0	0	0	0	0	0	1	0	0	1	2	2	0	0	2	1	0	1
0	3	0	1	0	0	0	2	0	0	0	2	0	0	0	0	0	1	0	2	0	0	0	0	1	1	0	0	2	0	0	0	0	0	0	1	3	0	0	1
0	1	1	0	2	0	1	0	0	0	0	0	1	1	0	0	1	0	1	0	0	0	1	1	2	1	1	0	0	0	0	1	1	0	1	0	0	2	1	2
1	0	0	0	1	1	0	0	1	1	1	0	0	2	1	0	0	0	0	1	3	0	2	2	1	4	0	1	0	0	1	0	3	0	0	1	1	0	1	0
0	2	1	1	0	1	1	0	0	0	1	1	0	0	3	1	1	0	0	1	0	1	0	2	5	2	1	1	0	1	2	0	0	1	1	0	1	2	0	0
0	0	0	0	0	2	0	1	1	1	2	0	0	1	1	2	1	0	1	0	0	3	2	1	4	5	0	2	1	1	1	1	2	0	2	0	0	1	0	1
0	0	1	1	2	0	0	0	1	0	0	1	1	0	0	0	0	0	2	0	0	1	2	2	1	0	0	3	3	1	1	0	1	0	0	0	0	0	1	0
1	0	1	1	0	0	1	1	2	2	1	1	0	0	0	0	0	1	0	0	2	1	1	0	0	0	0	0	1	1	0	0	1	1	0	0	2	0	0	2
0	0	1	1	1	1	1	0	0	0	2	2	1	2	0	0	0	2	1	0	0	0	0	0	1	1	0	3	0	0	1	2	0	7	1	0	2	0	0	2
0	1	1	1	1	2	2	2	0	0	2	0	3	1	0	1	0	1	0	0	1	0	0	0	1	1	1	3	1	0	1	0	2	1	2	1	0	0	0	1
0	2	1	0	0	0	2	1	2	0	0	0	0	0	1	0	3	0	1	1	0	0	0	1	0	0	1	0	0	0	2	2	1	1	0	1	0	1	1	0
0	0	0	0	1	0	0	2	0	0	0	0	0	0	0	1	1	0	0	1	1	0	1	0	0	1	1	0	1	1	1	2	0	1	0	2	1	0	1	1
2	0	0	1	2	0	0	0	0	0	1	0	0	1	1	2	1	3	2	0	0	0	0	0	0	0	0	0	1	0	0	0	1	1	1	1	0	2	1	0

Figure 3.2. Quadrat counts of houses from Matsui's data.

Matsui's original lattice several new lattices have been created by combining adjacent quadrats in various ways. Let t be the number of adjacent quadrats on a column, and s be the number of adjacent quadrats on a row of the original lattice (figure 3.2) which were combined to form a new quadrat. The combinations shown in table 3.6 were tried. Lattice 1 refers to figure 3.2. To show how monitoring changes in the parameters of a Poisson distribution with changes in quadrat size enables us to distinguish real from apparent contagion models, we fitted the negative binomial by maximum likelihood to the observed frequency distributions of quadrat counts of houses for lattices 1 to 9. The goodness-of-fit between the observed and expected frequency arrays was evaluated using X^2. The results are given in table 3.7, and indicate that the negative binomial is a good fit to the data for most lattices. The maximum likelihood estimates of the parameters k and p for the nine lattices are shown in table 3.8, together with the values we should 'expect' for lattices 2–9 from equations (3.6)–(3.7), and (3.11)–(3.12), given the results for lattice 1. Finally the percentage differences between the estimated and 'expected' values of the various parameters are presented. We define percentage difference as

$$100 \times \frac{|\text{estimated parameter value} - \text{`expected' parameter value}|}{\text{estimated parameter value}} .$$

If we compare the 'expected' parameter values with the maximum likelihood estimates and also examine the percentage differences between the 'expected' and estimated values, it appears that with the exception of lattice 3, the compound model holds better than the generalised model.

It is now possible to illustrate how to use the spatial autocorrelation measures to provide a further check. The degree of spatial autocorrelation between adjacent quadrats in lattices 1–9 was examined using I as given in equation (1.44). The moments of I were evaluated using the normality assumption (N) and under randomisation (R)—see equations (1.66)–(1.68).

Table 3.6. Lattices derived from Matsui's data.

Identity number	t	s	Lattice dimensions
1	1	1	30 × 40
2	1	2	30 × 20
3	2	1	15 × 40
4	2	2	15 × 20
5	3	1	10 × 40
6	3	2	10 × 20
7	1	4	30 × 10
8	2	4	15 × 10
9	3	4	10 × 10

Table 3.7. Fitting the negative binomial model to lattices 1–9.

Class value	Lattice number 1		2		3		4		5		6		7		8		9	
	O[a]	E[a]	O	E	O	E	O	E	O	E	O	E	O	E	O	E	O	E
0	584	590·2	151	153·4	137	145·9	14	21·7	49	52·3	2	4·2	20	21·0	0	1·1]	0	0·1]
1	398	392·3	189	188·4	207	191·9	56	50·0	97	95·4	13	14·0	46	49·2	2	4·5]	0	0·5]
2	168	154·7	138	133·8	139	139·3	72	63·4	98	96·6	31	25·2	67	63·2	17	9·8	0	1·5]
3	35	47·1	72	71·9	69	73·7	54	58·6	77	71·6	31	32·5	63	59·0	10	15·3	5	3·2]
4	9	12·2	37	32·4	33	31·8	43	44·1	44	43·3	34	33·4	48	44·6	18	19·1	3	5·2
5	4	2·8]	5	12·9	8	11·8	27	28·7	16	22·7	34	29·2	23	29·1	27	20·5	8	7·3
6	0	0·6]	2	4·7]	4	3·9]	18	16·6	13	10·6	13	22·5	18	16·9	22	19·5	11	9·1
7	1	0·1]	4	1·6]	1	1·2]	7	8·8	2	4·6]	13	15·7	4	9·0	15	16·8	16	10·2
8	0	0·0]	0	0·5]	1	0·3]	4	4·4	1	1·8]	12	10·1	4	4·4	10	13·5	11	10·5
9	1	0·0]	2	0·2]	0	0·1]	2	2·0]	1	0·7]	11	6·0	4	2·1]	6	10·1	8	10·1
10					1	0·0]	1	0·9]	1	0·3]	3	3·4	2	0·9]	9	7·1	5	9·2
11							0	0·4]	0	0·1]	0	1·8]	1	0·4]	6	4·8	7	7·9
12							2	0·2]	1	0·0]	1	0·9]	0	0·2]	2	3·1	6	6·5
13											0	0·5]			1	1·9]	6	5·2
14											0	0·2]			1	1·2]	2	4·0
15											1	0·1]			4	0·7]	5	2·9
16																	3	2·1]
17																	1	1·5]
18																	0	1·0]
19																	2	0·7]
20+																	1	1·5]
X^2	6·84 *		5·81		3·65		6·27		3·49		13·12		8·39		17·12 *		9·95	
df	3		4		4		7		5		9		7		10		12	

] = cells combined for purposes of X^2 test. [a] O = observed; E = expected.
Note: expected frequencies < minimum listed are put in the end group. * Significant at $\alpha = 0{\cdot}1$ level.

Table 3.8. Maximum likelihood estimates and 'expected' values of parameters k and p for the derived lattices from Matsui's data.

Parameter	Lattice 1	2	3	4	5	6	7	8	9
	Estimated values								
k	5·36	6·41	9·64	9·79	9·21	13·17	10·21	11·56	13·15
p	0·8760	0·8083	0·8636	0·7635	0·8018	0·7455	0·7708	0·6555	0·5904
	'Expected' values—generalised Poisson model								
k		10·72	10·72	21·44	16·08	32·16	21·44	42·88	64·32
p		0·8760	0·8760	0·8760	0·8760	0·8760	0·8760	0·8760	0·8760
	'Expected' values—compound Poisson model								
k		5·36	5·36	5·36	5·36	5·36	5·36	5·36	5·36
p		0·7794	0·7794	0·6385	0·7019	0·5407	0·6385	0·4690	0·3706
	Percentage differences—generalised Poisson model								
k		67·2	11·2	119·0	74·6	144·2	110·0	270·9	389·1
p		9·0	1·4	14·7	9·3	17·5	13·6	33·6	48·4
	Percentage differences—compound Poisson model								
k		16·4	44·4	22·6	41·8	59·3	47·5	53·6	59·2
p		3·6	9·7	16·4	12·5	27·5	17·2	28·5	37·2

Table 3.9. Results of tests for spatial autocorrelation in lattices from Matsui's paper[(a)].

Value of I	Lattice																	
	1		2		3		4		5		6		7		8		9	
	rook	queen	rook	queen	rook	queen	rook	queen	rook	queen	rook	queen	rook	queen	rook	queen	rook	queen
Expected	−0·00083		−0·00167		−0·00167		−0·00334		−0·00251		−0·00503		−0·00334		−0·00671		−0·01010	
Observed	0·0601	0·0731	0·0842	0·0826	0·1056	0·0843	0·1327	0·0943	0·0982	0·0645	0·1154	0·0863	0·1070	0·0731	0·1097	0·0640	0·0926	0·0424
σ_R	0·0147	0·0206	0·0209	0·0293	0·0209	0·0294	0·0297	0·0416	0·0259	0·0362	0·0365	0·0512	0·0299	0·0419	0·0423	0·0594	0·0517	0·0727
Standard deviate under R	4·16 ****	3·59 ****	4·12 ****	2·87 ****	5·13 ****	2·93 ****	4·58 ****	2·34 ****	3·89 ****	1·85 **	3·30 ****	1·79 **	3·69 ****	1·83 **	2·75 ****	1·19	1·99 **	0·72
σ_N	0·0147	0·0207	0·0209	0·0294	0·0210	0·0295	0·0298	0·0418	0·0260	0·0363	0·0367	0·0515	0·0300	0·0420	0·0424	0·0595	0·0520	0·0731
Standard deviate under N	4·15 ****	3·58 ****	4·10 ****	2·87 ****	5·11 ****	2·92 ****	4·57 ****	2·33 **	3·88 ****	1·84 **	3·28 ****	1·77 **	3·68 ****	1·82 **	2·74 ****	1·19	1·98 **	0·72

Rook = rook's case
Queen = queen's case
R = using randomisation
N = assuming normality

** Significant at 0·05 level (one-tailed test)
**** Significant at 0·01 level (one-tailed test)
(a) The testing procedure uses the approximation given in equation (2.47).

Two forms for $\boldsymbol{W}$ were tried:
(1) $w_{ij} = 1$ if the ith and jth quadrats had an edge in common, and $w_{ij} = 0$ otherwise (the rook's case);
(2) $w_{ij} = 1$ if the ith and jth quadrats had a common edge or vertex, and $w_{ij} = 0$ otherwise (the queen's case).
Matsui (1932) and Ginsberg (1958) have suggested that the settlement pattern in this part of Japan is one of nucleated villages, and so we would expect individual houses to be clustered, but clusters to be independent. However, the compound model suggests similar densities in neighbouring areas. We therefore postulate under H_1 positive spatial autocorrelation between quadrats and use a one-tailed test of significance. The results of the test are given in table 3.9. For all the lattices there is fairly clear evidence of positive spatial autocorrelation. From table 3.5 the results tend to confirm, for the negative binomial, the evidence of the parameter changes discussed above, namely that the compound model is more plausible than the generalised form.

The reader may recall from earlier in the section that Matsui originally fitted the simple Poisson to lattice 1. The authors repeated this exercise and also fitted the simple Poisson to the observed frequency arrays for lattices 2–9. The goodness-of-fit between the observed and the expected frequency arrays was again evaluated using X^2, and the results are given in table 3.10. It is evident from these results that the closest fit of the simple Poisson to the observed frequency distribution of quadrat counts of houses occurs for lattices 2, 3, 4, and 7. As table 3.9 shows, in all these lattices, there is a significant degree of spatial autocorrelation in both the rook's and queen's cases, although it is less marked in the queen's case for lattice 7. From table 3.5 these results suggest that we are again dealing with a compound Poisson process, although in the case of lattice 7 the apparent contagion is rather weak.

Table 3.10. Results of X^2 goodness-of-fit test between observed quadrat counts and simple Poisson expectations for lattices 1–9.

Item	Lattice number								
	1	2	3	4	5	6	7	8	9
X^2	7·87 **	7·21	3·68	8·56	12·04 *	19·5 ****	6·97	27·72 ****	17·28 ****
df	3	4	4	6	5	7	6	8	9

* Significant at 0·10 level
** Significant at 0·05 level
**** Significant at 0·01 level

To test the strength of the departure from the simple model we used the index of dispersion,

$$Di = \frac{\text{sample variance}}{\text{sample mean}}.$$

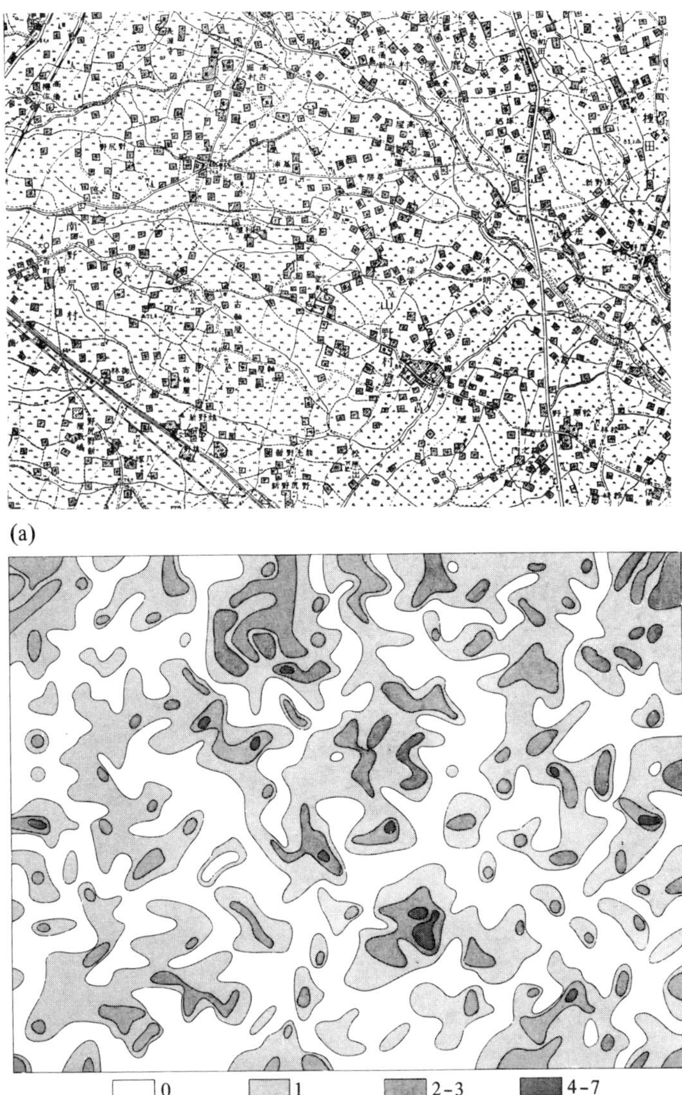

Figure 3. (a) A section of topographic map (1 : 20000 Military Land Survey) showing the western part of Hukuno town.
(b) Map showing the density of houses per 100 m^2 in the same part as figure 3 (a)

As Barko *et al.* (1968) have shown, given a sample of size n from a Poisson population, $(n-1)Di$ is approximately distributed as χ^2 with $(n-1)$ degrees of freedom, provided the population mean is not too small. Further, $E(Di) = 1$ for any sample size. For large n, therefore, the statistic

$$d = [2(n-1)Di]^{1/2} - (2n-1)^{1/2}$$

is approximately normally distributed with zero mean and unit variance. The values of Di and d for the nine lattices are as follows.

Lattice	Di	d	Lattice	Di	d	Lattice	Di	d
1	1·17	4·03	4	1·34	3·87	7	1·10	1·21
2	1·27	4·31	5	1·28	3·70	8	1·56	4·28
3	1·19	3·16	6	1·20	1·88	9	1·78	4·67

These results imply the rejection of the simple Poisson model in favour of the compound version, except for lattice 7. Although superficially different, this form of analysis is, in fact, very similar to the 'variance components' analysis carried out by Moellering and Tobler (1972).

Finally, using table 3.9, we note that, in confirmation of the earlier discussion of choice of quadrat size, the degree of spatial autocorrelation between adjacent quadrats generally declines as quadrat size increases. There is also much less spatial autocorrelation for the queen's case than for the rook's case, which reflects the chequered spatial arrangement of houses in the study area (figure 3.3).

3.3.1 Implications for settlement geography

As noted earlier, Matsui (1932, page 251) and Ginsberg (1958) suggested that the settlement pattern in the Tonami Plain is essentially one of nucleated villages. The better fits of the negative binomial model to the data (tables 3.7 and 3.10), as opposed to those obtained with the simple Poisson, and the values of Di, tend to confirm this. However, the tests for spatial autocorrelation indicate that the apparent, rather than the true, contagion version of the negative binomial model is the more plausible. This would seem to argue for a pattern of colonisation essentially random (Poissonian), but with varying propensities to settle in different parts of the region (because of different land quality, for example). It is apparent that the hypothesis of nucleated village settlement should not be accepted simply because the negative binomial model provides a good fit. If the reader is interested in a fuller discussion of this problem he should consult Harvey (1968).

4

Map comparison with application to diffusion processes

4.1 Introduction

In this chapter we show how the join count and I statistics may be used to evaluate the spatial goodness-of-fit between the observed and theoretical maps of some stochastic process. The rationale behind the proposed testing procedure is outlined in section 4.2.1. If the procedures are applied to diffusion processes, particular problems arise which are discussed in section 4.2.2. The use of the methods is illustrated in section 4.3, where we evaluate the spatial goodness-of-fit between some observed and theoretical maps of the diffusion of an innovation described in Hägerstrand (1953).

4.2 Map comparison

A common product of geographical research is a stochastic model of some spatial process, which yields, as its end product, a map from which we wish to evaluate the degree of spatial correspondence to the real world situation modelled. For example, it might be required to determine the spatial agreement between some theoretical arrangement of central places and the observed location of cities within Europe. This kind of map comparison is usually undertaken as part of an attempt to determine whether the model, which produced the theoretical map, is an acceptable description of reality. There is some discussion in the literature (see Tobler, 1965; Gale, 1971) of methods which can be used to compute the degree of spatial correspondence between theoretically derived and observed maps. In this chapter we look again at the problem in some detail, and illustrate how the join count statistics and a variant of the coefficient I may be used to provide an appropriate test.

4.2.1 The test

Suppose that it is desired to evaluate the degree of spatial correspondence between, for example, a theoretically derived, or *expected*, map showing the production of wheat in hundredweights per acre in the English counties, and the corresponding map of *observed* production figures. From these two maps a third map, showing the county-by-county *differences* between the expected and observed maps, can be constructed by calculating the quantity (observed − expected) county values. This is clearly analogous to constructing a map of residuals from regression. Zero residuals represent counties in which the theoretical and observed values are identical; positive residuals represent areas of underestimation by the model; negative residuals represent areas of overestimation of the actual county values by the model. Interest is centred upon the spatial arrangement in the differences map of the nonzero residuals. If the observed map is a realisation of the stochastic process underlying the theoretical map, then the nonzero residuals should be randomly located in the differences map; in other words, the observed and expected maps should differ only by chance. A nonrandom spatial arrangement of the nonzero residuals, for example systematic departures between the expected and observed maps indicated by clustering of positive and negative residuals, suggests that the observed map cannot be regarded as an outcome of the process underlying the theoretical map, and that the model is not an acceptable description of reality. This is not always straightforward, as is shown by the example in section 4.2.2.

Clearly, for this kind of analysis to work, we require the theoretical map to be the 'expected' outcome of the process postulated. If a model of the process is specified, but not the map itself, we can derive an expected map by obtaining several independent solutions for the model and then fixing the expected value of the ith county ($i = 1, 2, \ldots, n$) as the average of the values recorded in the ith county by the several solutions. If the expected map is so obtained, and a nonrandom spatial arrangement of the nonzero residuals in the differences map is then detected (that is, H_0 is rejected), the implication is that either:
(1) a correct inferential decision has been made—the theoretical and observed maps cannot be regarded as outcomes of the same process; or
(2) a type I error has been made. It might be that the observed map is in fact a true realisation of the process postulated, but that it is one of those outcomes which occur very rarely by chance (five times in a hundred for $\alpha = 0{\cdot}05$). That is, the observed map is a true but atypical outcome of the process.

We consider two ways of testing for a nonrandom spatial arrangement of the nonzero residuals in a differences map. The first is to create a three colour map by coding negative residuals black, B, positive residuals grey, G, and zero residuals white, W. We then test the distributions of BB, GG, and BG joins for departures from randomness using equations (1.41-1.42) and (1.60-1.63), or by using I and c given in equations (1.44-1.45). This is a sign test. In the second method, if the mean values of the random variable on the observed and expected maps are allowed to differ, we can use a variant of I which preserves the magnitude of the differences as well as the signs. The required variant is

$$I = \frac{n\sum_{(2)} w_{ij} x_i x_j}{W\sum_{(1)} x_i^2} , \tag{4.1}$$

where x_i is the value of the residual in county i. Note that in equation (4.1) the x values are not taken about their mean as in equation (1.44). As a result, when $x_i = 0$ (that is, for counties in which the observed and expected values are the same) no contribution is made either to the numerator or to the denominator of equation (4.1), and the coefficient therefore measures only the spatial autocorrelation in the nonzero residuals. We define the jth crude moment of the x's as

$$m_j = n^{-1}\sum_{(1)} x_i^j , \tag{4.2}$$

and

$$a_1 = \frac{nm_1^2}{m_2}, \qquad a_2 = \frac{m_4}{m_2^2}, \qquad a_3 = \frac{m_3 m_1}{m_2^2}.$$

Then, using randomisation, it can be shown that

$$\mathrm{E_R}(I) = (n-1)^{-1}(a_1 - 1), \tag{4.3}$$

and

$$\mathrm{E_R}(I^2) = \frac{1}{(n-1)^{(3)}W^2}\{n[(n^2-3n+3)S_1 - nS_2 + 3W^2] - a_2[(n^2-n)S_1 - 2nS_2 + 6W^2] - na_1[2nS_1 - (n-3)S_2 + 6W^2] + na_3[4(n-1)S_1 - 2(n-1)S_2 + 8W^2] + na_1^2(S_1 - S_2 + W^2)\}. \tag{4.4}$$

Apart from its particular use here, this model is of general interest, since it does not assume $\sum_{(1)} z_i = 0$, as in equations (1.66–1.68), to obtain the moments for I.

In the above discussion we have only considered methods for examining the degree of *spatial* correspondence between maps. In any real world problem, the researcher would also have to check the aspatial goodness-of-fit, for example by comparing the frequency distribution of the observed number of counties with 0, 1, 2, ..., k objects in them with the expected frequency distribution using chi-square. Care is needed in the interpretation of the results of such tests. As is shown by the example in section 4.3, a good spatial fit does not guarantee that the aspatial goodness-of-fit test will produce a satisfactory result or vice versa.

4.2.2 Application to diffusion processes

Suppose that the real world pattern modelled is a *diffusion* process, and that we wish to evaluate the goodness-of-fit between the observed and model maps of the process. We then face certain difficulties in applying the testing procedures outlined above. These have been pointed out by Brown and Moore (1969).

"Thus a viable comparative test of empirical and simulated diffusion patterns must have two important characteristics; it must preserve the property of relative location of individual cell values (i.e. the appropriate distance–decay characteristics), and it must be independent of specific directional bias.

Relatively little progress has been made towards the establishment of such a test. The contiguity ratio (i.e., the tests of spatial autocorrelation) which has been suggested as a method of evaluating differences between two spatial patterns, does not appear appropriate to the spatial diffusion situation. This is because random differences in the directional biases of observed and simulated patterns will produce systematic variation in the spatial distribution of individual cell differences."

The requirements of an appropriate test as specified by Brown and Moore may be summarised as follows:
(1) relative location of cell values must be preserved;
(2) the test must allow for systematic directional biases which occur by chance in the observed and simulated map patterns. An aspatial test such as chi-square fails on both counts, while the autocorrelation tests are affected by requirement (2). Let us now consider this problem of directional bias in the observed and expected maps in more detail. The problem appears to be specific to diffusion processes and, while the methods given in section 4.2.1 yield an appropriate test where this problem does not exist, a modified procedure is required to handle the diffusion situation.

The following example serves to illustrate Brown and Moore's point (2). Suppose that the county system is as shown in figure 4.1. The middle county contains a single adopter of an innovation, and every other county contains a single potential adopter. Suppose that the observed number of adopters of the innovation in each county at the end of the diffusion process is like that shown in figure 4.1a. We now model the process leading to this observed map in the following way:
(a) as on the observed map, the initial adopter is located in the middle county of the model plane.
(b) Each potential adopter accepts the innovation as soon as he is contacted by an adopter.
(c) In generation 1 of the model, the initial adopter contacts the potential adopter in the contiguous county to his right with probability 0·95 and the potential adopter in the contiguous county to his left with probability 0·05.
(d) In generations 2, 3, and 4, only the adopter who accepted in the previous time period may make a new contact, and he must contact the potential adopter in the county contiguous to the one in which he is located.

This model will produce a map either like that shown in figure 4.1b with probability equal to 0·95, or like that shown in figure 4.1c with probability equal to 0·05, yielding the map of expected values shown in figure 4.1d. Then the differences map (signs only) will be like map 4.1e of 4.1f, according to whether map b or c is observed. A conventional join count test, based on the assumption of independence between

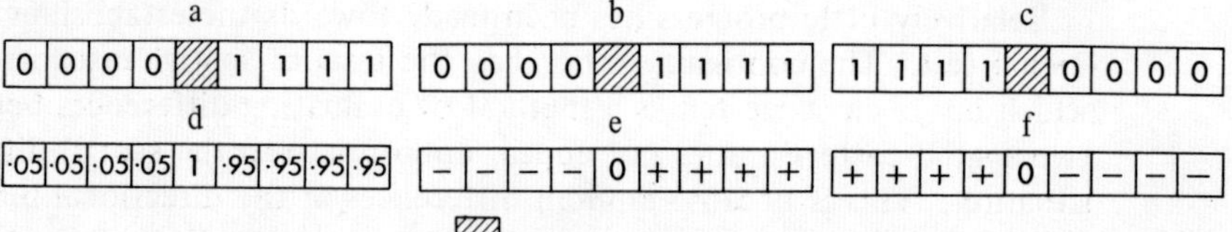

Figure 4.1. An example to illustrate Brown and Moore's point (2).

neighbouring cells, at $\alpha = 0\cdot05$ would reject H_0, given the pattern of signs shown in map e (or f) as

$$\text{prob(no plus-minus joins)} = \tfrac{1}{35},$$

whatever the outcome of the observed process. A valid test at $\alpha = 0\cdot05$ would reject H_0 whenever the observed process moved to the left.

It therefore appears that, if we apply the spatial autocorrelation tests to a differences map for a diffusion process and reject H_0, we must consider two possible explanations for this result:

1. the observed map is not a realisation of the process underlying the theoretical map;
2. we have committed a type I error, because the systematic variation in individual cell differences is due to chance differences in the directional orientation of the observed and modelled patterns of adopters. Moreover, the true probability of a type I error may be considerably greater than the 'nominal' level used in the test because of the directional bias which may arise by chance.

The problem of directional bias appears to be peculiar to the diffusion situation because phenomena such as the diffusion of innovations, the spread of diseases in human populations, and the spread of ghettoes in cities are basically contagious growth processes. Thus once the process moves off in a particular direction, often purely by chance, it will tend to retain that orientation because of the operation of the so-called 'neighbourhood effect' (Hägerstrand, 1953).

Can a test be constructed which deals with this problem? It is suggested that the procedure given below does so, but the cost in computing time is large. The method is based upon the Hope procedure described in section 2.6.

Step 1: generate m independent realisations of the diffusion model and, from these *and the observed map*, compute an 'averaged expected' map by simply averaging over the $(m+1)$ realisations.

Step 2: for each model map and for the observed map, compute a goodness-of-fit statistic between that map and the average expected map. For example, Pearson's product moment correlation coefficient or sums of squared differences could be used. Under the null hypothesis H_0, these $(m+1)$ statistics will be identically distributed and equi-correlated.

Step 3: rank the $(m+1)$ statistics and reject H_0 at the $100(j+1)/(m+1)\%$ level if the statistic between the observed and average expected map has rank $(m-j+1)$ or higher (one-tailed test). Rules for two-tailed tests may be formulated in a similar manner. In ranking the test statistics, if Pearson's r is used, call the highest positive value rank 1; if the sum of squared differences is used, call the smallest sum rank 1. In this procedure, we reject H_0 only if the difference in directional bias between the observed and expected maps is judged so severe that it cannot be regarded as a chance occurrence.

An alternative but less satisfactory approach is as follows:

Step 1: Construct m differences maps and carry out the testing procedure described in section 4.2.1.

Step 2: Rank the m test statistics obtained and reject H_0 at the $100(j+1)/(m+1)\%$ level if not more than j of the statistics are below expectation (one-tailed). An example serves to make the procedure clearer. Suppose that the BW join count statistic is calculated for each of the m differences maps. If the observed map is a realisation of the model process, we should expect some of the BW join counts to exceed $E(BW)$ and some to fall below. If too many exceed the expected value (or too few), this represents a bias more extreme than would be expected by chance. Thus if $m = 99$, we would reject H_0 at the 5% level if 4 or less of the BW join count statistics were above expectation (one-tailed test). A one-tailed test will usually be appropriate here, as a shortage of BW joins indicates an excess of positive spatial autocorrelation among the differences. The rationale for this alternative is the same as for the procedure outlined in section 4.2.1, and we are rejecting H_0 only if a significant systematic spatial departure between the observed and model maps is detected a sufficiently large number of times.

In the remainder of this chapter, we shall illustrate the various goodness-of-fit methods discussed for some maps given in Hägerstrand (1953).

4.3 Empirical example

4.3.1 The Hägerstrand Model

Hägerstrand selected the Asby district of Sweden to study the spatial pattern of acceptance of a subsidy which the Swedish government granted from 1928 onwards to farmers of small units (less than 8 hectares of tilled land) if they enclosed woodland on their farms and converted it to pasture. The study area was divided into 125, 5 x 5 km^2, cells. The total number of farms in each cell which had accepted the subsidy by the ends of 1929, 1930, 1931, and 1932 respectively was recorded. Hägerstrand then developed a Monte Carlo model to simulate the recorded numbers of adopters in each cell up to the end of the three observation years, 1930–1932. The model is described in detail in Hägerstrand's paper, but some discussion is required here to make interpretation of the results given later meaningful.

Hägerstrand assumed that the decision of any potential adopter to accept the subsidy was based solely upon information received orally at face to face meetings between the potential adopter and adopters or carriers. He further assumed that the probability of a potential adopter being paired with a carrier had a strong inverse relationship with geographical distance between the teller and receiver, in a way which could be determined by empirical estimate. Founded on these two assumptions, Hägerstrand developed a Monte Carlo model with the structure given below.

(1) The input number and spatial locations in the model of carriers and potential adopters (that is, all farms $\leqslant$ 8 hectares of tilled land which had not accepted the subsidy) were the actual configurations in 1929.
(2) A potential adopter accepted the subsidy as soon as he was contacted by a carrier.
(3) In each iteration of the model every carrier told one other person, carrier or non-carrier. The probability, P_i, that any given carrier would contact a receiver located in the ith cell of the model plane, is given for each cell in the diagram below. These probabilities were determined from an analysis of migration and telephone traffic data.

0·0096	0·0140	0·0168	0·0140	0·0096
0·0140	0·0301	0·0547	0·0301	0·0140
0·0168	0·0547	0·4431	0·0547	0·0168
0·0140	0·0301	0·0547	0·0301	0·0140
0·0096	0·0140	0·0168	0·0140	0·0096

It was assumed that the carrier was located in the centre cell of this target or Mean Information Field (MIF). Outside the target, $P_i = 0$. As in the study lattice, each cell of the target was 5 x 5 km^2. The address of a carrier's contact in each generation was determined in two steps. First, a random number m, from a rectangular distribution located the cell i according to the rule,

$$\sum_{r=1}^{i-1} Q_r < m < \sum_{r=1}^{i} Q_r,$$

where Q_i, the probability of a contact in cell i with population n_i, is

$$Q_i = \frac{P_i n_i}{\sum_{i=1}^{25} P_i n_i} .$$

A second random number from a rectangular distribution in the range 1 to n_i located the receiver in the cell. If he was identical with the teller, a new address was sampled.
(4) To take into account the reduction in interpersonal communication likely to be caused by physical features such as rivers and forests, two simplified types of barrier were introduced into the model plane, zero, and half contact barriers. When an address was directed over a zero contact barrier, the telling was cancelled. When the address crossed a half contact barrier, the telling was cancelled with probability 0·5. However, two half contact barriers in combination were considered equal to one zero contact barrier.

Using this model, Hägerstrand performed a series of computer runs to simulate the spatial pattern of acceptance of the improved pasture subsidy by farmers in the study area. The observed patterns and the results from three runs of the model are given by Hägerstrand (1953, pages 23–25). We wish to evaluate the spatial goodness-of-fit of the simulated to the observed maps.

4.3.2 Analysis of simulation results

To begin with we illustrate the method of analysis described in section 4.2.1. Differences maps were constructed for 1931 and 1932 for each of the three computer runs reported by Hägerstrand and they are shown in figure 4.2. For clarity, cells in which no observed and no simulated adopters were recorded are left blank. The nonfree sampling join count statistics defined in equations (1.41–1.42) and (1.60–1.63) were then applied to each of the differences maps to test for spatial autocorrelation in the nonzero residuals. The n_1 cells with a negative residual in the differences maps were coded B, and the n_2 cells with a positive residual were coded G. We set $w_{ij} = 1$ if two cells in the differences maps had a common edge or vertex, and $w_{ij} = 0$ otherwise. In the equations, $A = \frac{1}{2}W = 432$, and $D = 2700$. Nonfree, rather than free, sampling was used, since we had no *a priori* knowledge of the probability that a cell would be B or G, and these probabilities had to be estimated from the data. We estimated p_B by n_1/n and p_G by n_2/n, where $n = 125$, the total number of cells in the study area. Results were obtained for the distributions of BB, GG, and BG joins. In addition, results were computed for 1931 and 1932 for the average differences map over the three simulation series. The coefficient I, given in equations (4.1–4.4), was also evaluated for the differences maps from each of the three simulation runs, again with $n = 125$. The fact that this coefficient does not assume $\sum_{(1)} z_i = 0$ has advantages here. As discussed in item (3), page 75 for the simulation model, an iteration of the model was completed when each carrier had contacted one other person, carrier or non-carrier. As a result the total number of adopters on the simulated and observed maps is not the same for any given year (see Hägerstrand, 1953, pages 16, 23–25), and so $\sum_{(1)} z_i \neq 0$.

The results of the join count and I tests are given in tables 4.1 and 4.2. The findings appear very conclusive. There is a high degree of positive spatial autocorrelation in the nonzero residuals for the 1931 and 1932 differences maps in all cases except the I coefficients for simulation series two. Even here the same tendency is evident although the standard deviates are not significant, possibly because the differences are less in absolute size for simulation series two.

However, before returning the verdict, let us consider more closely the assumptions underlying the tests. The join count statistics assume under H_0 that the probability of a cell being coded a particular colour is the same for all cells; but a careful inspection of the differences maps suggests that a cell in the southeast corner, far away from the main region of

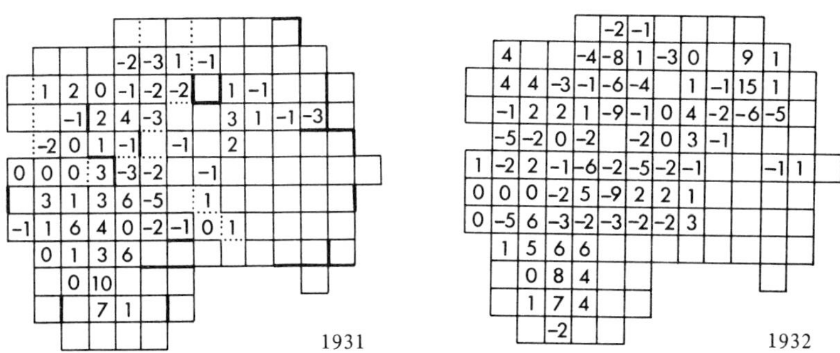

Simulation series one

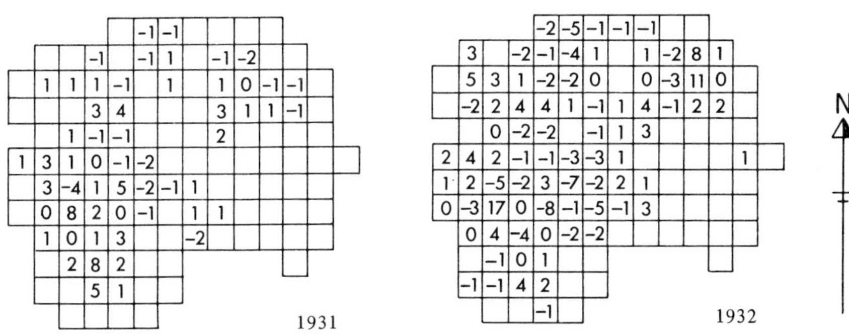

Simulation series two

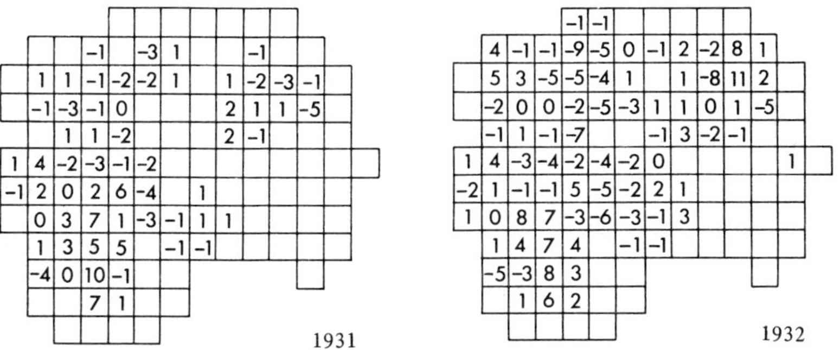

Simulation series three

—— zero contact barrier ...... half contact barrier

Figure 4.2. Differences maps for Hägerstrand's simulation series one, two, and three.

Table 4.1. The values of the join count statistics for the Hägerstrand differences maps[(a)].

Differences map	Year	n_1	n_2	*BB* joins				*GG* joins				*BG* joins			
				observed	expected	σ	standard deviate, z	observed	expected	σ	standard deviate, z	observed	expected	σ	standard deviate, z
Simulation series one	1931	21	26	26	11·71	2·97	4·81 ****	38	18·11	2·95	6·74 ****	31	30·43	7·25	0·08
	1932	38	32	61	39·19	4·89	4·46 ****	39	27·65	4·27	2·66 ****	84	67·78	6·61	2·45 ****
Simulation series two	1931	21	30	23	11·71	2·97	3·80 ****	42	24·25	4·05	4·38 ****	43	35·12	5·02	1·57
	1932	35	38	59	33·17	4·58	5·63 ****	58	39·19	4·89	3·85 ****	73	74·14	6·86	−0·17
Simulation series three	1931	27	29	33	19·57	3·70	3·63 ****	42	22·63	3·94	4·92 ****	61	43·65	5·53	3·14 ****
	1932	41	35	75	45·71	5·81	5·85 ****	52	33·17	4·55	4·14 ****	76	79·99	7·06	−0·57
Average of differences over the three simulation series	1931	32	36	51	27·65	4·27	5·46 ****	55	35·12	4·68	4·24 ****	83	64·21	5·94	3·16 ****
	1932	38	53	55	39·19	4·89	3·23 ****	108	76·81	6·12	5·10 ****	122	112·26	8·00	1·22

** Significant at 0·05 level ($|z| \geqslant 1{\cdot}9600$)
*** Significant at 0·01 level ($|z| \geqslant 2{\cdot}5758$)

(a) Because of the contagious growth nature of most diffusion processes noted earlier, and the contagious growth structure of the Hägerstrand model, we hypothesise that if the observed and simulated maps do have systematic spatial differences, then these differences will also exhibit positive spatial autocorrelation. We therefore apply one-tailed tests of significance to the standard deviates.

adopters, has a much higher chance of being coded W than a cell in the rest of the study area. Indeed, the low figures for the expected numbers of BB and GG joins in table 4.1 reflect the concentration of W cells in the southeast corner. A similar assumption is made in the case of I, namely that the probability of a cell in a differences map having a particular x_i value is the same for each cell.

In order to approximate more closely this assumption of equal probability in the join count and I statistics, the analysis for these coefficients was reworked, redefining n as the number of nonblank cells in the differences maps and considering only joins between cells which were not blank. The effective number of observations and the map structure varied for each differences map and, although the analysis was worked through for all differences maps and for the average differences map in the case of the join count statistics, for I we examined only the average differences map. The results are given in tables 4.3 and 4.4.

The picture now changes considerably. All the observed BB and GG counts continue to exceed expectation, but only five out of sixteen are significant at the 95% level. On the other hand the BG join counts are now much further away from their expectations under the null hypothesis, and indicate fewer such links than would be expected. The more powerful I statistic (for a discussion of relative efficiences, see chapter 7) now firmly rejects H_0 for 1931 and 1932. Criticisms can be made of both analyses, but the authors feel that the second is closer in spirit to the assumptions underlying the testing procedures.

The reader should note that in tables 4.1–4.4 we have tested the various coefficients for significance using the straightforward normal approximation. In the case of the variant of I used in tables 4.2 and 4.4, we have not undertaken any small sample studies to examine the suitability of this approximation in finite sized lattices. However, in the case of the join count statistics used in tables 4.1 and 4.3, the approximation given in equations (2.55) and (2.60) can be applied. This yields the results shown in table 4.5, and supports the comments made in previous paragraphs.

Table 4.2. Values of I for the Hägerstrand differences maps.

Value of I	Differences map					
	simulation series one		simulation series two		simulation series three	
	1931	1932	1931	1932	1931	1932
Expected	0·015	−0·008	0·034	−0·005	−0·001	−0·008
observed	0·275	0·176	0·115	0·064	0·247	0·235
σ	0·046	0·046	0·054	0·044	0·044	0·046
Standard deviate	5·67 ****	4·03 ****	1·49	1·56	5·60 ****	5·26 ****

**** Significant at $\alpha = 0·01$ level (one-tailed test)

Table 4.3. Values of the join count statistics for the reduced n Hägerstrand differences maps.

Differences map	Year	n_1	n_2	n	*BB* joins				*GG* joins				*BG* joins			
					observed	expected	σ	standard deviate, z	observed	expected	σ	standard deviate, z	observed	expected	σ	standard deviate, z
Simulation series one	1931	21	26	56	26	20·04	3·59	1·66 **	38	31·02	4·55	1·53	31	52·12	5·43	−3·89 ****
	1932	38	32	79	61	54·53	5·38	1·20	39	38·48	4·75	0·11	84	94·33	6·98	−1·48
Simulation series two	1931	21	30	56	23	19·08	3·48	1·13	42	39·55	4·71	0·52	43	57·27	5·49	−2·60 ****
	1932	35	38	82	59	44·07	5·15	2·90 ****	58	52·07	5·45	1·09	73	98·52	7·15	−3·57 ****
Simulation series three	1931	27	29	60	33	32·32	4·34	0·16	42	37·39	4·51	1·02	61	72·11	5·91	−1·88 **
	1932	41	35	80	75	64·09	5·52	1·98 **	52	46·51	4·97	1·10	76	112·17	7·30	−4·95 ****
Average of differences over the three simulation series	1931	32	36	71	51	41·72	4·64	2·00 **	55	52·59	4·95	0·41	83	96·89	6·78	−2·05 **
	1932	38	53	92	55	49·21	5·15	1·12	108	96·45	6·19	1·87 **	122	140·97	8·14	−2·33 **

** Significant at $\alpha = 0{\cdot}05$ level (one-tailed test)
**** Significant at $\alpha = 0{\cdot}01$ level (one-tailed test)

It is, of course, possible that the fairly conclusive rejection of H_0 by the above analyses for the various differences maps is caused by Brown and Moore's point—that the autocorrelation tests are not independent of directional biases in the observed and simulated maps. We therefore look to the Hope-type and 'alternative approach' Hope-type procedures outlined in section 4.2.2 for further evidence.

The Hope-type procedure. Hägerstrand has given the results for three simulation series, and we have generated another 96 expected maps for 1931, and 1932 respectively, yielding, together with Hägerstrand's results, m (= 99) model maps for each of those years (2). The steps in the procedure were then

Step 1: from the 99 generated maps and the corresponding observed map (k = 100 maps in all) we computed, for 1931 and 1932, an 'average expected' map, where $\bar{x}_i$, the number of adopters in the ith cell of the average map, was given by

$$\bar{x}_i = \frac{1}{100}\sum_{k=1}^{100} x_{ik}, \qquad i = 1, 2, \ldots, 125.$$

Step 2: the spatial goodness-of-fit of each of the k (= 100) maps to the corresponding average map was determined as follows. We converted each of the k maps into a differences map by calculating the quantities,

$$z_{ik} = x_{ik} - \bar{x}_i, \qquad i = 1, 2, \ldots, 125; \qquad k = 1, 2, \ldots, 100,$$

where x_{ik} is the number of adopters in the ith cell of the kth map. We then computed for the kth differences map the test statistic, I_k given in equation (4.1), using the $\{z_{ik}\}$. Binary weights were employed as before.

Step 3: the I_k (k = 1, 2, ..., 100) were ranked from smallest (rank 1) to largest (rank 100). The values of I_k (in standard deviate form) and ranks are given in table 4.6. Clearly, given the procedure outlined above, the maps which correspond 'best' with the average map have the lowest degree of spatial autocorrelation in the differences map.

Table 4.4. Values of I for the reduced n Hägerstrand average differences map.

Year	Statistic				
	n	I	E(I)	σ	Standard deviate
1931	71	0·3034	0·0303	0·0605	4·51 ****
1932	92	0·2051	−0·0108	0·0555	3·89 ****

**** Significant at α = 0·01 level (one-tailed test)

(2) We are indebted to E. Sheppard for making a FORTRAN programme of the Hägerstrand model operational, whilst an undergraduate in the Geography Department at Bristol.

Table 4.5. Results of tests of significance for Hägerstrand's differences maps using the approximations given in equations (2.55) and (2.60).

Simulation series differences map		Year	*BB* joins			*GG* joins			*BG* joins		
			observed	BB_α from equation (2.55)		observed	GG_α from equation (2.55)		observed	BG_α from equation (2.60)	
				$\alpha = 0{\cdot}05$	$\alpha = 0{\cdot}01$		$\alpha = 0{\cdot}05$	$\alpha = 0{\cdot}01$		$\alpha = 0{\cdot}05$	$\alpha = 0{\cdot}01$
Corresponding to table 4.1	one	1931	26 ****	16·86	19·41	38 ****	23·12	25·47	31	42·03	46·64
		1932	61 ****	47·45	51·24	39 ****	34·91	38·30	84 ****	78·33	82·50
	two	1931	23 ****	16·86	19·41	42 ****	31·15	34·40	43	43·06	46·13
		1932	59 ****	40·93	44·52	58 ****	47·45	51·24	73	62·30	56·79
	three	1931	33 ****	26·31	29·35	42 ****	29·36	32·53	61 ****	52·43	55·85
		1932	75 ****	55·53	60·04	52 ****	40·88	44·44	76	67·83	62·17
	average	1931	51 ****	34·91	38·30	55 ****	43·04	46·49	83 ****	73·66	77·37
		1932	55 ****	47·45	51·24	108 ****	87·04	91·60	122	125·09	130·22
Corresponding to table 4.2	one	1931	26	26·18	29·08	38	38·74	42·33	31 ****	42·63	38·10
		1932	61	63·57	67·64	39	46·50	50·18	84	82·30	76·70
	two	1931	23	25·03	27·86	42	47·50	51·13	43 ****	47·68	43·11
		1932	59 ****	52·76	56·72	58	61·54	65·38	73 ****	86·21	80·49
	three	1931	33	39·67	43·05	42	45·00	48·48	61 **	61·83	56·97
		1932	75 **	73·34	77·47	52	54·87	58·66	76 ****	99·61	93·79
	average	1931	51 **	49·54	53·09	55	60·90	64·63	83 **	85·19	79·73
		1932	55	57·87	61·79	108 **	106·76	111·31	122 **	127·03	120·64

** Significant at $\alpha = 0{\cdot}05$ level (one-tailed test)
**** Significant at $\alpha = 0{\cdot}01$ level (one-tailed test)

Table 4.6. Values of standard deviates of I for Hope procedure applied to Hägerstrand data.

1931				1932			
Rank	Standard deviate	Rank	Standard deviate	Rank	Standard deviate	Rank	Standard deviate
1	−2·95	51	−0·29	1	−2·52	51	0·62
2	−2·94	52	−0·29	2	−1·89	52	0·66
3	−2·61	53	−0·25	3	−1·61	53	0·69
4	−2·40	54	−0·24	4	−1·53	54	0·69
5	−2·37	55	−0·13	5	−1·38	55	0·82
6	−2·21	56	−0·07	6	−1·19	56	0·86
7	−2·02	57	−0·05	7	−1·09	57	0·99
8	−2·01	58	−0·02	8	−1·05	58	1·03
9	−1·89	59	0·00	9	−0·97	59	1·05
10	−1·74	60	0·04	10	−0·96	60	1·13
11	−1·70	61	0·08	11	−0·96	61	1·17
12	−1·69	62	0·15	12	−0·92	62	1·17
13	−1·67	63	0·17	13	−0·84	63	1·17
14	−1·64	64	0·18	14	−0·75	64	1·18
15	−1·52	65	0·21	15	−0·69	65	1·21
16	−1·48	66	0·29	16	−0·56	66	1·28
17	−1·46	67	0·36	17	−0·52	67	1·28
18	−1·41	68	0·38	18	−0·42	68	1·43
19	−1·40	69	0·42	19	−0·32	69	1·43
20	−1·39	70	0·45	20	−0·30	70	1·48
21	−1·38	71	0·49	21	−0·29	71	1·50
22	−1·37	72	0·49	22	−0·26	72	1·55
23	−1·36	73	0·50	23	−0·24	73	1·56
24	−1·33	74	0·54	24	−0·18	74	1·90
25	−1·29	75	0·54	25	−0·14	75	1·91
26	−1·27	76	0·54	26	−0·13	76	1·96
27	−1·27	77	0·57	27	−0·13	77	1·98
28	−1·23	78	0·61	28	−0·12	78	1·98
29	−1·22	79	0·63	29	−0·05	79	1·99
30	−1·18	80	0·68	30	−0·03	80	2·14
31	−1·17	81	0·84	31	0·01	81	2·16
32	−1·15	82	1·10	32	0·04	82	2·33
33	−1·15	83	1·15	33	0·15	83	2·34
34	−0·93	84	1·26	34	0·16	84	2·37
35	−0·91	85	1·31	35	0·17	85	2·44
36	−0·84	86	1·33	36	0·17	86	2·56
37	−0·84	87	1·36	37	0·25	87	2·66
38	−0·84	88	1·47	38	0·28	88	2·71
39	−0·71	89	1·57	39	0·29	89	2·77
40	−0·66	90	1·68	40	0·30	90	2·78
41	−0·65	91	1·72	41	0·30	91	2·91
42	−0·60	92	1·77	42	0·37	92	3·02
43	−0·51	93	1·92	43	0·38	93	3·08
44	−0·45	94	2·37	44	0·39	94	3·40
45	−0·41	95	2·46	45	0·42	95	3·43
46	−0·40	96	2·52	46	0·45	96	3·66
47	−0·39	97	3·14	47	0·51	97	4·24
48	−0·37	98	3·73	48	0·51	98	4·26
49	−0·30	99	4·49	49	0·56	99	5·23
50	−0·30	100	5·36	50	0·58	100	5·56

Step 4: the test statistic between the observed map and the average map for 1931 ranked 100, while that for 1932 ranked 98. As discussed in section 4.2.2, we can reject H_0 for 1931 at the $\alpha = 0 \cdot 01$ level, and for 1932 at the $\alpha = 0 \cdot 03$ level (one-tailed test).

The 'alternative approach' Hope-type procedure. Following the procedure described in section 4.2.2, we compared each simulated map with the corresponding observed map using I given in equation (4.1). The standard deviates for I, ranked from largest to smallest, appear in table 4.7. In all cases, the standard deviate is positive, implying that $I > E_R(I)$ throughout. Therefore $j = 0$ for 1931 and 1932, and we can reject H_0 for both years at the $\alpha = 0 \cdot 01$ level (one-tailed test).

The results of both Hope-type analyses support the conclusions drawn earlier in this section. We have used one-tailed tests throughout, anticipating that deviations from H_0 would show up as positive spatial autocorrelation. However, a two-sided alternative could easily be used instead.

4.3.3 Interpretation of the results

If the differences maps (figure 4.2) are compared with the spatial locations of the original adopters in 1929 (Hägerstrand, 1953, figure 6) which, as noted in item (1), page 75, formed the starting point for the Monte Carlo model, it will be noticed that the areas in which the simulation model overestimated numbers of adopters (negative residuals in figure 4.2), are clustered very closely along the line of the original adopters of the innovation in 1929. Conversely, areas in which the simulation produced less adopters than actually occurred (positive residuals) form a 'tyre' shaped ring around the hub of overestimation, and are therefore removed from the regions of original 1929 adopters. This basic pattern is evident in all the difference maps of figure 4.2, and accounts for the several significant negative values of the standard deviate for BG joins in tables 4.1 and 4.3. We consider two possible reasons for these findings.

First. The probabilities in the MIF might be too large in the centre cell and in the cells surrounding the centre cell of the target, and too small in the border cells of the target. This increases considerably the probability that a carrier will contact 'near' potential adopters in a generation of the model, as opposed to potential adopters located further away. Since each carrier makes one contact in a generation, most new adopters will be added very close to existing adopters. Naturally this will rapidly lead to over-concentration of adopters in areas of original adopters, and to underestimation of new adopters in regions away from areas of original adopters.

Such an interpretation is supported by Tinline (1971). Tinline's approach was to take the observed maps for two particular years, say 1930 and 1931, and to find the 5×5 matrix operator which transformed the 1930 map into the 1931 map with the minimum amount of error.

Table 4.7. Values of standard deviates of *I* for "alternative approach" Hope-type procedure applied to Hägerstrand data.

1931				1932			
Rank	Standard deviate	Rank	Standard deviate	Rank	Standard deviate	Rank	Standard deviate
1	8·05	51	3·78	1	5·78	51	3·22
2	6·16	52	3·76	2	5·52	52	3·21
3	5·82	53	3·76	3	5·44	53	3·08
4	5·76	54	3·74	4	5·33	54	3·07
5	5·64	55	3·70	5	5·26	55	3·00
6	5·62	56	3·65	6	5·17	56	2·97
7	5·60	57	3·60	7	5·12	57	2·91
8	5·54	58	3·59	8	4·97	58	2·87
9	5·44	59	3·51	9	4·89	59	2·81
10	5·38	60	3·48	10	4·79	60	2·65
11	5·34	61	3·42	11	4·77	61	2·52
12	5·24	62	3·41	12	4·77	62	2·52
13	5·17	63	3·41	13	4·73	63	2·52
14	5·15	64	3·40	14	4·68	64	2·52
15	5·04	65	3·39	15	4·62	65	2·49
16	4·98	66	3·38	16	4·59	66	2·48
17	4·96	67	3·38	17	4·52	67	2·45
18	4·92	68	3·26	18	4·48	68	2·37
19	4·89	69	3·25	19	4·35	69	2·36
20	4·85	70	3·20	20	4·34	70	2·27
21	4·84	71	3·15	21	4·20	71	2·27
22	4·84	72	3·11	22	4·20	72	2·26
23	4·81	73	3·10	23	4·20	73	2·12
24	4·69	74	3·09	24	4·16	74	2·09
25	4·51	75	2·94	25	4·04	75	2·04
26	4·45	76	2·93	26	4·03	76	2·03
27	4·44	77	2·91	27	4·01	77	1·96
28	4·40	78	2·87	28	4·01	78	1·84
29	4·39	79	2·82	29	3·99	79	1·83
30	4·36	80	2·77	30	3·96	80	1·81
31	4·32	81	2·73	31	3·95	81	1·79
32	4·31	82	2·70	32	3·83	82	1·77
33	4·23	83	2·49	33	3·73	83	1·71
34	4·21	84	2·47	34	3·73	84	1·56
35	4·21	85	2·46	35	3·72	85	1·55
36	4·16	86	2·45	36	3·71	86	1·51
37	4·13	87	2·23	37	3·68	87	1·51
38	4·12	88	1·99	38	3·65	88	1·46
39	4·12	89	1·94	39	3·62	89	1·44
40	4·10	90	1·87	40	3·59	90	1·40
41	4·09	91	1·80	41	3·56	91	1·34
42	4·02	92	1·77	42	3·49	92	1·27
43	4·02	93	1·58	43	3·46	93	1·15
44	4·01	94	1·49	44	3·41	94	1·14
45	4·01	95	1·49	45	3·37	95	1·07
46	4·00	96	1·27	46	3·37	96	1·01
47	3·98	97	0·81	47	3·37	97	0·96
48	3·93	98	0·42	48	3·33	98	0·86
49	3·91	99	0·01	49	3·33	99	0·53
50	3·79			50	3·26		

Least squares (LS) and minimum absolute deviations (MAD) were both used by Tinline as criteria for obtaining the 5 x 5 operator; his LS and MAD operators for 1930–1931 are given below.

LS

0·70	0·83	0·54	0·56	0·48
0·15	−0·14	0·17	−0·07	0·49
−0·98	−0·30	1·02	0·31	−0·65
1·35	0·50	0·51	0·52	−0·02
−1·63	0·43	0·62	−0·88	−1·10

MAD

0·35	0·72	0·79	0·68	0
0·28	0·09	0	0	0·21
0·33	0	1·02	0	0
0	0	0	0	0·17
0	0·58	1·59	0	0

They are the nonprobabilistic moving average schemes (in contrast to the probabilistic MIF) which best transform the 1930 map into the 1931 map according to the LS and MAD criteria. There is a tendency in both the operators for the coefficients in the border cells of the operators to be higher than the values in the inner cells (exclusive of the central weight). The MAD operator is an excellent caricature of this pattern and is described by Tinline (1971, page 90) as "doughnut-shaped, with an outer ring of higher values and an inner ring of lower values". This may be contrasted with the negative exponential decay of the probabilities postulated by Hägerstrand in his MIF, and by comparison with the operators overestimate in the inner ring and underestimate in the outer ring.

Second. The system of half and zero contact barriers evidently reduces too severely the probability of contact over barriers. Since the barriers intervene between areas of original adopters and peripheral regions of the study lattice (figure 4.2), they increase further the chance of underestimation of numbers of new adopters in marginal areas. This is particularly noticeable in all the 1932 differences maps with the half contact barrier in the southeast part of the map. The division between overestimation and underestimation of numbers of adopters by the model follows exactly the configuration of this barrier, with overestimation on the western side of the barrier where the original adopters were located, and underestimation on the eastern side.

Since a single half barrier stops the innovation with probability 0·5, one possibility would be to allow two half barriers in combination to stop with probability $1-(0\cdot5)^2 = 0\cdot75$, rather than 1·0 as done by Hägerstrand. However, it is doubtful whether this alone would be sufficient to counteract the tendencies noted above.

5

The analysis of regression residuals—theory

5.1 Introduction

In the first four chapters of this monograph we have considered spatial autocorrelation among sample data, where these data have not been modified by any statistical procedure. On many occasions we wish to carry out a regression analysis and look for autocorrelation, not in the original data, but among the residuals from the regression.

If autocorrelation (temporal or spatial) is detected among the regression residuals, it could imply:

1. the presence of nonlinear relationships between the dependent and independent variables;
2. the omission of one or more regressor variables;
3. that the regression model should have an autoregressive structure.

The presence of autocorrelation among the population error terms leads to biased estimates of the residual variance and inefficient estimates of the regression coefficients when the method of ordinary least squares (OLS) is used. Therefore some check for autocorrelation should always be applied and remedial action taken when necessary.

When situation '1' above is believed to be important, different models can be specified and interaction terms among the independent variables included [see regressions 1(a) and 1(b) in section 6.2]. If '2' is the main cause of autocorrelation, additional variables may be suggested by plotting the residuals on a map and searching for regular patterns in the residuals [see the discussion on regression (2) in section 6.2, and Taaffe *et al.* (1963)]. Finally, if '3' is thought to be the main cause, some kind of transformation must be carried out (see sections 5.8 and 6.6).

In this chapter the problems caused when the population error terms are autocorrelated are outlined in section 5.2. In section 5.3 we give the different statistics which may be used to test for autocorrelation among the population error terms, and the assumptions which underly the use of these statistics in testing procedures. Section 5.4 is devoted to the evaluation of the moments of the statistics and in section 5.5 we explore the alternative BLUS procedure. In section 5.6 some asymptotic distribution theory is developed. This is used to provide approximations to the sampling distributions of the statistics; alternative procedures are also considered. In section 5.7, various estimates for autoregressive models are considered, and the question of examining the residuals from such models is reviewed. Finally, in section 5.8, we discuss various methods for handling case '3' above.

In conclusion a test for autocorrelation will tell us whether a given model is adequate, or whether a different form is required. We have no desire to remove spatial autocorrelation as such, but simply to make allowances for it so that valid estimating procedures can be adopted.

Indeed, as Gould (1970) has pointed out "...it is precisely the lack of independence—the interdependence—of spatial phenomena that allows us to substitute pattern, and therefore predictability and order, for chaos and apparent lack of interdependence of things in time and space". If this interdependence is ignored, we cannot hope to have a very realistic model of an observed process.

5.2 The general model and alternative hypotheses

5.2.1 The classical regression model

Suppose that, for each of the n counties in a study area, the observation y_i has been recorded on the variate Y_i $(i = 1, 2, ..., n)$. In vector notation, let $\boldsymbol{y}'$ $(= y_1, y_2, ..., y_n)$ be the $(n \times 1)$ vector of observed values corresponding to the variate vector $\boldsymbol{Y}'$ $(= Y_1, Y_2, ..., Y_n)$. $\boldsymbol{Y}$ is assumed to have the mean vector $\boldsymbol{X\beta}$ and covariance matrix $\sigma^2\boldsymbol{V}$; that is,

$$\mathrm{E}(\boldsymbol{Y}) = \boldsymbol{X\beta}, \tag{5.1}$$

and

$$\mathrm{var}(\boldsymbol{Y}) = \sigma^2\boldsymbol{V}, \tag{5.2}$$

where $\boldsymbol{X}$ is an $(n \times k)$ matrix of nonstochastic regressor variables,

$$\boldsymbol{X} = \begin{bmatrix} 1 & X_{12} & \dots & X_{1k} \\ 1 & X_{22} & \dots & X_{2k} \\ \vdots & \vdots & & \vdots \\ 1 & X_{n2} & \dots & X_{nk} \end{bmatrix}, \tag{5.3}$$

with the elements in the first column corresponding to the constant term. The vector $\boldsymbol{\beta}$ is of order $(k \times 1)$, and contains the parameters β_i $(i = 1, 2, ..., k)$; that is $\boldsymbol{\beta}' = (\beta_1, \beta_2, ..., \beta_k)$, and $\boldsymbol{V}$ is an $(n \times n)$ matrix with elements $\{v_{ij}\}$.

The OLS model specifies the regression equation

$$\boldsymbol{Y} = \boldsymbol{X\beta}+\boldsymbol{\epsilon}, \tag{5.4}$$

where $\boldsymbol{\epsilon}$ is an $(n \times 1)$ vector of random error terms. It follows from equation (5.1) and the assumption of nonstochastic X variables that

$$\mathrm{E}(\boldsymbol{\epsilon}) = \boldsymbol{0}. \tag{5.5}$$

Further, if $\mathrm{var}(\boldsymbol{\epsilon}) = \sigma^2\boldsymbol{V}$ reduces to

$$\mathrm{var}(\boldsymbol{\epsilon}) = \sigma^2\boldsymbol{I}_n, \tag{5.6}$$

where

$\boldsymbol{I}_n$ $(\equiv \boldsymbol{I})$ is the unit matrix of order n, and $\boldsymbol{X}$ is of rank k (that is, full rank), (5.7) then the OLS estimators

$$b = (X'X)^{-1}X'y, \tag{5.8}$$

are the best linear unbiased estimators for β (cf. Johnston, 1972, pp.123–127).

It follows from these assumptions that the unobservable error terms ϵ can be estimated by

$$e = y - Xb \tag{5.9}$$

while the best unbiased estimator for σ^2 is

$$\begin{aligned}\hat{\sigma}^2 &= (n-k)^{-1}e'e = (n-k)^{-1}\sum_{i=1}^{n} e_i^2 \\ &= (n-k)^{-1}(y'y - b'X'y).\end{aligned} \tag{5.10}$$

The estimated variance–covariance matrix for the b is

$$\hat{\text{var}}(b) = \hat{\sigma}^2(X'X)^{-1}. \tag{5.11}$$

The overall goodness-of-fit of the model is then measured by the coefficient of multiple correlation,

$$R^2 = \frac{b'X'y - n\bar{y}^2}{y'y - n\bar{y}^2}, \tag{5.12}$$

where $n\bar{y} = \sum_{i=1}^{n} y_i$.

If, in addition to the assumptions already made, we assume that the ϵ are normally distributed, the null hypothesis

$$H_0\colon \beta_2 = \beta_3 = \ldots \beta_k = 0,$$

may be tested using the statistic

$$F = \frac{R^2/(k-1)}{(1-R^2)/(n-k)}, \tag{5.13}$$

which is distributed under H_0 as Snedecor's F with $(k-1)$, $(n-k)$ degrees of freedom (df). Finally, for individual coefficients in the regression, we may test H_0: $\beta_i = 0$ using the t statistic

$$t_i = \frac{b_i}{\hat{\sigma}(a_{ii})^{1/2}}, \tag{5.14}$$

with $(n-k)$ df, where a_{ii} is the ith element on the leading diagonal of $(X'X)^{-1}$. Note that this test is conditional upon the other variables being included in the regression equation. For further details, see Johnston (1972, pp.137–138).

5.2.2 Consequences of autocorrelated errors

Equation (5.6) embodies the crucial assumption, H_0: that there is no autocorrelation among the error terms[3]. If, as often happens, this assumption is violated, the estimators (5.8) are inefficient, while the variance estimator (5.10) is downwards biased, thereby inflating the observed value of R^2. Clearly, if H_0 is violated, the error terms must be autocorrelated in some way, and we now consider in detail an alternative hypothesis H_1, which specifies the structure of the autocorrelation among the error terms. See also appendix 1.

5.2.3 Detailed specification of H_1

In a regression analysis of serially ordered data (time series), an often used alternative to H_0 is the assumption that the error terms in the model arise from a first order Markovian scheme, that is

$$\epsilon_i = \rho\epsilon_{i-1} + u_i, \qquad i = 1, 2, ..., n, \tag{5.15}$$

where it is assumed that ϵ_0 is known and u_i is uncorrelated with ϵ_{i-1}, ϵ_{i-2}, ... and all other u_j. The covariance matrix of $\boldsymbol{\epsilon}$ for scheme (5.15), under an alternative hypothesis which specifies a value of ρ different from zero, is of the form

$$\sigma^2 V = \sigma^2[(I-\rho A)'(I-\rho A)]^{-1}, \tag{5.16}$$

where the matrix A has elements

$$\begin{aligned} a_{ij} &= 1, \qquad \text{if } j = i-1, \\ &= 0, \qquad \text{otherwise.} \end{aligned} \tag{5.17}$$

For regression errors with a geographic ordering, we consider the first order Markovian scheme

$$\epsilon_i = \rho\sum_j w_{ij}\epsilon_j + u_i, \qquad i = 1, 2, ..., n, \tag{5.18}$$

where the $\{w_{ij}\}$ are the general weights specified in chapter 1, and the summation is taken over all $j \neq i$. Either standardised (that is, $\sum_j w_{ij} = 1$) or unstandardised weights could be used. In this instance we shall employ standardised weights, as this gives a natural interpretation to the value of ρ, akin to that in equation (5.15).

From model (5.18), in matrix terms, we have that

$$\boldsymbol{\epsilon} = \rho W\boldsymbol{\epsilon} + \boldsymbol{u},$$

or

$$\boldsymbol{\epsilon} = (I-\rho W)^{-1}\boldsymbol{u}, \tag{5.19}$$

[3] Equation (5.6) also implies that the error terms are homoscedastic, that is they have equal variances. In the remainder of this chapter, and in chapter 6, we accept the assumption of homoscedasticity without further comment. The interested reader should consult Johnston (1972, pp.214-221).

if we assume that $\boldsymbol{I}-\rho \boldsymbol{W}$ is positive definite. If the covariance matrix of $\boldsymbol{u}$ is $\sigma^2 \boldsymbol{I}$, then the covariance matrix of $\boldsymbol{\epsilon}$ is

$$\begin{aligned} \mathrm{E}(\boldsymbol{\epsilon}\boldsymbol{\epsilon}') &= (\boldsymbol{I}-\rho \boldsymbol{W})^{-1}\mathrm{E}(\boldsymbol{u}\boldsymbol{u}')(\boldsymbol{I}-\rho \boldsymbol{W}')^{-1} \\ &= \sigma^2[(\boldsymbol{I}-\rho \boldsymbol{W}')(\boldsymbol{I}-\rho \boldsymbol{W})]^{-1} = \sigma^2 \boldsymbol{V}, \text{ say.} \end{aligned} \tag{5.20}$$

Then

$$\boldsymbol{V}^{-1} = [\boldsymbol{I}+\rho^2 \boldsymbol{W}'\boldsymbol{W}-\rho(\boldsymbol{W}+\boldsymbol{W}')]. \tag{5.21}$$

Clearly, if we set $\boldsymbol{W} = \boldsymbol{A}$, equation (5.20) reduces to (5.16).

5.3 The choice of test statistic

As noted in section 5.2.1, the error terms ϵ_i $(i = 1, 2, \ldots, n)$ are unobservable and so any test for autocorrelation among the errors must be based upon the calculated residuals e_i $(i = 1, 2, \ldots, n)$. It is evident that we could use the BB or BW join counts as our test statistic by adopting the convention that $x_i = 1$ if $e_i \geqslant 0$, and $x_i = 0$ if $e_i < 0$. Equations (1.41) and (1.42) could then be used. Similarly the I or c coefficients could be used if we replaced z_i and x_i by e_i in equations (1.44) and (1.45).

When several alternative statistics are available for testing a null hypothesis H_0, we choose that one which is most efficient (has the greatest power against the alternative hypothesis H_1, under consideration) provided that this test is

(a) consistent, that is,

$$\text{prob(reject } \mathrm{H}_0 \,|\, \mathrm{H}_1 \text{ true}) \to 1 \quad \text{as } n \to \infty,$$

where n is the sample size, and

(b) unbiased in the parameter space of H_1, that is,

$$\text{prob(reject } \mathrm{H}_0 \,|\, \mathrm{H}_1 \text{ true}) \geqslant \alpha,$$

where

$$\begin{aligned} \alpha &= \text{prob(reject } \mathrm{H}_0 \,|\, \mathrm{H}_0 \text{ true)} \\ &= \text{prob(type I error).} \end{aligned}$$

For further details see Kendall and Stuart (1967, chapter 24). We leave considerations of efficiency until chapter 7, but we do proceed now to look at properties (a) and (b) for the join count, I, and c statistics.

5.3.1 Correlation among the sample residuals under H_0

Under the usual assumptions of regression analysis, the least squares estimators $\boldsymbol{e}$, of the error terms $\boldsymbol{\epsilon}$, have zero means and covariance matrix

$$\begin{aligned} \mathrm{E}(\boldsymbol{e}\boldsymbol{e}') &= \sigma^2[\boldsymbol{I}-\boldsymbol{X}(\boldsymbol{X}'\boldsymbol{X})^{-1}\boldsymbol{X}'] \\ &= \sigma^2 \boldsymbol{M}, \text{ say.} \end{aligned} \tag{5.22}$$

For simplicity we assume that the distribution of each e_i is continuous and symmetric, although this does not affect the overall argument in any fundamental way. From this assumption and equation (5.22) it follows that

$$\text{prob}(e_i \geqslant 0) = \text{prob}(e_i < 0) = \tfrac{1}{2}, \qquad \text{for all } i,$$

but that

$$\text{prob}(e_i \geqslant 0 \text{ and } e_j \geqslant 0) \neq \text{prob}(e_i \geqslant 0)\,\text{prob}(e_j \geqslant 0).$$

Generally the n estimators follow a multivariate distribution which spans $(n-k)$ dimensions, because of the parameters already estimated, and

$$\text{prob}(e_1 \geqslant 0, e_2 \geqslant 0, \ldots, e_m \geqslant 0) \neq \text{prob}(e_1 \geqslant 0)\,\text{prob}(e_2 \geqslant 0) \ldots \text{prob}(e_m \geqslant 0), \qquad m \leqslant n. \tag{5.23}$$

In other words, the sample residuals $\boldsymbol{e}$ are correlated under H_0, whether or not the population errors $\boldsymbol{\epsilon}$ are autocorrelated.

From result (5.23) it follows that, for regression residuals, the expected values of the join count statistics in free sampling under H_0 will differ from the values given in equations (1.54) and (1.56). The same argument holds for nonfree sampling [equations (1.60) and (1.62)].

Thus the join count statistics are not unbiased, although they remain consistent provided that the matrix $\boldsymbol{X}'\boldsymbol{X}/n$ converges to a limit in probability as n increases. The correct moments could be evaluated, but this involves the evaluation of $\frac{1}{2}na$ bivariate integrals, where a is the average number of joins with nonzero weights per county.

For the I and c statistics we could operate under either assumption N or assumption R (see section 2.3). Anticipating the results of the next section (equations 5.34 and 5.47), we find that the tests are consistent and unbiased under assumption N, although the moments are more complicated. To make assumption R operational, we must consider the $n!$ random permutations of the n vectors $(y_i, X_{2i}, \ldots, X_{ki})$, which is equivalent to considering the randomisation of the $\{e_i\}$. This means that the moments given in section 2.3.2 apply (with e_i replacing z_i), but this in turn implies that the tests are biased. This bias could be removed by correcting the first moment, but the test would still ignore autocorrelation among the regressor variables and therefore would be inefficient.

We can conclude that the only operational tests available that are both consistent and unbiased are those based on the I and c statistics under assumption N. We now give the first two moments of these coefficients.

5.4 The moments of the *I* and *c* statistics

The methods used in this section are the same as in section 2.3, although the moments are more involved because of the correlation between the variates under H_0. The OLS model is assumed, as outlined in section

5.2.1, and it is also assumed that the random error terms are normally distributed. We first develop the results for I for a single regressor variable and then quote the results for I (several variables) and c (single variable).

5.4.1 Moments of I for a single regressor variable

We consider the population regression model

$$\boldsymbol{y} = \mathbf{1}\alpha + \boldsymbol{x}\beta + \boldsymbol{\epsilon}, \tag{5.24}$$

where $\boldsymbol{y}$, $\boldsymbol{x}$, $\mathbf{1}$, and $\boldsymbol{\epsilon}$ are $(n \times 1)$ vectors, α and β are parameters and $\mathbf{1}' = (1, 1, \ldots, 1)$. The x_i are measured about their mean, so that $\bar{x} = 0$. Under the null hypothesis H_0 (no autocorrelation among the error terms) we know that

$$\mathrm{E}(\boldsymbol{\epsilon}) = \mathbf{0} \qquad \text{and} \qquad \mathrm{E}(\boldsymbol{\epsilon\epsilon}') = \sigma^2 \boldsymbol{I},$$

and we shall set $\sigma^2 = 1$, without loss of generality. The least squares estimator for β is

$$b = (\boldsymbol{x}'\boldsymbol{x})^{-1}\boldsymbol{x}'\boldsymbol{y}, \tag{5.25}$$

and the OLS estimator for α is $a = \bar{y}$. From equations (5.9) and (5.25), the sample residual in county i is

$$e_i = y_i - \bar{y} - bx_i, \qquad i = 1, \ldots, n. \tag{5.26}$$

From equation (5.26)

$$e_i = y_i - \bar{y} - x_i S^{-1} \textstyle\sum x_j y_j,$$

where $S = \boldsymbol{x}'\boldsymbol{x}$, so that

$$\begin{aligned} \boldsymbol{e} &= [\boldsymbol{I}_n - \frac{1}{n}\mathbf{1}\mathbf{1}' - \boldsymbol{x}(\boldsymbol{x}'\boldsymbol{x})^{-1}\boldsymbol{x}']\boldsymbol{y} \\ &= \boldsymbol{My}, \text{ say.} \end{aligned} \tag{5.27}$$

Then the test statistic I, in terms of the residuals, is

$$I = \frac{n\sum_{(2)} w_{ij} e_i e_j}{W\sum_{(1)} e_i^2} = \frac{n}{W}\frac{\boldsymbol{e}'\boldsymbol{We}}{\boldsymbol{e}'\boldsymbol{e}}\,. \tag{5.28}$$

We now proceed to evaluate the moments of I, using the Pitman–Koopman's theorem given in section 2.3.1. Direct application of this theorem implies that

$$\mathrm{E}(I^p) = \left(\frac{n}{W}\right)^p \frac{\mathrm{E}[(\boldsymbol{e}'\boldsymbol{We})^p]}{\mathrm{E}[(\boldsymbol{e}'\boldsymbol{e})^p]}\,, \qquad p = 1, 2, \ldots, \tag{5.29}$$

as I and $\boldsymbol{e}'\boldsymbol{e}$ are independently distributed. Further, $\boldsymbol{e}'\boldsymbol{e}$ is distributed as chi-square with $(n-2)$ degrees of freedom [$(n-k)$ df in the general case], so that

$$\mathrm{E}(\boldsymbol{e}'\boldsymbol{e}) = n - 2, \tag{5.30}$$

or $(n-k)$ generally and

$$E[(\boldsymbol{e}'\boldsymbol{e})^2] = n(n-2), \tag{5.31}$$

or $(n-k)(n-k+2)$ generally.

Mean of I.
Since $\boldsymbol{M}$ is idempotent, it follows that

$$\begin{aligned} E(\boldsymbol{ee}') &= E(\boldsymbol{Myy}'\boldsymbol{M}) \\ &= \boldsymbol{M}. \end{aligned}$$

Therefore

$$E(e_i e_j) = m_{ij} = -n^{-1} - x_i S^{-1} x_j, \qquad i \neq j. \tag{5.32}$$

Thus, from equation (5.32), we see that

$$\begin{aligned} E(\boldsymbol{e}'\boldsymbol{We}) &= -n^{-1} \textstyle\sum_{(2)} w_{ij} - S^{-1} \textstyle\sum_{(2)} w_{ij} x_i x_j \\ &= -n^{-1} W - S^{-1} \boldsymbol{x}'\boldsymbol{Wx}. \end{aligned} \tag{5.33}$$

Then, from equations (5.29), (5.30), and (5.33), it follows that

$$\begin{aligned} E(I) &= \frac{n}{W(n-2)} \left(-\frac{W}{n} - \frac{\boldsymbol{x}'\boldsymbol{Wx}}{S} \right) \\ &= -\frac{(1+I_{1x})}{(n-2)} , \end{aligned} \tag{5.34}$$

where $I_{1x} = n\boldsymbol{x}'\boldsymbol{Wx}/WS$ is the spatial autocorrelation coefficient for X.

Variance of I
If we ignore constants, the numerator of I^2 is

$$\begin{aligned} \left(\textstyle\sum_{(2)} w_{ij} e_i e_j\right)^2 = \tfrac{1}{2} \textstyle\sum_{(2)} (w_{ij} + w_{ji})^2 e_i^2 e_j^2 + \textstyle\sum_{(3)} (w_{ij} + w_{ji})(w_{ik} + w_{ki}) e_i^2 e_j e_k \\ + \textstyle\sum_{(4)} w_{ij} w_{kl} e_i e_j e_k e_l . \end{aligned} \tag{5.35}$$

Let $\boldsymbol{m}_i$ denote the ith column vector of $\boldsymbol{M} = \{\boldsymbol{m}_1, \boldsymbol{m}_2, \ldots, \boldsymbol{m}_n\}$. Then

$$E(e_i^2 e_j^2) = \boldsymbol{m}_i' E\{\boldsymbol{yy}'\boldsymbol{m}_j \boldsymbol{m}_i' \boldsymbol{yy}'\} \boldsymbol{m}_j , \tag{5.36}$$

with $E(e_i^2 e_j e_k)$ and $E(e_i e_j e_k e_l)$ similarly defined.
Now,

$$E(y_i^4) = 3, \; E(y_i^2 y_j^2) = 1, \text{ and } E(y_i y_j y_k y_l) = 0 \text{ otherwise,}$$

since $E(y_i^2) = 1$.

After some algebra, we find that

$$\left. \begin{aligned} E(e_i^2 e_j^2) &= 2m_{ij}^2 + m_{ii} m_{jj} \\ E(e_i^2 e_j e_k) &= m_{ii} m_{jk} + 2m_{ij} m_{ik} \\ E(e_i e_j e_k e_l) &= m_{ij} m_{kl} + m_{ik} m_{jl} + m_{il} m_{jk}. \end{aligned} \right\} \tag{5.37}$$

Taking the expected value of equation (5.35) and substituting (5.37) into this expectation we find, after some simplification, that

$$\text{var}(I) = \frac{1}{(n-2)n}\left[\frac{n^2S_1 - nS_2 + 3W^2}{W^2} + 2I_{1x}^2 - \left(\frac{n}{W}\right)^2 \frac{\sum_{(1)}(v_i - \bar{v})^2}{S}\right] - \frac{1}{(n-2)^2} \tag{5.38}$$

where

$$w_{i.} = \sum_{j=1}^{n} w_{ij}, \qquad w_{.i} = \sum_{j=1}^{n} w_{ji},$$

$$v_i = \sum\nolimits_{(1)}(w_{ij} + w_{ji})x_j, \qquad n\bar{v} = \sum\nolimits_{(1)} v_i,$$

$$S_1 = \tfrac{1}{2}\sum\nolimits_{(2)}(w_{ij} + w_{ji})^2,$$

and

$$S_2 = \sum\nolimits_{(1)}(w_{i.} + w_{.i})^2.$$

If we replace $(n-2)$ by $(n-1)$ throughout and drop all terms in x, (5.38) reduces to var(I) for testing the original data, as given by equation (1.67).

5.4.2 Examples

We now give a few examples, showing var(I) for particular cases.

Example 1: A circular time series autocorrelation coefficient;

$$w_{i,i+1} = 1, \qquad i = 1, 2, \ldots, \text{mod}(n);\ W = n.$$

We obtain

$$\text{var}(I) = \frac{1}{n(n-2)}[(n-3) + 2(I_{1x}^2 - I_{2x})] - \frac{1}{(n-2)^2} \tag{5.39}$$

where

$$I_{2x} = \frac{\sum x_i x_{i+2}}{\sum x_i^2}.$$

Result (5.39) corresponds to that of Moran (1950b), after correcting a minor algebraic error [for $(n+1)/n$, in equation (12) of that paper, read $(n-3)/(n-2)$]. The extension to testing for tth order autocorrelation is immediate, on defining $w_{i,i+t} = 1$, $w_{ij} = 0$ otherwise.

Example 2: A noncircular time series; $w_{i,i+1} = 1, \quad i = 1, 2, \ldots, n-1$; $W = n-1$.

We obtain

$$\text{var}(I) = \frac{n}{(n-1)^2(n-2)}\left[\frac{n^3 - 4n^2 + 3}{n^2} + 2(I_{1x}^2 - I_{2x}) + \frac{(x_1 + x_n)^2}{nS} + \frac{x_1^2 + x_n^2}{S}\right] - \frac{1}{(n-2)^2}, \tag{5.40}$$

where

$$I_{jx} = \frac{\sum_{i=1}^{n-j} x_i x_{i+j}}{S},$$

reducing to equation (5.39) asymptotically. Here, $S = \boldsymbol{x}'\boldsymbol{x}$.

Example 3: The spatial equivalent of a circular time series is mapping a regular lattice onto a torus. Using symmetric binary weights, we then have $w_{i.} = w_{.i} = W/n = a$, say, for all i. Then $S_1 = 2W$, $S_2 = 4Wa$ and

$$\text{var}(I) = \frac{1}{na^2(n-2)}\left[a(2n-a)+2a^2I_{1x}^2 - \frac{4\sum_i\{\sum_j w_{ij}x_j\}^2}{S}\right] - \frac{1}{(n-2)^2}\,. \quad (5.41)$$

Values of a, in practice, range from 2 to 8 (inclusive), with the maximum occurring for the queen's case.

5.4.3 Extension to several variables

When there are k regressor variables in the regression (including the constant term), the OLS estimator of $\boldsymbol{\beta}$ is

$$\boldsymbol{b} = (\boldsymbol{X}'\boldsymbol{X})^{-1}\boldsymbol{X}'\boldsymbol{y},$$

where $\boldsymbol{b}$ is a $(k \times 1)$ vector, and $\boldsymbol{X}$ is an $(n \times k)$ matrix in which X_1 represents the constant term. Then the $(n \times 1)$ vector of sample residuals is

$$\boldsymbol{e} = \boldsymbol{y} - \boldsymbol{X}\boldsymbol{b} = [\boldsymbol{I}_n - \boldsymbol{X}(\boldsymbol{X}'\boldsymbol{X})^{-1}\boldsymbol{X}']\boldsymbol{y} \equiv \boldsymbol{M}\boldsymbol{y}. \quad (5.42)$$

By the same argument as in section 5.4.1, we find that

$$\text{E}(I) = -\frac{1+I_{1x}}{n-k}, \quad (5.43)$$

where

$$I_{1x} = \frac{n}{W}\sum_{(2)} w_{ij}d_{ij},$$

and

$$d_{ij} = \boldsymbol{x}_i'(\boldsymbol{X}'\boldsymbol{X})^{-1}\boldsymbol{x}_j. \quad (5.44)$$

Equations (5.37) continue to hold but, because $\boldsymbol{x}_i'$ is now a row vector rather than a scalar, the expression for the variance is rather more complex. We obtain, eventually,

$$\begin{aligned}\text{var}(I) = \frac{n}{(n-k)W^2}\Bigg\{&\frac{n^2S_1 - nS_2 + 3W^2}{n^2} + \frac{1}{n}\sum_{i=1}^{n}\sum_{j=1}^{n}(w_{i.}+w_{.i})(w_{j.}+w_{.j})d_{ij} \\ &+ 2\Big(\sum_{(2)} w_{ij}d_{ij}\Big)^2 \\ &- \Big[\sum_{(3)}(w_{ik}+w_{ki})(w_{jk}+w_{kj})d_{ij} + \sum_{(2)}(w_{ij}+w_{ji})^2 d_{ii}\Big] \\ &+ \frac{1}{n}\sum_{(3)}(w_{ij}+w_{ji})(w_{ik}+w_{ki})(d_{ii}d_{jk}-d_{ij}d_{ik})\Bigg\} - \frac{1}{(n-k)^2}\,. \end{aligned} \quad (5.45)$$

The first four terms inside the brace bracket in equation (5.45) reduce to those of equation (5.38) when $k = 2$, while the fifth term vanishes.

5.4.4 The moments of *c*

The moments of the c statistic may be evaluated in the same way. If we redefine c as

$$c = \frac{n-k}{2W} \frac{\sum_{(2)} w_{ij}(e_i - e_j)^2}{\sum e_i^2}, \tag{5.46}$$

we obtain

$$\mathrm{E}(c) = 1 - c_{1x}(n-1)^{-1}, \tag{5.47}$$

where

$$c_{1x} = \frac{n-1}{2W} \sum_{(2)} w_{ij}(\boldsymbol{x}_i - \boldsymbol{x}_j)'(X'X)^{-1}(\boldsymbol{x}_i - \boldsymbol{x}_j). \tag{5.48}$$

When $k = 2$, equation (5.48) reduces to

$$c_{1x} = \frac{n-1}{2W} \frac{\sum_{(2)} w_{ij}(x_i - x_j)^2}{\sum x_i^2}.$$

Unfortunately the number of terms in the variance expression is considerably greater than for I. For example, when $k = 2$,

$$\mathrm{var}(c) = \frac{(2S_1 + S_2)(n-2) - 4W^2}{2nW^2} + \frac{[4c_{1x} - (\frac{1}{2}n - 3)c_{1x}^2]}{n(n-1)} + \frac{4[2\sum_{(2)}(w_{ij} + w_{ji})^2(x_i - x_j)^2 + 2\sum(w_{i.} + w_{.i})x_i v_i - \sum v_i^2]}{W^2}, \tag{5.49}$$

reducing to result (1.70) when n is replaced by $(n+1)$ throughout, and the terms in the regressor variables are dropped. For $k > 2$, the result is considerably more complex for c than that for I in equation (5.45), and so I is recommended in preference to c.

Geary (1954) has evaluated the first two moments of c under the assumption that "the error terms are normally distributed *and* the $n!$ random permutations of the vectors $(X_{2i}, ..., X_{ki})$ are considered".

It seems to the authors that this randomisation, while simplifying the results, reduces the power of the test by ignoring autocorrelation among the regressor variables. A test based on this assumption is also biased unless equation (5.47) is used in place of $\mathrm{E}(c) = 1$. This approach is not considered further.

5.5 The BLUS procedure

We recall from section 5.3.1 that the biasedness of the join counts, and of I and c under assumption R (randomisation), when used for regression residuals, was due to the correlation among the sample residuals under null hypothesis H_0. In making allowances for this autocorrelation, the moments of the statistics become more complicated. To avoid the complications raised by the correlation among the sample residuals under H_0, we could construct different residuals which were uncorrelated (and hence independent if ϵ is taken to be normally distributed). Theil (1965) has suggested the use of BLUS estimators (Best Linear Unbiased estimators with a Scalar covariance matrix), and we shall now explore this approach.

5.5.1 Derivation of the estimates

Given that there are k regressor variables in equation (5.4), we nominate $(n-k)$ counties and estimate the $(n-k)$ vector of residuals $\boldsymbol{z}'$ $(= z_1, z_2, \ldots, z_{n-k}$ say), such that

$$\mathrm{E}(\boldsymbol{z}) = \boldsymbol{0}, \quad \text{and} \quad \operatorname{var}(\boldsymbol{z}) = \sigma^2 \boldsymbol{I}_{n-k}.$$

The counties may be renumbered so that the residuals are estimated for the first $(n-k)$ counties only. These estimators, the BLUS estimators, are related to the OLS estimators by

$$\boldsymbol{z} = \boldsymbol{B}\boldsymbol{e}, \tag{5.50}$$

where $\boldsymbol{B}$ is an $(n-k) \times n$ matrix such that $\boldsymbol{BMB}' = \boldsymbol{I}_{n-k}$, $\boldsymbol{M}$ being defined by equation (5.22). $\boldsymbol{B}'$ is the matrix of eigenvectors corresponding to the $(n-k)$ eigenvalues equal to one in the idempotent matrix $\boldsymbol{M}$. For details of the calculation of $\boldsymbol{z}$, see Theil (1965).

Given the BLUS estimates, an I, c, or join count test may be carried out in the usual way, working with the reduced county system of size $(n-k)$ and adjusted weights, as we now show. For example, consider the test statistic

$$I' = \frac{n-k}{W'} \frac{\sum'_{(2)} \omega_{ij} z_i z_j}{\sum' z_j^2}, \tag{5.51}$$

where

$$\textstyle\sum'_{(2)} \equiv \sum\limits_{i=1}^{n-k} \sum\limits_{\substack{j=1 \\ i \neq j}}^{n-k}, \qquad \sum' = \sum\limits_{j=1}^{n-k}, \qquad W' = \sum'_{(2)} \omega_{ij},$$

and ω_{ij} represent the revised weights. These revised weights might be simply $\omega_{ij} = w_{ij}$ or $\omega_{ij} = w_{ij}/\sum' w_{ij}$; the choice of revised weights is considered further in section 7.3.6.

5.5.2 Moments of I'

If we apply the methods of section 5.4, it follows that

$$\mathrm{E}(I') = 0, \tag{5.52}$$

and, putting $t_{ij} = \omega_{ij} + \omega_{ji}$, we also have

$$\operatorname{var}(I') = \frac{(n-k)\sum'_{(2)} t_{ij}^2}{2(W')^2(n-k+2)}, \tag{5.53}$$

with

$$\mu_3(I') = \frac{(n-k)^2 \sum'_{(3)} t_{ij} t_{jm} t_{mi}}{2(W')^3(n-k+2)(n-k+4)}, \tag{5.54}$$

and

$$\mu_4(I') = (n-k)^3[\tfrac{9}{2}\textstyle\sum'_{(2)} t_{ij}^4 + 9\sum'_{(3)} t_{ij}^2 t_{im}^2 + \tfrac{3}{4}\left(\sum'_{(2)} t_{ij}^2\right)^2$$
$$+ 3\textstyle\sum'_{(4)} t_{ij} t_{jm} t_{ml} t_{li}]/(W')^4(n-k+2)(n-k+4)(n-k+6), \tag{5.55}$$

where $\sum'_{(3)} = \sum_{i \neq j \neq m}$, i, j, and m are defined over 1 to $(n-k)$, and $\sum'_{(4)}$ is defined similarly. From expressions (5.52–5.55) it is clear that, once the z_i have been computed, the analysis is simpler because of the zero correlations among these residuals.

The principal difficulty with the Theil procedure lies in the choice of the k counties to be dropped. In time series studies, the first k are often dropped, while for spatial data several rules come to mind, such as: choose the k counties

(1) on the borders of the study area;
(2) at random;
(3) in one particular subarea.

We shall make an attempt to devise a suitable rule in section 7.3.6, but also show that some loss in power is usually entailed.

5.6 Distributions of the test statistics

Our treatment of the distributions of the test statistics considered in sections 5.4 and 5.5 falls into two parts. First, we demonstrate the asymptotic normality of the statistics under general conditions, and second, we outline a randomisation procedure for use with small samples or in situations where assumption N cannot be employed.

5.6.1 Asymptotic normality of the test statistics

The asymptotic normality of the I and c statistics was proved in section 2.4, subject to condition (2.44) on the eigenvalues of the matrix

$$\boldsymbol{T} = \boldsymbol{MWM}, \tag{5.56}$$

where $\boldsymbol{M}$ was given by equation (2.35). Let the eigenvalues of $\boldsymbol{T}$ be ν_i $(i = 1, ..., n)$. Then, in the regression residuals case, with $\boldsymbol{M}$ defined by

$$\boldsymbol{M} = \boldsymbol{I}_n - X(X'X)^{-1}X', \tag{5.57}$$

it follows that I and c will be asymptotically normally distributed provided that

$$\phi_j(\nu) = \frac{\sum_{i=1}^{n} (\nu_i - \bar{\nu})^j}{\sigma_\nu^j n^{j/2}} \quad \text{is o(1),} \tag{5.58}$$

where o means 'of smaller order than', and

$$n\sigma_v^2 = \sum_{i=1}^{n} (v_i - \bar{v})^2. \tag{5.59}$$

Again a sufficient condition, akin to equation (2.45) and deriving from equation (5.58), is that

$$\max_i \frac{|v_i - \bar{v}|}{\sigma_v} \text{ is } O(n^{-1/2}). \tag{5.60}$$

In more intuitive terms these conditions reduce to the requirement that the matrix $n^{-1}X'X$ should stabilise (converge in probability) as n increases, and that no definite subset of the counties should dominate the lattice. Condition (2.46), which requires that

$$\max_i \left(\frac{w_{i.} + w_{.i}}{W}\right), \tag{5.61}$$

should be of order n^{-1}, again gives a guide as to whether the application of a normal approximation is reasonable. The star lattice with a single articulation point once more proves to be an exception (see the example in section 2.4). However, the beta distribution proves to be a good approximation for the star lattice (see Cliff and Ord, 1972).

The argument leading to asymptotic normality is essentially the same for the statistic based on the BLUS estimates. Again a normal approximation may be used; alternatively, the simpler form of the moments allows the use of approximations involving higher moments. A beta approximation is recommended, following the results for the d statistic (Durbin and Watson, 1971).

5.6.2 A random permutations procedure

From equation (5.42) it is known that

$$\boldsymbol{e} = \boldsymbol{M}\boldsymbol{y},$$

which reduces to

$$\boldsymbol{e} = \boldsymbol{M}\boldsymbol{\epsilon}. \tag{5.62}$$

Given $\boldsymbol{M}$ for a particular regression analysis, and that the ϵ_i are independently distributed, the parameters of the distribution can be estimated from the observed residuals. A set of n drawings can then be generated from this distribution, and a 'dummy' vector $\boldsymbol{e}_g$ constructed from equation (5.62). If the ϵ_i are uncorrelated but not independent, a single drawing from a specified n variate distribution will have to be made; otherwise the procedure is unchanged. Usually, it will be assumed that ϵ_i is $N(0, \sigma^2)$. No estimate for σ^2 is required, since the test statistics are scale free functions of $\boldsymbol{\epsilon}$. To achieve full comparability between the observed and generated $\boldsymbol{e}$ vectors, the generated values should be adjusted to have zero mean. Given $\boldsymbol{e}_g$, the selected test statistic may be evaluated and the value recorded. Following the procedure of section 2.7, generate m such values. On the assumption that the upper tail is the critical region, the null hypothesis H_0, of no spatial autocorrelation, is rejected at the $100(j+1)/(m+1)$ percent level if the observed value of the statistic exceeds at least the $(m-j)$ smallest generated values. This Hope procedure is the same as that given in section 2.7, except that the generated variables must be transformed by equation (5.62) before the statistic is computed.

In accordance with the results given earlier, m set equal to 49 or 99 is suggested as a suitable number of generated values.

5.7 The treatment of lagged variables

The specification of the regression model in section 5.2.1 requires the regressor variables to be nonstochastic. Yet, in many applications, a model containing temporal or spatial lags is often useful, such as the simple autoregressive scheme.

$$y_t = \alpha + \beta L y_t + \epsilon_t, \tag{5.63}$$

where α and β are parameters, ϵ_t is the error term with zero mean and variance σ^2, and L is a *lag operator*. Thus for a time series model, we might use the first order lag operator

$$L y_t = y_{t-1}, \tag{5.64}$$

while the spatial first order lag might be represented as

$$L y_t = \sum_{s \neq t} w_{ts} y_s, \tag{5.65}$$

where $\sum_{s \neq t} w_{ts} = 1$. This is of the same form as the Markov scheme given for the error terms in equation (5.18).

The OLS estimator for β is

$$\tilde{\beta} = \frac{\sum (y_t - \bar{y})(L y_t - \bar{y}_L)}{\sum (L y_t - \bar{y}_L)^2}, \tag{5.66}$$

where $n\bar{y} = \sum y_t$ and $n\bar{y}_L = \sum L y_t$. For the time series model (5.64) this estimator is consistent and asymptotically unbiased. Further, when the ϵ_t are independent and normally distributed, $\tilde{\beta}$ is the maximum likelihood estimator. Unfortunately, when the model is multilateral (that is, the dependence extends in all directions, as in the spatial case) $\tilde{\beta}$ is no longer the maximum likelihood estimator. Worse still it is inconsistent and asymptotically biased (Whittle, 1954). Whittle has outlined a large sample procedure for finding the maximum likelihood estimator for β, but this is computationally feasible only when the lattice is regular. Mead (1967) has given the exact maximum likelihood solution as that value of β, $\hat{\beta}$, say, which minimises

$$|I_n - \beta W|^{-2/n} \sum [y_t - \bar{y} - \beta(Ly_t - \bar{y}_L)]^2, \tag{5.67}$$

where $|I_n - \beta W|$ is the determinant of the nth order matrix enclosed by the lines. Given $\hat{\beta}$, $\hat{\alpha} = \bar{y} - \hat{\beta}\bar{y}_L$, and

$$n\sigma^2 = \sum [y_t - \bar{y} - \hat{\beta}(Ly_t - \bar{y}_L)]^2. \tag{5.68}$$

The reader should see Mead's paper for details. For small samples, n in equation (5.68) might be replaced by $(n-2)$, analogous to the OLS estimator. Unfortunately the computational burden of solving equation (5.67) is heavy when n is not small and/or the lattice is irregular. However, Ord (1973) has developed a method of computation which is very rapid once the eigenvalues of W are known. A summary of this method is given in Appendix 3.

To fit the more general model.

$$Y = \beta WY + X\gamma, \tag{5.69}$$

where γ is a $(k \times 1)$ vector of unknown parameters, we have that

$$\hat{\gamma} = (X'X)^{-1}X'(Y - \hat{\beta}WY), \tag{5.70}$$

$n\sigma^2$ is the residual sum of squares, as in equation (5.68), and $\hat{\beta}$ is that value of β which minimises

$$|I_n - \beta W|^{-2/n} Y'(I_n - \beta W')M(I_n - \beta W)Y, \tag{5.71}$$

where M is defined as in equation (5.22).

Once equation (5.69) has been fitted, we may wish to test the residuals for autocorrelation as previously. However, as Nerlove and Wallis (1966) and Durbin (1970) have pointed out, although the test statistics given in sections 5.4 and 5.5 may still be used to analyse the residuals from such models (and are equally efficient), the sampling distributions of the statistics are different, even asymptotically. If the Durbin–Watson tables, or any of the approximations given earlier, are used, serious underestimation of the significance of the results may occur. At this stage we are not in a position to suggest suitable modifications, but only to warn of the dangers as the extent of the bias is unknown for any particular case. Further work is required in this area, probably by adapting the tests given in Durbin (1970) and Wickens (1972) for the time series model.

5.8 Estimation in the presence of spatial autocorrelation

If a fitted regression has a high R^2 value, no autocorrelation is detected, and no other problems arise, we can be satisfied with our result! If autocorrelation, or any other difficulty, is encountered, the model must be modified. In section 5.1, three possible causes of autocorrelated residuals are listed. Remedies for the first two causes, by specifying different models or adding further variables, are not considered further in this section. However, in the case of the third, if it is decided that an autoregressive structure is required because the residuals are autocorrelated, we must adopt a different procedure for estimating the parameters of the regression model. One possibility is to carry out a transformation as follows.

Suppose that the initial model is

$$y_j = \beta_1 x_{1j} + \ldots + \beta_s x_{sj} + \epsilon_j, \tag{5.72}$$

and the ϵ_j are supposed to follow a first order autoregressive scheme such as

$$\epsilon_j = \rho \mathrm{L}\epsilon_j + u_j. \tag{5.73}$$

Then, if $\rho \mathrm{L} y_j$ is subtracted from both sides, it yields, on substitution,

$$y_j - \rho \mathrm{L} y_j = \beta_1 x_{1j} - \rho\beta_1 \mathrm{L} x_{1j} + \beta_2 x_{2j} - \rho\beta_2 \mathrm{L} x_{2j} + \ldots$$
$$+ \beta_s x_{sj} - \rho\beta_s \mathrm{L} x_{sj} + \epsilon_j - \rho \mathrm{L}\epsilon_j ,$$

or

$$y_j = \rho \mathrm{L} y_j + \beta_1 x_{1j} + \ldots + \beta_s x_{sj} - \gamma_1 \mathrm{L} x_{1j} - \ldots - \gamma_s \mathrm{L} x_{sj} + u_j, \tag{5.74}$$

where

$$\gamma_i = \rho\beta_i, \qquad i = 1, \ldots, s. \tag{5.75}$$

While this approach appears to provide an equation with uncorrelated error terms, it is only valid when ρ is known *or* when the autocorrelation among the ϵ_j happens to be the same as that among the y_j, when the method of equations (5.70) and (5.71) can be used. Typically the transformation will over-correct (see the empirical results in section 6.6). Further, when ρ is *un*known, the estimators for the parameters should be derived subject to the s constraints in equation (5.75). This method has not been developed in detail but three variants are tried out in section 6.6. These are

1. Use some arbitrary value of ρ, ρ_0 say, to construct new variables

$$\left.\begin{aligned} y_j^* &= y_j - \rho_0 \mathrm{L} y_j, \\ &\text{and} \\ x_{ij}^* &= x_{ij} - \rho_0 \mathrm{L} x_{ij}, \qquad i = 1, \ldots, s, \end{aligned}\right\} \tag{5.76}$$

and then estimate the s parameters $\beta_1, \ldots, \beta_s$ by OLS. Often ρ_0 is put equal to unity, corresponding to the use of first differences. While this removes linear trends, it tends to overadjust for autocorrelation, and lower values are sometimes used. In general, the resulting estimators for β will be unbiased but inefficient. However, the loss of efficiency will be slight if ρ_0 is near ρ.

2. Estimate equation (5.74) by OLS without imposing any constraints.

3. Estimate equation (5.74) by OLS subject to the constraints in equation (5.75).

Note that variants '2' and '3' will yield *inconsistent* estimators.

To develop an approach which will apply for any value of ρ we turn to Cochrane and Orcutt (1949) and the general discussion in Johnston (1972, pp.259–265). An iterative procedure which yields consistent estimators is as follows.

4. *Step 1*: compute the simple LS residuals from equation (5.72), e_j say.

Step 2: estimate ρ from the equations

$$e_j = \rho \mathrm{L} e_j + \tilde{u}_j, \qquad j = 1, \ldots, n, \tag{5.77}$$

using the maximum likelihood method of equation (5.67).

Call this estimate $\tilde{\rho}$.

Step 3: construct the new variables,

$$\tilde{y}_j = y_j - \tilde{\rho} \mathrm{L} y_j, \quad \text{and} \quad \tilde{x}_{ij} = x_{ij} - \tilde{\rho} \mathrm{L} x_{ij}, \qquad i = 1, \ldots, s.$$

Step 4: apply OLS to $\tilde{y}_j$ on the $\tilde{x}_{ij}$, yielding $\tilde{\beta}$ as estimates for β. Then construct $\boldsymbol{e} = \boldsymbol{y} - \boldsymbol{X}\tilde{\beta}$ and return to step 2. Repeat until the process converges to a steady value for ρ.

(4) For a recent discussion and extension of the theory for temporal autocorrelation, see Pierce (1971a, 1971b).

6

The analysis of regression residuals–some empirical examples

6.1 Introduction

In this chapter the methods developed in chapter 5 will be illustrated by considering the residuals from regressions given in O'Sullivan (1968), and Taaffe *et al.* (1963). We shall also examine regression residuals calculated from data given in Kendall (1939) and Yule and Kendall (1958), and from a trend surface analysis of unemployment in southwest England. In the final section of the chapter the use of autoregressive models will be discussed.

Throughout the chapter, tests are based on the assumption that the tail areas of the normal distribution adequately approximate those of the distribution of I under null hypothesis H_0. Although this assumption holds asymptotically (see section 5.6.1), its validity has not been examined empirically for small lattices.

6.2 Regressions from the data of O'Sullivan (1968)

O'Sullivan determined the accessibility on the arterial road network of each of the 26 counties of Eire shown in figure 3.1. The accessibility of a vertex i, in a road network N, was defined by O'Sullivan as

$$\mathrm{A}(i, N) = \sum_{j=1}^{n} d_{ij}\,, \tag{6.1}$$

where n is the number of vertices in the network, and d_{ij} is the distance in miles by road on the shortest path between the ith and jth vertices. The road network taken by O'Sullivan was all T (trunk) class roads in Eire, and the vertices were the 31 towns of over 5000 population in the 1961 census. Equation (6.1) was applied to each vertex. County accessibility values were approximated by taking the value of the largest town in the county if it was one of the 31, or alternatively, by interpolating a value from an isopleth map of accessibility. With the accessibility on the arterial road network (ARA) defined in this way, it is evident that the ARA of eastern and southern counties will be 'better', and the ARA of western counties 'worse', than in reality because most of the 31 towns of over 5000 population are located in counties bordering the south and east coasts of Eire. There is no doubt that the eastern and southern counties of Eire do have considerably better transport services than the western counties (O'Sullivan, 1969) but, as constructed, the ARA index emphasises these differences.

O'Sullivan then used these county accessibility values as the independent variable in several regressions in which various measures of intensity of economic activity in the counties of Eire formed the dependent variable.

From O'Sullivan's work[5], the following least squares regressions were selected:

Regression (1)

y = the 1961 population as a percentage of the 1926 population by county,

x = the ARA,

1(a) $y = 133{\cdot}45 - 0{\cdot}0103x \qquad R^2 = 0{\cdot}40,$
$\qquad\qquad (0{\cdot}0026)$

1(b) $\log y = 4{\cdot}19 - 0{\cdot}6210 \log x \quad R^2 = 0{\cdot}52.$
$\qquad\qquad (0{\cdot}1225)$

Note that here and elsewhere in this chapter the number in brackets below each estimate is its estimated standard error, while the logarithms are to the base 10.

Regression (2)

y = the percentage, in value terms, of the gross agricultural output of each county consumed by itself;

x = the ARA,

$y = -8{\cdot}49 + 0{\cdot}0053x \qquad R^2 = 0{\cdot}70.$
$\qquad\qquad (0{\cdot}0007)$

In addition, as an example where x was not the ARA, we took

Regression (3)

y = the value of retail sales (£000) by county.

x = the total personal income (£000) by county.

$y = -2393{\cdot}8 + 0{\cdot}5405x \qquad R^2 = 0{\cdot}987.$
$\qquad\qquad (0{\cdot}0126)$

The county values for all variables, and the regression residuals, are given in table 6.1. The county serial letters refer to figure 3.1. The residuals were tested for spatial autocorrelation using I as defined in equation (5.28). In this equation we tried three forms for $\boldsymbol{W}$:

1. $w_{ij} = 1$ if counties i and j had a length of county boundary in common, and $w_{ij} = 0$ otherwise (binary weights);
2. the unstandardised boundary length/distance between county centres weights defined in equation (3.1);
3. the standardised form of '2' defined in equation (3.2).

We recall, from section 5.2.3, that we have used weights scaled as in '3' in much of the theory of chapter 5. The moments of I were evaluated under assumption N [equations (5.34) and (5.38)], and under assumption R (see section 5.3.1) when equations (1.66) and (1.68) were used. Positive spatial autocorrelation was suspected and so the upper tails were used as critical regions. The results of the analysis are given in table 6.2.

From table 6.2 we note that in all cases the residuals are positively spatially autocorrelated, and that 10 of the 12 values of the standardised deviate are lower under R than under N. This difference arises because

(5) The authors wish to thank Dr. O'Sullivan for making the full computer results of his study available to them.

Table 6.1. Eire regression data and regression residuals.

County serial letter	1961 population as % of 1926 population[a]	ARA	%, in value terms, of gross agricultural output of each county consumed by itself[b]	Value of retail sales[c] (£000)	Total personal income[d] (£000)	Regression residuals			
						1(a)	1(b)	2	3
A	97·0	3664	8·6	2962	7185	1·437	0·0067	−1·933	1472·5
B	69·0	5000	15·0	4452	9459	−12·749	−0·0574	−3·014	1733·4
C	78·0	4321	19·0	3460	12435	−10·769	−0·0435	4·585	−867·1
D	90·0	4118	9·0	28402	65901	−0·868	0·0057	−4·339	−4822·6
E	75·0	7500	27·0	7478	17626	19·100	0·0882	−4·264	345·3
F	142·0	3078	9·4	89424	164631	40·379	0·1252	1·173	2837·5
G	88·0	4537	21·9	8972	26950	1·464	0·0220	6·440	−3200·2
H	78·0	5140	17·0	6341	20510	−2·301	0·0033	−1·756	−2350·5
I	111·0	3200	9·0	4803	14703	10·640	0·0287	0·526	−749·9
J	87·0	3708	8·0	4321	13585	−8·108	−0·0374	−3·166	−627·7
K	87·0	3455	10·3	3128	9280	−10·724	−0·0564	0·175	506·1
L	60·0	5000	23·1	1885	5709	−21·749	−0·1181	4·986	1193·2
M	95·0	4018	11·4	10786	27395	3·098	0·0225	−1·809	−1626·7
N	77·0	4250	19·0	1960	5297	−12·504	−0·0536	4·961	1490·9
O	107·0	3948	10·1	7059	12156	14·374	0·0694	−2·438	2882·7
P	71·0	6815	30·0	6758	19201	8·018	0·0386	2·367	−1226·0
Q	103·0	4008	8·7	3356	14512	10·994	0·0569	−3·756	−2093·7
R	72·0	4500	13·0	3960	8396	−15·919	−0·0673	−2·364	1815·9
S	98·0	4108	14·3	3817	10320	7·028	0·0420	1·714	633·0
T	71·0	4500	23·0	2821	10223	−14·919	−0·0734	7·636	−310·5
U	75·0	5997	22·0	3535	9461	3·560	0·0279	−1·298	815·3
V	88·0	3926	9·0	9226	26424	−4·854	−0·0170	−3·322	−2661·9
W	91·0	3691	8·0	7526	15696	−4·283	−0·0191	−3·076	1436·4
X	93·0	3872	16·0	3822	10842	−0·412	0·0033	3·965	355·9
Y	87·0	3940	8·6	8231	15582	−5·709	−0·0210	−3·396	2203·0
Z	102·0	3600	10·2	4865	11921	5·776	0·0238	−0·594	815·7

[a] Census of Population, 1966, Preliminary Report, table 8 (Central Statistics Office, 1967).

[b] Attwood and Geary (1963), table 3 $\left(\frac{\text{column 12}}{\text{column 11}}\right) \times 100$.

[c] Attwood and Geary (1963), table 6, column 2.

[d] Attwood and Geary (1963), table 2, column 6.

Table 6.2. Results of tests for spatial autocorrelation in regression residuals from O'Sullivan (1969).

Value of I	Binary weights: regression				Unstandardised boundary length/county centre distance weights: regression				Standardised boundary length/county centre distance weights: regression			
	1(a)	1(b)	2	3	1(a)	1(b)	2	3	1(a)	1(b)	2	3
Assumption N												
I	0·1908	0·1301	0·3968	0·2297	0·2467	0·1890	0·4539	0·2281	0·1553	0·0803	0·4361	0·2928
E(I)	−0·0556	−0·0581	−0·0556	−0·0421	−0·0575	−0·0602	−0·0575	−0·0418	−0·0589	−0·0616	−0·0589	−0·0419
σ(I)	0·1137	0·1129	0·1137	0·1173	0·1438	0·1430	0·1438	0·1456	0·1391	0·1388	0·1391	0·1444
Standard deviate	2·17 **	1·67 **	3·98 ****	2·32 **	2·12 **	1·74 **	3·56 ****	1·85 **	1·54	1·02	3·56 ****	2·32 **
Assumption R												
I	0·1908	0·1301	0·3968	0·2297	0·2467	0·1890	0·4539	0·2281	0·1553	0·0803	0·4361	0·2928
E(I)	−0·0400	−0·0400	−0·0400	−0·0400	−0·0400	−0·0400	−0·0400	−0·0400	−0·0400	−0·0400	−0·0400	−0·0400
σ(I)	0·1108	0·1157	0·1175	0·1158	0·1384	0·1448	0·1471	0·1450	0·1363	0·1427	0·1449	0·1428
Standard deviate	2·08 **	1·47	3·72 ****	2·33 ****	2·07 **	1·58	3·36 ****	1·85 **	1·43	0·84	3·28 ****	2·33 ****

** Significant at $\alpha = 0{\cdot}05$ level (one-tailed test)
**** Significant at $\alpha = 0{\cdot}01$ level (one-tailed test)

under R we are assuming, falsely, that the sample residuals are uncorrelated under H_0, whereas by using assumption N we are allowing for the correlation among the sample residuals under H_0. The amount and direction of the bias introduced when we make assumption R depends critically on the correlation structure among the regressor variables. However, from the results given in tables 6.8, 6.10, and 6.14, the general tendency is for the test under R to be more conservative than under N, if the residuals are positively spatially autocorrelated. This conservatism increases rapidly as the number of regressor variables increases, and reaches gross proportions for some examples in table 6.14.

As regards the regression equations individually, several points emerge.

Regression (1). As shown in table 6.2, whatever the form of W, the positive spatial autocorrelation among the residuals from regression 1(a) is stronger than among the residuals from regression 1(b). One of the causes of autocorrelated disturbances mentioned in section 5.1 is that of making an incorrect specification of the form of the relation between the dependent and independent variables. For example, suppose we specify a linear relation between y and x when the true relation is, say, a quadratic. Even though the disturbance term in the true relation may be nonautocorrelated, the disturbance term associated with the linear relation will contain a term in x^2. If there is any autocorrelation in the x^2 values, then we shall have autocorrelation in the composite disturbance term. In the case of regression (1), the relation between y and x was originally specified by the simple linear equation 1(a). However, if we plot y against x (figure 6.1), it appears that the true relation is probably better described by a power curve of the form

$$y = \alpha x^{\beta} + \gamma, \tag{6.2}$$

with $\beta < 0$. By using regression equation 1(a), rather than equation (6.2), the disturbance term associated with it will contain a term in x^{β}. In addition, x is highly spatially autocorrelated [applying equations (1.44), (1.66), and (1.68) with binary weights to the ARA values, we obtained $I = 0{\cdot}335$, $\mathrm{E}(I) = -0{\cdot}040$, $\sigma(I) = 0{\cdot}110$, and the standard deviate $= 3{\cdot}42$; the 1% cutoff point is $I = 0{\cdot}2158$]. This suggests that the cause of autocorrelated disturbances mentioned above may account in part for the result for regression 1(a) in table 6.2. Now if we assume $\gamma = 0$, a relation of the form of 6.2 can be reduced to a linear form by taking logarithms of both sides, as done by O'Sullivan in regression 1(b). We are now specifying a linear relation between $\log y$ and $\log x$. As a result, there is a drop in the spatial autocorrelation in the residuals from this regression as compared with 1(a). Although it is not attempted here, it appears that if equation (6.2) were fitted using nonlinear methods, better results than those obtained for regression 1(b) would be achieved.

Regression (2). This model is a measure of subsistence. The more remote and inaccessible Irish counties (essentially the western littoral and west-central counties) would be expected to consume more of their own agricultural produce than the less isolated eastern counties. While a high value for R^2 is obtained, the striking feature is the degree of positive spatial autocorrelation in the residuals for all forms of $\boldsymbol{W}$ (table 6.2). The regression model overestimated the amount of their own agricultural produce consumed internally in (a) all counties on and south of a line from Limerick (M) to Wicklow (Z), (b) counties O, Q, and R, which form a block in the northeast part of the Irish Republic, and (c) U and E. Elsewhere, underestimation occurred. This spatial pattern of residuals suggests several alternative independent variables which might improve the model.

The areas of overestimation are counties which are served by the principal railways from Dublin, whereas the areas of underestimation are poorly linked by rail to Dublin, the latter being the chief market for agricultural produce in the country. We examined three independent variables which might measure the importance of rail transport to each county;

(i) rail accessibility measured by applying equation (6.1) to the largest town in each county—we defined d_{ij} as the distance in miles by rail on the shortest route between the ith and jth vertices;

(ii) a binary variable, with a county being coded 1 if it was linked by a through freight train service to Dublin, and 0 otherwise;

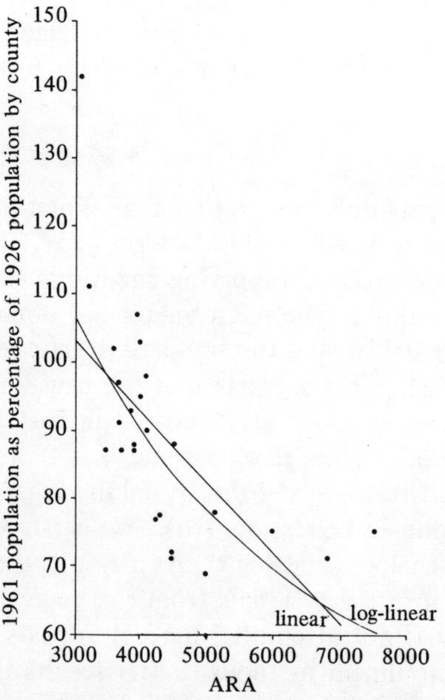

Figure 6.1. Graph of data and regression lines for O'Sullivan's regressions 1(a) and 1(b).

(iii) a measure of cost accessibility by rail of each county, which we defined for the ith county as

$$c_i = \sum_{j=1}^{n} c_{ij}, \tag{6.3}$$

where c_{ij} is the cost in shillings of shipping one ton of goods by freight train between the ith and jth counties (data from Coras Iompair Eireann, 1966).

The areas of overestimation by the regression model are also those which are closest to the chief ports of Eire for the export of agricultural goods. From the Statistical Abstract of Ireland for 1961 (Central Statistics Office, 1962), the following ports each exported more than 180000 tons of cargo: Cork (including Cohb and Whitegate), Drogheda, Dublin (including Dun Laoghaire), Sligo, and Waterford. All others exported less than 26000 tons each. We therefore tried (iv) distance in miles between the largest town in each county and the nearest of these major ports.

O'Sullivan (1969, p.18 and personal communication) suggests that the areas where the amount of their own agricultural produce consumed internally is overestimated, are the chief commercial farming areas of Eire with large farm units, whereas the areas of underestimation coincide broadly with the subsistence farming areas with small farm units. To quantify this pattern, we looked at two variables:
(v) the number of agricultural holdings above 100 acres, June 1960, as a percentage of the total number of holdings by county [source: Statistical Abstract of Ireland (Central Statistics Office) 1961, table 80];
(vi) the number of males aged 18 years and over, who were members of the family engaged on their own family farm, as a percentage of the total male population, June 1960, by county [source: Statistical Abstract of Ireland 1961 (Central Statistics Office, 1962, tables 8 and 75)]. We hoped

Table 6.3. Values of simple correlation coefficients and R^2 for new independent variables tried in O'Sullivan's regression (2).

New independent variable added as x_2	r_{y,x_1}	r_{y,x_2}	r_{x_1,x_2}	R^2
(i)	0·8346	0·2924	0·5910	0·759 **
(ii)	0·8346	−0·5992	−0·5664	0·720
(iii)	0·8346	0·3116	0·5791	0·741 **
(iv)	0·8346	0·2894	0·0329	0·765 **
(v)	0·8346	−0·7249	−0·5738	0·787 **
(vi)	0·8346	0·7569	0·6056	0·796 **

** Increase in R^2 judged significant at 0·05 level using F test.

that variable (v) would pick out the areas of Eire in which the larger commercial farming units were located, whereas (vi) would pick out the subsistence farming areas.

We tried a series of two independent variable multiple regressions, with y as the percentage, in value terms, of gross agricultural output of each county consumed by itself, x_1 as the ARA, and x_2 set equal, in turn, to each of the independent variables (i)–(vi) described above. The values of R^2 obtained are shown in table 6.3.

The new independent variables postulated produced some increase in the value of R^2. However, even for the best, (vi), the sign of the residual from the regression was changed in only four counties when compared with the signs for the original simple regression. All the sets displayed significant positive spatial autocorrelation when tested using I. Thus, we were unable to break up the pattern of spatial autocorrelation in the residuals. It therefore appeared that an autoregressive model might be worth considering, since such a model would allow for the persistence of regional variations. We shall return to this approach in section 6.6.

Regression (3). Despite the extraordinarily large R^2 value, the regression residuals display a high degree of spatial autocorrelation. Three points can be made. First, the y variable, the gross value of retail sales, is a well-known surrogate measure of gross personal income (the x variable), which accounts in part for the inflated R^2 value. Second, the regression provides an example of the way in which the position of a regression line fitted by the usual least squares method can be dominated by a few very large [Cork (D) and Dublin (F)] and very small [Leitrim (L) and Longford (N)] y and x values. When this happens a high R^2 value is obtained, while the regression equation may be a poor estimator of the relationship between nonextreme y and x values. This appears to have happened in the regression considered here. The limited usefulness of the regression equation as a predictor of retail sales for nonextreme county values is revealed in the autocorrelated residuals. Third, the regression model consistently overestimates retail sales in the poorer counties west of and including a line from Cork (D), Tipperary (V), to Mayo (P).

6.3 Regressions from Taaffe, Morrill, and Gould (1963)

In this well-known paper, Taaffe *et al.* examined the degree of internal accessibility of underdeveloped countries as measured by the extent of their road networks. They postulated that this accessibility would be a function of such factors as population level, physical environment, rail competition, and degree of commercialisation. Regression analysis was used to quantify the relationship between the size of the road network and these factors. Ghana and Nigeria were used as examples[6]. The data

[6] The authors wish to thank Professor Taaffe and his colleagues for supplying us with the data used in their work.

Table 6.4. Basic regression data for Ghana.

Recording unit		y^a	x_1^b	x_2	Recording unit		y^a	x_1^b	x_2
Identity number	name	highway mileage	population (in thousands)	area (in tens of square miles)	Identity number	name	highway mileage	population (in thousands)	area (in tens of square miles)
1	Accra	284	225	92	21	Kumasi 1–2	259	157	39
2	Axim	168	74	151	22	Kumasi 3	205	70	81
3	Sekondi	140	106	37	23	Kumasi 4	287	84	395
4	Akwapim[c]	115	114	40	24	Kumasi 5	139	65	76
5	Kibi	286	219	225	25	Mampong E.	83	13	460
6	Mpraeso N.	16	6	200	26	Mampong W.	262	90	236
7	Mpraeso S.	129	73	82	27	Wenchi	359	73	681
8	Oda	162	72	94	28	Sunyani	238	109	248
9	Cape Coast	435	269	208	29	Dagomba E.	424	121	672
10	Dunkwa	103	40	93	30	Dagomba W.	308	104	289
11	Winneba	333	187	92	31	Gonja E.	226	52	578
12	Ho	432	173	246	32	Gonja W.	307	33	869
13	Keta	205	190	116	33	Krachi	194	32	338
14	Ada	90	114	80	34	Fra Fra	132	164	79
15	Sefwi	146	65	270	35	Gambaga	239	78	279
16	Volta River	201	165	146	36	Kusasi	266	148	124
17	Enchi	52	10	125	37	Navrongo	178	142	155
18	Tarkwa	256	121	346	38	Lawra	169	89	110
19	Bekwai	247	91	128	39	Tumu	214	30	273
20	Obuasi	169	67	94	40	Wa	333	85	340

[a] Source: *Road Map of the Gold Coast*, 1:500000, Department of Surveys, Accra, 1950. Only first and second class roads were used and no weighting system was applied.
[b] Source: *The Gold Coast, Census of Population, 1948, Report and Tables*, The Government Printing Department, Accra, Gold Coast (Ghana), 1950.
[c] Includes New Juaben.

Table 6.5. Basic regression data for Nigeria.

Recording unit		y[a]	x_1[b]	x_2	Recording unit		y	x_1	x_2
Identity	name	highway mileage	population (in thousands)	area (in tens of square miles)	Identity	name	highway mileage	population (in thousands)	area (in tens of square miles)
1	Adamawa	545	799	1856	26	Kontagora	534	251	1322
2	Muri	444	260	1101	27	Minna	289	142	576
3	Numan	131	121	221	28	Emaa[d]	390	417	396
4	Bauchi	680	512	1452	29	Lowland	129	194	480
5	Gombe	402	477	648	30	Pankshin	192	279	380
6	Katagum	385	434	512	31	Argungu	213	171	336
7	Idoma	204	319	375	32	Gwandu	375	489	751
8	Lafia	144	132	395	33	Sokoto	1059	2021	2561
9	Nasarawa	251	162	556	34	Zaria	780	806	1649
10	Tiv	491	719	986	35	Abeokuta	448	630	427
11	Wukari	107	137	622	36	Benin	772	901	846
12	Bedde–Potiskum	111	160	367	37	Colony	101	510	135
13	Bornu	1339	1006	3299	38	Delta	315	590	644
14	Dikwa	330	265	515	39	Ibadan	617	1661	452
15	Biu	210	164	392	40	Ijebu	211	348	247
16	Borgu	312	100	1091	41	Ondo	695	946	816
17	Ilorin	339	460	265	42	Oyo	644	783	970
18	Lafiaga	170	70	416	43	Bamenda	252	429	693
19	Igala	353	361	498	44	Calabar	730	1841	625
20	Kabba[c]	310	303	497	45	Kumba–Victoria	211	224	532
21	Katsina	823	1483	947	46	Mamfe	136	100	432
22	Kano	1135	2933	1293	47	Ogoja	571	1082	749
23	Northern	302	424	370	48	Onitsha	770	1768	489
24	Abuja	189	101	395	49	Owerri	860	2080	387
25	Bida	299	221	574	50	Rivers	207	747	701

[a] Source: *Mobil Road Map of Nigeria, 1957*, from the Federal Survey Department, Lagos, at the scale of 1:750000. Maps of the Survey Department at a scale of 1:500000 were used to enumerate additional local roads in Onitsha and Owerri.
[b] Source: *Population Census of Nigeria, 1952–1953*, Government Statistician, Lagos, 1954.
[c] Includes the Kabba, Igbirra, Koto–Kaaifi districts of Kabba Province.
[d] Includes the Emaa, Jos, and southern districts of Plateau Province.

are reproduced here in tables 6.4 and 6.5. The locations of the recording units are shown in figures 6.2 and 6.3, and the identity numbers of the recording units correspond with those given in tables 6.4 and 6.5. respectively. The basic regression equations obtained by Taaffe *et al.*, were as follows:

Ghana

(a) $y = 130{\cdot}636 + 0{\cdot}8654x_1$ $\quad R^2 = 0{\cdot}284$
$\qquad\qquad(0{\cdot}2230)$

(b) $\log y = 1{\cdot}2774 + 0{\cdot}5263 \log x_1$ $\quad R^2 = 0{\cdot}491$
$\qquad\qquad(0{\cdot}0869)$

(c) $y = 166{\cdot}993 + 0{\cdot}2298x_2$ $\quad R^2 = 0{\cdot}195$
$\qquad\qquad(0{\cdot}0757)$

(d) $\log y = 1{\cdot}7326 + 0{\cdot}2461 \log x_2$ $\quad R^2 = 0{\cdot}100$
$\qquad\qquad(0{\cdot}1199)$

(e) $\log y = 0{\cdot}1625 + 0{\cdot}6293 \log x_1 + 0{\cdot}4118 \log x_2$ $\quad R^2 = 0{\cdot}756$
$\qquad\qquad(0{\cdot}0630) \qquad (0{\cdot}0647)$

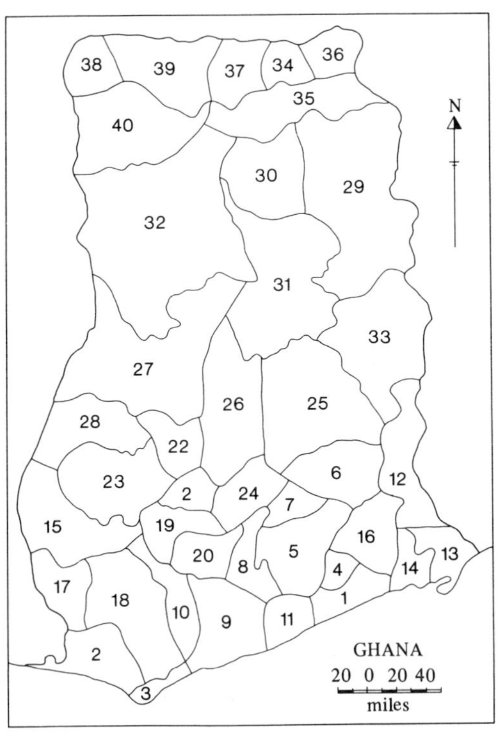

Figure 6.2. A map showing the location and identity numbers of recording units in Ghana.

Nigeria

(a) $y = 194 \cdot 178 + 0 \cdot 3742 x_1$ $\qquad R^2 = 0 \cdot 657$
$\qquad (0 \cdot 0390)$

(b) $\log y = 1 \cdot 0213 + 0 \cdot 5805 \log x_1$ $\qquad R^2 = 0 \cdot 650$
$\qquad (0 \cdot 0615)$

(c) $y = 159 \cdot 941 + 0 \cdot 3628 x_2$ $\qquad R^2 = 0 \cdot 541$
$\qquad (0 \cdot 0482)$

(d) $\log y = 0 \cdot 4272 + 0 \cdot 7596 \log x_2$ $\qquad R^2 = 0 \cdot 487$
$\qquad (0 \cdot 1124)$

(e) $y = 60 \cdot 733 + 0 \cdot 2892 x_1 + 0 \cdot 2510 x_2$ $\qquad R^2 = 0 \cdot 883$
$\qquad (0 \cdot 0247) \quad (0 \cdot 0264)$

(f) $\log y = 0 \cdot 0104 + 0 \cdot 4512 \log x_1 + 0 \cdot 4848 \log x_2$ $\qquad R^2 = 0 \cdot 817$
$\qquad (0 \cdot 0491) \quad (0 \cdot 0743)$

The residuals from each of these regressions are shown in tables 6.6 and 6.7. We tested each of the sets of residuals for spatial autocorrelation using the following statistics:

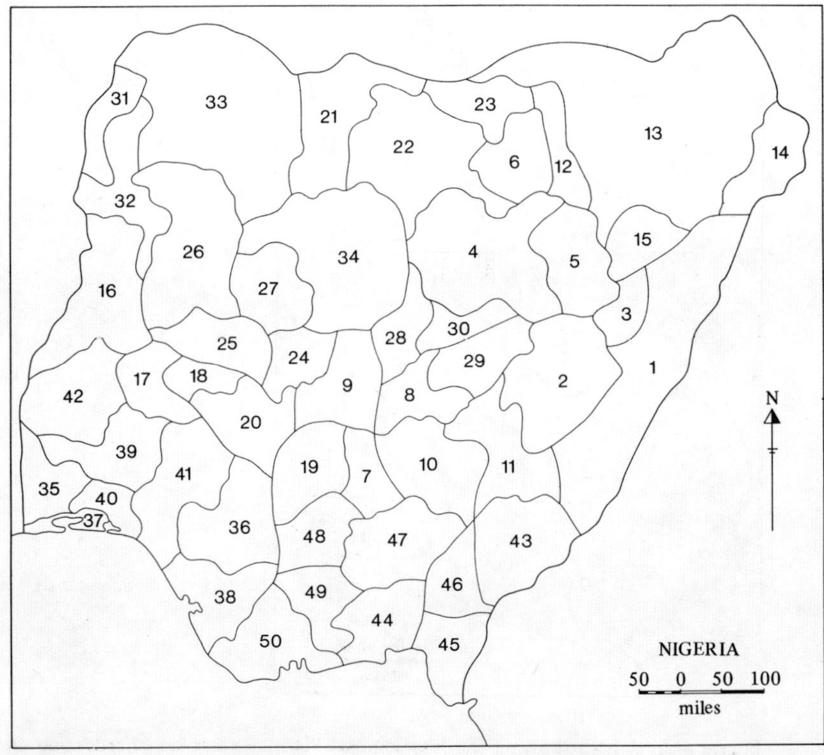

Figure 6.3. A map showing the location and identity numbers of recording units in Nigeria.

(1) I as defined in equation (5.28) under assumption N [equations (5.34), (5.38), (5.43), and (5.45)] and under assumption R [equations (1.66) and (1.68)];
(2) BB and BW as defined in equations (1.41) and (1.42). Here we coded a county B if it had a positive residual and W if it had a negative residual. The moments of BB and BW were evaluated under free sampling [equations (1.54–1.57)] and under nonfree sampling [equations (1.60–1.63)]. Throughout the analysis we put $w_{ij} = 1$ if the ith and jth

Table 6.6. Residuals from Ghana regressions.

Recording unit identity number	Regression				
	(a)	(b)	(c)	(d)	(e)
1	−41·35	−0·0620	95·87	0·2374	0·0035
2	−26·68	−0·0359	−33·69	−0·0435	−0·0111
3	−82·37	−0·1972	−35·50	0·0276	0·0630
4	−114·29	−0·2993	−61·19	−0·0662	−0·0549
5	−34·16	−0·0528	67·30	0·1449	−0·1479
6	−119·83	−0·4828	−196·95	−1·0948	−0·3960
7	−64·81	−0·1475	−56·84	−0·0930	−0·0129
8	−30·94	−0·0454	−26·59	−0·0087	0·0654
9	71·57	0·0823	220·21	0·3354	−0·0080
10	−62·25	−0·1077	−85·36	−0·2042	0·0318
11	40·53	0·0494	144·87	0·3066	0·1222
12	151·65	0·1802	208·48	0·3145	0·0794
13	−90·06	−0·1650	11·35	0·0711	−0·1347
14	−139·29	−0·4057	−95·38	−0·2467	−0·2860
15	−40·89	−0·0672	−83·04	−0·1666	−0·1457
16	−72·43	−0·1413	0·46	0·0379	−0·1462
17	−87·29	−0·0877	−143·72	−0·5326	0·0604
18	20·65	0·0347	9·50	0·0508	−0·1096
19	37·61	0·0843	50·59	0·1415	0·1348
20	−19·62	−0·0106	−19·59	0·0097	0·1034
21	−7·50	−0·0198	83·04	0·2891	0·2138
22	13·79	0·0633	19·39	0·1095	0·2018
23	83·67	0·1677	29·24	0·0863	0·0148
24	−47·89	−0·0885	−45·46	−0·0525	0·0648
25	−58·89	0·0554	−189·70	−0·4688	−0·0413
26	53·48	0·1124	40·77	0·1017	0·0485
27	165·19	0·2970	35·51	0·1253	0·0324
28	13·04	0·0269	14·02	0·0547	−0·0544
29	188·65	0·2538	102·58	0·1990	−0·0106
30	87·36	0·1496	74·59	0·1503	0·0462
31	50·36	0·1736	−73·82	−0·0582	−0·0260
32	147·81	0·4105	−59·69	0·0312	0·0158
33	35·67	0·2182	−50·67	−0·0672	0·1363
34	−140·56	−0·3225	−53·15	−0·0790	−0·2165
35	40·86	0·1052	7·89	0·0439	0·0178
36	7·28	0·0053	70·51	0·1771	0·0343
37	−75·52	−0·1597	−24·61	−0·0212	−0·1688
38	−38·66	−0·0755	−23·27	−0·0071	−0·0023
39	57·40	0·2756	−15·73	−0·0017	0·2370
40	128·81	0·2296	87·88	0·1668	0·1029

Table 6.7. Residuals from Nigeria regressions.

Recording unit identity number	Regression					
	(a)	(b)	(c)	(d)	(e)	(f)
1	51·84	0·0302	−288·30	−0·1736	−212·87	−0·1686
2	152·53	0·2242	−115·38	−0·0904	31·59	0·0723
3	−108·46	−0·1131	−109·12	−0·0907	−20·22	0·0303
4	294·23	0·2385	−6·73	0·0035	106·58	0·0664
5	29·33	0·0280	6·96	0·0414	40·60	0·0219
6	28·42	0·0331	39·31	0·1003	70·19	0·0713
7	−109·55	−0·1651	−91·99	−0·0728	−43·15	−0·0787
8	−99·57	−0·0939	−159·25	−0·2412	−54·10	−0·0680
9	−3·80	0·0958	−110·66	−0·1127	3·80	0·0612
10	27·77	0·0115	−26·66	−0·0103	−25·26	−0·0601
11	−138·44	−0·2323	−278·60	−0·5200	−149·55	−0·2999
12	−143·05	−0·2555	−182·09	−0·3300	−88·16	−0·2032
13	768·38	0·3625	−17·82	0·0270	159·00	0·0555
14	36·66	0·0905	−16·78	0·0314	63·31	0·0998
15	−45·55	0·0152	−92·16	−0·0748	3·40	0·0550
16	80·40	0·3119	−243·76	−0·2406	−51·62	0·1083
17	−27·31	−0·0368	82·92	0·2623	78·70	0·1433
18	−50·37	0·1381	−140·87	−0·1862	−15·44	0·1175
19	23·74	0·0418	12·38	0·0718	62·81	0·0755
20	2·44	0·0296	−30·25	0·0160	36·84	0·0538
21	73·88	0·0533	319·49	0·2274	95·59	0·0309
22	−156·71	0·0209	505·96	0·2642	−98·61	−0·0287
23	−50·84	−0·0665	7·82	0·1020	25·74	0·0388
24	−42·97	0·0917	−114·25	−0·1231	−0·13	0·1026
25	22·12	0·0935	−69·19	−0·0472	30·21	0·0696
26	245·90	0·3132	−105·56	−0·0705	68·70	0·1209
27	41·69	0·1902	−79·91	−0·0631	42·56	0·1408
28	39·78	0·0488	86·39	0·1907	109·23	0·1388
29	−137·77	−0·2388	−205·09	−0·3533	−108·37	−0·2322
30	−106·58	−0·1577	−105·81	−0·1035	−44·84	−0·0815
31	−45·17	0·0108	−68·84	−0·0178	18·44	0·0854
32	−2·16	−0·0084	−57·40	−0·0375	−15·74	−0·0442
33	108·56	0·0847	−30·07	0·0087	−229·30	−0·1298
34	284·22	0·1837	21·80	0·0211	72·09	0·0103
35	18·08	0·0050	133·14	0·2260	97·85	0·1023
36	240·67	0·1511	305·13	0·2368	238·26	0·1245
37	−284·02	−0·5887	−107·92	−0·0411	−141·12	−0·2608
38	−99·96	−0·1315	−78·58	−0·0625	−78·07	−0·1244
39	−198·72	−0·1004	293·07	0·3462	−37·57	0·0393
40	−113·40	−0·1724	−38·55	0·0796	−12·40	0·0069
41	146·83	0·0932	239·01	0·2031	155·78	0·0769
42	156·82	0·1078	132·14	0·1129	113·25	0·0445
43	−102·71	−0·1480	−159·36	−0·1836	−106·82	−0·1743
44	−153·08	−0·0533	343·31	0·3124	−20·07	0·0240
45	−67·00	−0·0613	−141·95	−0·1735	−48·11	−0·0684
46	−95·60	−0·0488	−180·67	−0·2956	−62·14	−0·0573
47	−28·06	−0·0260	139·32	0·1460	9·28	−0·0167
48	−85·76	−0·0200	432·65	0·4165	75·19	0·1067
49	−112·51	−0·0129	559·66	0·5417	100·58	0·1722
50	−266·71	−0·3733	−207·26	−0·2728	−245·79	−0·3708

recording units shared a length of common boundary, and $w_{ij} = 0$ otherwise. The results are given in table 6.8. Given the assumption of independent, identically normally distributed residuals, the test based upon the coefficient I evaluated under assumption N is the efficient test, and we may judge the performance of the other coefficients using these results as our benchmark. As we wished to detect positive spatial autocorrelation, one-tailed critical regions were used. We note that:

(a) I evaluated under assumption R is on all occasions more conservative than I evaluated under assumption N in detecting positive spatial autocorrelation, and more liberal in detecting negative spatial autocorrelation. However, at the nominal $\alpha = 0{\cdot}05$ level of significance, we would reach the same decision whether or not to accept the null hypothesis, H_0, of no spatial autocorrelation among the regression residuals.

(b) For the join counts, we note that neither BB nor BW provides a strictly valid test of spatial autocorrelation among regression residuals for the reasons discussed in section 5.3.1. However, despite this limitation, we found that for BW under both free and nonfree sampling we would reach the same decision as for I under N as to whether or not to accept H_0 at the $\alpha = 0{\cdot}05$ level for 10 of the 11 regressions. There is also little to choose between the results for BW under free and nonfree sampling. Conversely, for BB we would reach the same inferential decision as for I under N on only 6/11 occasions for free sampling, and on 4/11 occasions for nonfree sampling. There are also quite dramatic differences between the results under free and nonfree sampling, and with no consistent pattern to these differences.

(c) As regards the analysis carried out by Taaffe *et al.* we note that, for Nigeria, the multiple regression produced a significant drop in the degree of spatial autocorrelation among the regression residuals compared with the results using either x_1 or x_2 alone. For Ghana, the multiple regression did not reduce autocorrelation significantly compared with x_2 alone. For both Nigeria and Ghana, the high values of R^2 for the multiple regressions, and the very small degree of spatial autocorrelation among the residuals, would suggest that these models are acceptable descriptions of reality. Taaffe *et al.* found that little was gained by adding to the regressions the further independent variables postulated in their paper.

6.4 Analysis of data from Kendall (1939), and Yule and Kendall (1968)

Data giving the yield of wheat in hundredweights per acre in each of the 48 counties of England in 1936 were taken from Yule and Kendall (1968, p.311). These data were regressed against a measure of productivity by county, p, defined in Kendall (1939, pp.25–29). p_i is the score of county i on the first principal component of the correlation matrix for the yields of ten crops in each of the English counties. The data and the

Table 6.8. Results of tests for spatial autocorrelation in the Taaffe, Morrill, and Gould (1963) regression residuals[a].

Standard deviate	Regression residuals										
	Ghana					Nigeria					
	a	b	c	d	e	a	b	c	d	e	f
I_N	2·59 ****	3·39 ****	−0·35	0·67	0·81	1·14	2·37 ****	2·37 ****	3·89 ****	0·90	−0·24
I_R	2·48 ****	3·36 ****	−0·47	0·62	0·62	1·06	2·24 **	2·34 ****	3·85 ****	0·72	−0·34
BB (free sampling)	0·60	0·36	−0·36	−1·33	0·84	0·28	−0·23	2·08 **	1·38	0·88	2·98 ****
BW (free sampling)	−2·04 **	−2·45 ****	0·20	−0·20	0·00	0·44	−2·55 ****	−2·91 ****	−2·91 ****	−0·26	−3·26 ****
BB (nonfree sampling)	0·94	1·11	−0·73	−0·62	0·75	−1·14	0·88	0·92	1·47	1·66 **	2·22 **
BW (nonfree sampling)	−2·39 ****	−2·85 ****	−0·50	−0·06	−0·16	−0·53	−2·85 ****	−2·65 ****	−3·13 ****	−0·50	−2·80 ****

[a] The results in this table were computed by Mr. T. Dobson, Department of Geography, University of Bristol, as part of his undergraduate dissertation.

** Significant at $\alpha = 0{\cdot}05$ level (one-tailed test)
**** Significant at $\alpha = 0{\cdot}01$ level (one-tailed test)

Table 6.9. Data and regression residuals for Kendall's (1939) and Yule and Kendall's (1968) studies.

County	Wheat yield (cwts per acre)	p	Residual
Bedford	16·0	−0·656	0·6004
Berkshire	13·8	−1·860	−0·7005
Buckingham	15·2	0·595	−1·1337
Cambridge	16·4	−1·279	1·4656
Chester	17·7	2·727	−0·2257
Cornwall	15·4	0·584	−0·9255
Cumberland	17·5	−0·565	2·0325
Derby	15·2	0·606	−1·1419
Devon	14·4	−0·826	−0·8726
Dorset	11·2	−2·265	−2·9981
Durham	16·4	0·438	0·1835
Essex	17·7	1·528	0·6696
Gloucester	13·2	−0·898	−2·0189
Hampshire	12·8	−2·794	−1·0031
Hereford	14·4	−1·782	−0·1588
Hertford	15·3	0·241	−0·7694
Huntingdon	16·0	−2·867	2·2514
Isle of Ely	20·5	5·527	0·4835
Isle of Wight	12·0	−4·321	−0·6629
Kent	18·5	1·369	1·5883
Lancaster	19·2	3·551	0·6590
Leicester	15·8	−1·159	0·7760
Lincs (Holland)	21·8	6·701	0·9068
Lincs (Kesteven)	15·5	−1·903	1·0316
Lincs (Lindsey)	15·8	−0·374	0·1899
Middlesex	16·5	0·107	0·5307
Norfolk	16·9	1·048	0·2280
Northampton	14·3	−0·952	−0·8785
Northumberland	18·5	1·907	1·1866
Nottingham	15·6	−1·657	0·9479
Oxford	14·1	0·232	−1·9626
Rutland	16·6	0·027	0·6904
Salop	16·5	1·490	−0·5020
Soke of Peterborough	14·4	−1·311	−0·5105
Somerset	13·4	−0·182	−2·3535
Stafford	17·1	1·486	0·1010
Suffolk, E.	16·3	2·328	−1·3278
Suffolk, W.	18·2	0·468	1·9611
Surrey	12·7	−2·042	−1·6646
Sussex, E.	15·7	−1·177	0·6895
Sussex, W.	14·3	−3·784	1·2362
Warwick	15·4	−0·437	−0·1631
Westmorland	15·8	−4·333	3·1461
Wiltshire	13·8	0·369	−2·3649
Worcester	14·2	−1·135	−0·8419
Yorks, E. Riding	16·1	−0·485	0·5727
Yorks, N. Riding	17·0	0·940	0·4087
Yorks, W. Riding	16·9	0·492	0·6432

regression residuals are given in table 6.9, while the estimating equation is

$$\text{wheat yield} = \underset{(0\cdot0889)}{15\cdot8894+0\cdot7467p} \qquad R^2 = 0\cdot605.$$

The residuals from the regression were tested for spatial autocorrelation using the coefficient I defined by equation (5.28). The moments of I were evaluated under assumptions N [equations (5.34) and (5.38)] and R [equations (1.66) and (1.68)]. In these equations we put $w_{ij} = 1$ if the ith and jth counties had a length of county boundary in common, and $w_{ij} = 0$ otherwise. Positive spatial autocorrelation was suspected and so a one-tailed test has been used. The results of the analysis are given in table 6.10. From this table we note that, despite a fairly high R^2, the regression residuals are highly spatially autocorrelated. The method of generating the p scores means that the R^2 value is slightly inflated, but this does not affect our present analysis. These results suggest that productivity alone is not sufficient to account for the spatial variation in wheat yields in the English counties, and that additional variables such as rainfall or soil type should be considered. We note again that the residuals are positively autocorrelated and that the results under R are more conservative than the results under N.

Table 6.10. Results of tests for spatial autocorrelation in regression residuals from the crop yield data.

Statistic	Assumption N	Assumption R
I	0·3979	0·3979
$E(I)$	−0·0256	−0·0213
$\sigma(I)$	0·0874	0·0879
Standard deviate	4·84 ****	4·77 ****

**** Significant at $\alpha = 0\cdot01$ level (one-tailed test)

6.5 Trend surface analysis of unemployment data

For this example, we took the percentage of the total workforce unemployed in January, 1967, in the 37 employment exchange areas in the southwest of England whose locations are shown in figure 6.4. The exchange identity numbers correspond with those in table 6.11, where the unemployment rates and the x_1(E–W) and x_2(N–S) cartesian coordinates of the exchanges according to the grid shown in figure 6.4 are given. We then fitted linear. quadratic, and cubic trend surfaces to the data using the method of least squares.

The dependent variable in the trend surface model was the observed unemployment level in the various exchanges, while the independent variables were functions of the x_1 and x_2 coordinates. The coefficients obtained for the various surfaces, and the values of t and R^2 are given in table 6.12, while the analysis of variance is recorded in table 6.13. The calculated unemployment rates $\hat{Y}$ and the residuals $(Y-\hat{Y})$ for each surface are quoted in table 6.11. In checking the overall goodness-of-fit of the trend surface, these regression residuals should always be tested for spatial autocorrelation and appropriate action taken when it is detected at a significant level.

Table 6.11. Southwest unemployment data, cartesian coordinates of exchanges, calculated values, and residuals from the trend surfaces.

Exchange identity number	Coordinates		Workforce unemployed (%) January 1967[a]	Calculated values and residuals from surfaces					
				linear		quadratic		cubic	
	x_1	x_2		$\hat{Y}$	$Y-\hat{Y}$	$\hat{Y}$	$Y-\hat{Y}$	$\hat{Y}$	$Y-\hat{Y}$
1	382	216	2·4	2·23	0·17	4·34	−1·94	1·83	0·57
2	402	202	1·9	1·88	0·02	1·97	−0·07	2·91	−1·01
3	384	205	1·4	2·26	−0·86	3·33	−1·93	2·31	−0·91
4	372	181	2·0	2·69	−0·69	2·68	−0·68	2·50	−0·50
5	365	168	1·6	2·93	−1·33	2·54	−0·93	2·37	−0·77
6	332	160	5·1	3·72	1·38	3·91	1·19	2·88	2·22
7	385	165	2·1	2·51	−0·41	1·54	0·56	2·51	−0·41
8	390	165	2·1	2·40	−0·30	1·33	1·33	2·59	−0·49
9	415	185	5·4	1·71	3·69	0·58	4·82	3·60	1·80
10	363	143	2·4	3·14	−0·74	2·19	0·21	2·10	0·29
11	349	137	1·4	3·49	−2·09	2·66	1·26	2·08	−0·68
12	323	124	2·5	4·16	−1·66	3·50	−1·00	2·32	0·18
13	388	145	2·5	2·57	−0·07	1·39	1·11	2·27	0·23
14	388	106	3·4	2·84	0·56	2·88	0·52	2·50	0·90
15	355	115	1·5	3·51	−2·01	2·83	−1·33	2·50	−1·00
16	369	90	0·9	3·37	−2·47	4·02	−3·12	4·06	−3·16
17	414	130	1·6	2·10	−0·50	1·29	0·31	1·70	−0·10
18	182	61	9·1	7·71	1·39	7·42	1·68	7·56	1·54
19	147	30	8·7	8·70	0·00	8·27	0·43	7·97	0·73
20	167	42	6·3	8·17	−1·87	7·79	−1·49	7·40	−1·10
21	181	34	7·4	7·92	−0·52	7·76	−0·36	7·52	−0·12
22	207	68	4·1	7·11	−3·01	6·79	−2·69	6·08	−1·98
23	222	106	8·2	6·52	1·68	7·03	1·17	8·94	−0·74
24	251	146	12·1	5·61	6·49	7·78	4·32	11·57	0·53
25	232	85	3·1	6·44	−3·34	6·16	−3·06	5·22	−2·12
26	296	146	3·4	4·61	−1·21	5·17	−1·77	4·49	−1·09
27	259	96	4·4	5·77	−1·37	5·41	−1·01	4·05	0·35
28	277	75	5·8	5·51	0·29	5·37	0·43	4·89	0·91
29	295	113	3·3	4·85	−1·55	4·37	−1·07	2·90	0·40
30	330	100	3·4	4·16	−0·76	3·75	−0·35	3·23	0·17
31	292	55	14·1	5·31	8·79	6·38	7·72	9·07	5·03
32	287	51	7·1	5·45	1·65	6·64	0·46	9·82	−2·72
33	301	81	6·9	4·94	1·96	4·86	2·04	4·69	2·21
34	225	65	8·6	6·73	1·87	6·43	2·17	5·41	3·19
35	257	55	2·9	6·09	−3·19	6·38	−3·48	7·27	−4·37
36	248	75	5·4	6·15	−0·75	5·82	−0·42	4·66	0·74
37	404	79	3·4	2·66	0·74	5·33	−1·93	2·79	0·61

[a] Source: Department of Employment, Southwest Regional Office.

We tested the residuals from the three trend surfaces for spatial autocorrelation using the coefficient I given in equation (5.28). The moments of I were evaluated under assumptions N [equations (5.43) and (5.45)] and R [equations (1.66) and (1.68)]. In these equations the following forms for $\boldsymbol{W}$ were used:

(1) $w_{ij} = 1$ if the ith and jth exchanges were first nearest neighbours in terms of airline distance in miles between them, and $w_{ij} = 0$ otherwise.

(2) $w_{ij} = 1$ if the ith and jth exchanges were first or second nearest neighbours, and $w_{ij} = 0$ otherwise.

(3) $w_{ij} = d_{ij}^{-a}$, where d_{ij} was the airline distance in miles between the ith employment exchange and its first nearest neighbour j, and $w_{ij} = 0$ otherwise. We tried $a = 1$ and $a = 2$.

(4) $w_{ij} = d_{ij}^{-a}$ if j was the first or second nearest neighbour of i, and $w_{ij} = 0$ otherwise. We took $a = 2$.

The results of the analysis are given in table 6.14. In this case two-tailed critical regions were used as we had no prior reasons to expect positive or negative spatial autocorrelation.

If we use tables 6.11 and 6.12, and figure 6.4, to compare the fitted trend surfaces with the observed unemployment levels, we find that the linear surface falls from the southwest to the northeast parts of the map and reflects, as one would expect, the significantly higher levels of

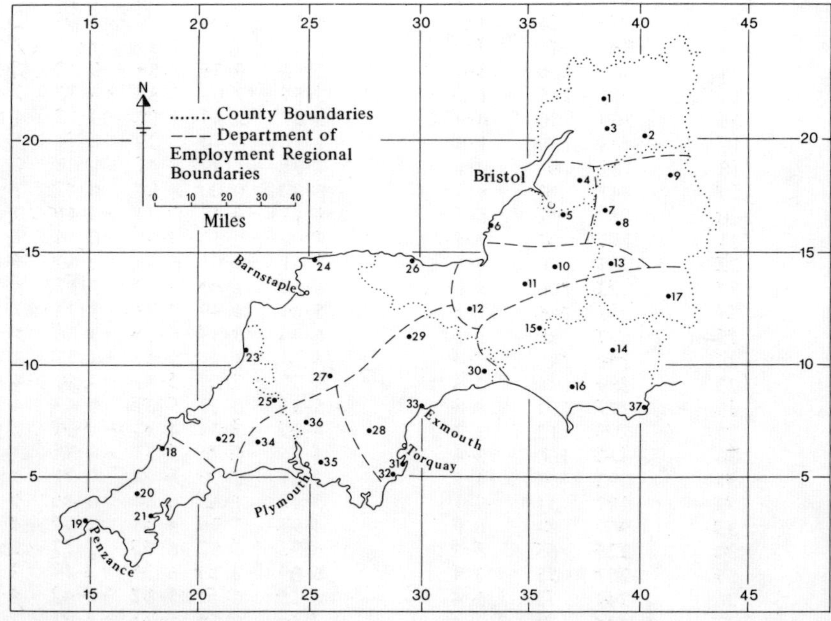

Figure 6.4. The locations and identity numbers of the 37 employment exchanges in the southwest of England.

unemployment in the extreme southwest, where the economy is heavily reliant upon tourism and mining, compared with the Bristol region in the northeast. The quadratic surface does not significantly improve upon this basic pattern. The cubic surface, however, produces a substantial improvement by better fitting to the seaside areas, for example exchanges 24 and 31.

Looking now at table 6.14, we again find that I evaluated under assumption R is consistently more conservative than I evaluated under

Table 6.12. Trend surface analysis for southwest region unemployment data (January, 1967).

Terms in regression	Surface					
	linear		quadratic		cubic	
	coefficient	t value	coefficient[a]	t value	coefficient[a]	t value
Constant	12·1625	-	11·4171	-	29·4010	-
x_1	−0·02220	−2·75 ****	−0·03256	−0·55	−0·45403	−1·20
x_2	−0·00671	−0·55	0·03960	0·58	0·79074	2·19 **
x_1^2			1·2232	0·96	29·305	1·81
x_1x_2			−6·3266	−2·03 **	−94·959	−3·73 ****
x_2^2			6·6782	2·19 **	61·928	3·72 ****
x_1^3					0·4608	2·16 **
$x_1^2x_2$					1·6105	2·96 ****
$x_1x_2^2$					0·7956	0·88
x_2^3					0·6641	1·00
Degrees of freedom		34·0		31·0		27·0
R^2	0·404		0·489		0·695	

** Significant at $\alpha = 0{\cdot}05$ level (two-tailed test)
**** Significant at $\alpha = 0{\cdot}01$ level (two-tailed test)
[a] The coefficients of the quadratic terms in x_1 and x_2 have been multiplied by 10^4, and those of the cubic terms by 10^5.

Table 6.13. Analysis of variance for trend surface study.

Source	Degrees of freedom	Sums of squares	Observed F values
Linear	2	144·2	$F_{2,34} = 11{\cdot}85$ ****
Addition of quadratic	3	30·6	$F_{3,31} = 1{\cdot}79$
Addition of cubic	4	73·3	$F_{4,27} = 4{\cdot}77$ ****
Residual	27	109·2	
	36		

**** Significant at $\alpha = 0{\cdot}01$ level.

Table 6.14. Results of tests for spatial autocorrelation in southwest unemployment trend surface residuals.

Statistic	Form of ***W***														
	(1)			(2)			(3) $a = 1$			(3) $a = 2$			(4)		
	trend surface			trend surface			trend surface			trend surface			trend surface		
	linear	quadratic	cubic	linear	quadratic	cubic	linear	quadratic	cubic	linear	quadratic	cubic	linear	quadratic	cubic
I	0·124	0·002	−0·448	0·118	0·047	−0·311	0·346	0·120	−0·782	0·585	0·227	−1·133	0·475	0·182	−0·948
Using N															
E(*I*)	−0·112	−0·186	−0·265	−0·110	−0·178	−0·240	−0·114	−0·199	−0·296	−0·114	−0·209	−0·321	−0·113	−0·199	−0·298
σ(*I*)	0·204	0·234	0·270	0·155	0·194	0·224	0·260	0·276	0·311	0·408	0·391	0·401	0·328	0·325	0·346
Standard deviate	1·16	0·80	−0·68	1·48	1·16	−0·32	1·78	1·16	−1·56	1·72	1·17	−2·03 **	1·79	1·17	−1·88
Using R															
E(*I*)	−0·028	−0·028	−0·028	−0·028	−0·028	−0·028	−0·028	−0·028	−0·028	−0·028	−0·028	−0·028	−0·028	−0·028	−0·028
σ(*I*)	0·186	0·191	0·194	0·132	0·135	0·137	0·250	0·255	0·260	0·411	0·420	0·427	0·328	0·335	0·341
Standard deviate	0·81	0·16	−2·17 **	1·11	0·56	−2·06 **	1·50	0·58	−2·90 ****	1·49	0·61	−2·59 ****	1·53	0·63	−2·70 ****

** Significant at $\alpha = 0{\cdot}05$ level (two-tailed test)
**** Significant at $\alpha = 0{\cdot}01$ level (two-tailed test)

assumption N when searching for positive spatial autocorrelation, and more liberal when searching for negative spatial autocorrelation. It is also evident, remembering that the linear, quadratic, and cubic trend surfaces are equivalent to 3, 6, and 10 independent variable regressions respectively, that the conservatism becomes more marked as the number of independent variables increases. As regards the different forms of $\boldsymbol{W}$ tried, we note that the distance weights (3) and (4) above emphasise the spatial autocorrelation among the residuals more strongly than do the binary weights.

If we now ask how well the fitted surfaces account for the observed spatial autocorrelation in unemployment rates, the following point may be noted. We tested the *original* data (column 4 in table 6.11) for spatial autocorrelation using I under assumption R [equations (1.44), (1.66), and (1.68)] for each of the forms of $\boldsymbol{W}$ used in the analysis of the residuals, and obtained the results given in table 6.15. These indicate that there is strong positive spatial autocorrelation in the unemployment rates. However, the results given in table 6.14 in general indicate that, at conventional significance levels the residuals from the linear, quadratic, and cubic trend surfaces are spatially random. Taken with the results in tables 6.12 and 6.13, the findings imply that the major component of the spatial autocorrelation in the raw data is the linear southwest-northeast trend referred to earlier. Removal of this trend appears to eliminate most of the systematic spatial variation in the raw data. Finally, it is interesting to note from table 6.14 that the residuals from the linear and quadratic trend surfaces are slightly positively spatially autocorrelated, whereas for the cubic surface, a negative pattern is evident. This is possibly due to the effect of cubic terms in a N–S direction in the western part of the study area, where frequently there are only two or three exchanges in a N–S strip.

Table 6.15. Results of tests for spatial autocorrelation in observed levels of unemployment in the southwest.

Statistic	Form of $\boldsymbol{W}$				
	(1)	(2)	(3) $a = 1$	(3) $a = 2$	(4)
I	0·463	0·470	0·712	0·978	0·867
$\mathrm{E}(I)$	−0·028	−0·028	−0·028	−0·028	−0·028
$\sigma(I)$	0·195	0·138	0·261	0·430	0·343
Standard deviate	2·52 ****	3·60 ****	2·83 ****	2·34 ****	2·61 ****

**** Significant at $\alpha = 0{\cdot}01$ level (one-tailed test)

6.6 The use of an autoregressive model

We mentioned in section 6.2 that the persistence of a pattern of positive spatial autocorrelation among the residuals from O'Sullivan's regression (2) suggested the use of an autoregressive model. Following the procedure outlined in section 5.8, we specify the equations

$$y_i = \alpha + \beta x_i + \epsilon_i , \tag{6.4}$$

and

$$\epsilon_i = \rho \mathrm{L}\epsilon_i + u_i, \qquad i = 1, 2, ..., n, \tag{6.5}$$

where the lag operator L is defined by equation (5.65), and $\boldsymbol{W}$ is of form '3' in section 6.2. These equations yield the transformed relationship,

$$\begin{aligned} y_i &= \alpha(1-\rho) + \beta x_i + \rho \mathrm{L}y_i - \rho\beta \mathrm{L}x_i + u_i \\ &= \gamma_1 + \gamma_2 x_i + \gamma_3 \mathrm{L}y_i + \gamma_4 \mathrm{L}x_i + u_i . \end{aligned} \tag{6.6}$$

This equation should, however, be estimated subject to the constraint that

$$\gamma_4 + \gamma_2\gamma_3 = 0. \tag{6.7}$$

We now use the various methods described in section 5.8 to estimate the parameters of equation (6.6) for O'Sullivan's regression (2) data. The

Table 6.16. Results of autoregressive analyses of O'Sullivan's regression (2) data.

Regression	Equation	R^2	Proportion of variance accounted for $= \dfrac{\text{Error variance}}{\text{Variance }(y)}$
Original variables	$y = -8{\cdot}49 + 0{\cdot}00527x$ $(0{\cdot}00070)$	0·700	0·700
First differences	$y^* = -0{\cdot}038 + 0{\cdot}00245x^*$ $(0{\cdot}00067)$	0·356	0·880
Full regression	$y = 0{\cdot}625 + 0{\cdot}00245x$ $(0{\cdot}00068)$ $-0{\cdot}00265\mathrm{L}x + 1{\cdot}018\mathrm{L}y$ $(0{\cdot}00213) \quad (0{\cdot}2325)$	0·882	0·882
Constrained regression	$y = -0{\cdot}036 + 0{\cdot}00260x$ $(0{\cdot}00067)$ $-0{\cdot}00265\mathrm{L}x + 1{\cdot}018\mathrm{L}y$ $(0{\cdot}00106) \quad (0{\cdot}1143)$	0·881	0·881
Iterative method	$\tilde{y} = -1{\cdot}32 + 0{\cdot}00387\tilde{x}$ $(0{\cdot}00067)$	-	-

Note: for the constrained regression, the standard errors of the coefficients of x and Ly were obtained by the asymptotic maximum likelihood formula. For the coefficient of Lx, the standard error was calculated using the asymptotic formula for the variance of a product. For the iterative method, the asymptotic maximum likelihood formula for the standard error was used.

methods are:

1. First differences. The new variables, y_i^* $(= y_i - \mathrm{L}y_i)$ and x_i^* $(= x_i - \mathrm{L}x_i)$, were computed and the relationship, $y_i^* = \delta_1 + \delta_2 x_i^*$, estimated by OLS. This assumes an *a priori* value of $\rho = 1$ in equation (6.5), but satisfies the constraint (6.7).

2. Full regression. Equation (6.6) was estimated by OLS ignoring the constraint (6.7) on the coefficients.

3. Constrained regression. This uses equations (6.4–6.7). The estimates were obtained by a direct search procedure to minimise the residual sum of squares, subject to constraint (6.7).

The use of methods '2' and '3' is subject to the reservations expressed in section 5.8, particularly that OLS is not a consistent estimating procedure for this model. Therefore we have also estimated the model using '4', the iterative method given in that section. The method of computation is discussed in Ord (1973) and appendix 3. Successive values of the estimates for ρ were 0·433, 0·496, 0·5037, 0·5046, 0·5047, the last value being correct to four decimal places. Little is changed after two rounds of the iterative procedure.

The results are presented in tables 6.16–18, together with the values of R^2, the standard errors of the coefficients, and the proportion of the variance accounted for, which we define as the ratio of the error variance to the variance of the *original* dependent variable y. The coefficients for

Table 6.17. Coefficients implied by the autoregressive equations.

Regression	x[a]	Lx[a]	Ly
Original variables	0·530	0	0
First differences	0·245	−0·245	1
Full regression	0·245	−0·265	1·018
Constrained regression	0·260	−0·265	1·018
Iterative method	0·387	−0·195	0·505

[a] Coefficient multiplied by 100.

Table 6.18. Measures of spatial autocorrelation among residuals from autoregressive models.

Residuals	I	Standard deviate
Original	0·4361	3·56
First differences	−0·3874	−2·45
Full regression	−0·3918	−2·5[a]
Constrained regression	−0·4075	−2·6[a]
Iterative method	0·2382	+2·0[a]

[a] Using randomisation (assumption R). This is not a valid procedure (see latter part of section 5.7) and the approximate standard deviates are given for guidance only.

the three regressor variables yielded by methods '1'–'3' above are listed in table 6.17. Finally, measures of spatial autocorrelation among the residuals are presented in table 6.18. The following points are worth noting.

(1) The variance of Ly is much smaller than that of y (less than one-fifth in the present case), which means that the OLS estimate of the coefficient of Ly in the various regressions is greater than one. For the time series model, var(Ly)/var(y) $\rightarrow$ 1 as $n \rightarrow \infty$, but there is no such guarantee for the spatial model, and the limiting ratio will usually be less than one.

(2) For these data, taking first differences yields results very close to the full and constrained regressions. The level of fit and pattern of residuals are very similar for these three models.

(3) The constrained regression appears to fit better than the full regression (since the variance estimate for the random error term is higher for the unconstrained version). Further, the standard errors of the coefficients γ_3 and γ_4 in the constrained regression are half the size of the unconstrained standard errors. However, the lack of consistency of the estimators prevents us from placing too great a reliance on these results. This is confirmed by the quite different estimates given by the maximum likelihood (ML) iterative procedure.

(4) The ML iterative procedure does not eliminate all the spatial autocorrelation (see the discussion in section 8.3).

(5) The initial estimate for ρ is very close to the value of I for the original variables in table 6.18, suggesting that this is a good initial value from which to start the iterations.

(6) The ML estimates are quite different from both the OLS and the inconsistent procedures, indicating the need for efficient estimation methods.

7

Comparisons of tests for spatial autocorrelation

7.1 Introduction

In the first six chapters of this monograph a variety of different tests have been used to search for spatial autocorrelation in data. The purpose of this chapter is to undertake a study of these tests with a view to trying to recommend which test should be used in given circumstances. We shall also make recommendations about the form the weighting matrix $\boldsymbol{W}$ should take.

The general question which may be asked is 'which test or combination of tests is best?' Naturally, this implies some criterion by which 'best' can be assessed. The standard approach, due to Neyman and Pearson, is to consider the *power* of a test, which is defined as 'the probability of rejecting the null hypothesis, H_0, when it is false'. That is,

$$\text{power} = 1 - \text{probability (type II error)}.$$

The power is examined at given levels of the *size* of the test, where size is defined as 'the probability of rejecting the null hypothesis, H_0, when it is true'. That is,

$$\text{size} = \text{probability (type I error)}.$$

Unfortunately, for the problem in hand, small sample results cannot be obtained by analytical methods. Therefore three alternative approaches are used in this chapter.

(1) Asymptotic relative efficiency (ARE).
Instead of computing the full power curve, we can assess the local efficiency of the test as the parameter value(s), under the alternative hypothesis H_1, approach those specified under H_0, and the sample size n goes to infinity. This measure was first used by Pitman (1948) and is reviewed briefly in section 7.2. For a fuller discussion, see Kendall and Stuart (1967, chapter 25). The ARE measures are evaluated for the various tests of spatial autocorrelation in section 7.3. In section 7.4, the correlation between the BB and BW join count statistics is found and a combined test of significance is considered.

(2) Field trials.
In section 7.5 results are reported for two sets of real data, and the performances of the various statistics are compared.

(3) Monte Carlo studies.
In section 7.6, the power functions of the test statistics are evaluated for several lattices, allowing small sample comparisons to be made. The chapter ends with a list of conclusions drawn from these studies.

7.2 Asymptotic relative efficiency

Suppose that we wish to test the null hypothesis, H_0: $\psi = 0$, against the alternative hypothesis, H_1: $\psi \neq 0$, where ψ is some parameter. Let h denote any test statistic under consideration and suppose that, without loss of generality, the expected value of h under H_0 is zero; that is

$$E(h \mid H_0) = 0. \tag{7.1}$$

Further, we shall assume that the variance of h exists, defined as

$$\text{var}(h \mid H_0) = \omega^2, \qquad \text{say}, \tag{7.2}$$

and that h is asymptotically normally distributed. Given certain conditions, which are satisfied in all the cases we shall consider (see Kendall and Stuart, 1967, pp.265 ff), we may examine alternative hypotheses for which h is asymptotically normally distributed and

$$E(h \mid H_1) = \psi b + O(\psi^{1+\delta}), \tag{7.3}$$

where $\delta > 0$, O denotes terms of this order or higher in ψ, and b is some function independent of ψ. Then as $n \to \infty$, if we consider alternatives of the form $\psi \propto n^{-1/2}$, the asymptotic *efficacy* of a test based on h is defined as

$$F(h) = \frac{b^2}{\omega^2}\,. \tag{7.4}$$

From equation (7.4), the asymptotic relative *efficiency* (ARE) of a test based on h_1 to one based on h_2 is defined as

$$\text{ARE}(h_1, h_2) = \frac{F(h_1)}{F(h_2)}\,. \tag{7.5}$$

The ARE is a useful measure because it is related to power, as defined in section 7.1, in the following way.

Let $P(h, \psi)$ be the power of a test based on h when the parameter has the value ψ under H_1. Then

$$\text{ARE}(h_1, h_2) = \lim_{n \to \infty} \left[\frac{P(h_1, \psi)}{P(h_2, \psi)}\right]^{1/2}, \tag{7.6}$$

where $\psi \propto n^{-1/2}$.

Thus the ARE is a measure of the comparative asymptotic local power of a test. This may seem to be a measure of strictly limited value but, in practice, the ARE of two tests often gives a fair guide to their relative power for alternatives not too far from the null hypothesis.

7.3 The ARE of tests for spatial autocorrelation

Throughout this section it is assumed that the data are drawn from normal populations (that is assumption N of sections 1.3.2 and 2.3). As in equation (5.18), we specify a first order Markov scheme as the alternative hypothesis H_1; that is,

$$x_i = \rho \sum_j d_{ij} x_j + u_i \,, \qquad i = 1, 2, \ldots, n, \tag{7.7}$$

where the $\{u_i\}$ are independent and identically distributed normal variates with common variance σ^2 (see also appendix 1). Thus, the precise form of H_1 is specified through the $\{d_{ij}\}$, which are any non-negative constants, such that $\sum_j d_{ij} = 1$ $(i = 1, 2, \ldots, n)$. The following example illustrates the point.

Example. Observations are taken on a regular square grid and the researcher postulates a north–south pattern of spatial autocorrelation under H_1 (figure 7.1). Then the appropriate specification of the Markov scheme would be

$$d_{ij} = \tfrac{1}{2},$$

if county j is due north or due south of county i and contiguous to it,

$$d_{ij} = 0 \text{ otherwise.}$$

For simplicity, all counties are taken to have four neighbouring counties, so that there are no complicating edge effects. Clearly $\sum_j d_{ij} = 1$ for all i, while equation (7.7) for county i will include terms on the right hand side for the two shaded counties in figure 7.1.

We may express equation (7.7) in vector notation as

$$\boldsymbol{x} = \rho \boldsymbol{D}\boldsymbol{x} + \boldsymbol{u} \tag{7.8}$$

where

$$\boldsymbol{x} = \begin{pmatrix} x_1 \\ \vdots \\ x_n \end{pmatrix}, \quad \boldsymbol{u} = \begin{pmatrix} u_1 \\ \vdots \\ u_n \end{pmatrix}, \quad \text{and } \boldsymbol{D} = \begin{pmatrix} 0 & d_{12} & \cdots & d_{1n} \\ d_{21} & 0 & & \vdots \\ \vdots & & \ddots & \vdots \\ d_{n1} & \cdots & \cdots & 0 \end{pmatrix}.$$

For simplicity we assume that the means of the X variates are known, and that the variables have been adjusted to have mean zero. That is,

$$\mathrm{E}(\boldsymbol{X}) = \mathrm{E}(\boldsymbol{u}) = \boldsymbol{0}, \tag{7.9}$$

where $\boldsymbol{X}$ is the variate vector corresponding to the observed values $\boldsymbol{x}$. This assumption does not affect the *asymptotic* results, but makes the analysis simpler. From the assumption that

$$\mathrm{E}(\boldsymbol{u}\boldsymbol{u}') = \sigma^2 \boldsymbol{I}_n \,, \tag{7.10}$$

and equation (7.9), it follows that

$$\operatorname{var}(X) = \mathrm{E}(XX') = \sigma^2(I_n - \rho D)^{-1}(I_n - \rho D')^{-1} = \sigma^2 V(\rho), \text{ say.} \tag{7.11}$$

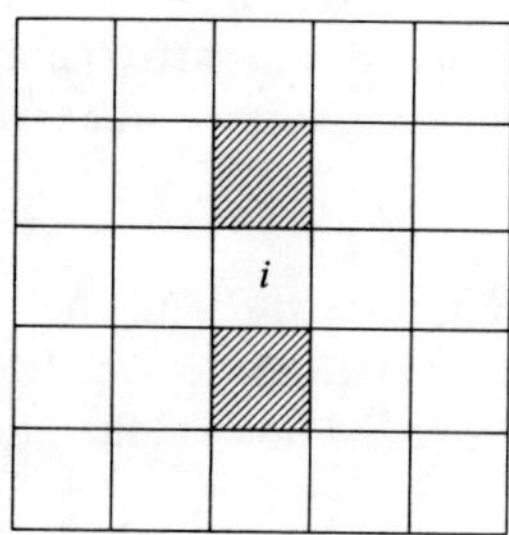

Figure 7.1. Lattice used for example in section 7.3.

7.3.1 The likelihood ratio test

Since the ARE criterion compares two tests, we need a statistic to serve as a benchmark. An obvious candidate is the likelihood ratio (LR) statistic. Under H_1: $\rho = \rho_1 > 0$, and σ^2 known, the log-likelihood function is

$$L_1 \propto n \ln \sigma - \tfrac{1}{2}\ln|V_1| - \tfrac{1}{2}\frac{x'V_1^{-1}x}{\sigma^2}\ , \tag{7.12}$$

where $V_1 = V(\rho_1)$. Likewise, under H_0: $\rho = 0$, σ^2 known, then

$$L_0 \propto -n \ln \sigma - \frac{x'x}{2\sigma^2}\ . \tag{7.13}$$

The likelihood ratio test then rejects H_0 in favour of H_1 if

$$L_1 - L_0 > k\ , \tag{7.14}$$

where k is some suitable constant. This suggests a test statistic of the form,

$$\frac{x'V^{-1}x}{x'x}\ . \tag{7.15}$$

If we ignore constants and terms of order ρ_1^2, this reduces to the statistic

$$\frac{x'(D+D')x}{x'x} \equiv \frac{\sum_{(2)}(d_{ij}+d_{ji})x_i x_j}{\sum x_i^2}\ ;$$

this is equivalent to

$$\frac{\sum_{(2)} d_{ij} x_i x_j}{\sum x_i^2}\ , \tag{7.16}$$

since $x'Dx = x'D'x$. Equation (7.16) is the form of the I statistic used in earlier chapters. Thus equation (7.16) approaches the LR statistic as $\rho_1 \to 0$ and, since no uniformly most powerful test is available (Anderson, 1948), we conjecture that (7.16) will provide a satisfactory test. This argument parallels that of Durbin and Watson (1950, pp.423–424) for the analysis of time series, although they used the statistic

$$\frac{\sum_{(2)} d_{ij}(x_i - x_j)^2}{\sum x_i^2}, \tag{7.17}$$

which is equally satisfactory in that case (see section 7.3.3). *Equations (7.16) and (7.17) imply that the weights used in the test statistic should correspond to the weights postulated for the first order Markov scheme given in equation (7.7).*

7.3.2 Large sample moments for I and c

Let us consider the statistic

$$h = \frac{x'Tx}{x'x}, \tag{7.18}$$

where T is a matrix of constant coefficients $\{t_{ij}\}$. Both I and c can be expressed in the form of equation (7.18), when the population mean is set equal to zero. If we assume that $\sum_{(2)} w_{ij} = W = n$, we have for I that $T = W$, and for c that $T = \Omega - W$, where Ω is a diagonal matrix with elements $\Omega_{ii} = \frac{1}{2}\sum_j (w_{ij} + w_{ji})$. If we use the methods of section 2.3.1 it follows that, under H_0,

$$E(h \mid H_0) = \frac{1}{n}\sum_{i=1}^{n} t_{ii} = \frac{1}{n}\mathrm{tr}(T), \tag{7.19}$$

where tr is the trace operator which sums elements on the leading diagonal of the matrix T. Likewise, we find that

$$\mathrm{var}(h \mid H_0) = \frac{1}{n(n+2)}\left\{\mathrm{tr}[T(T+T')] - \frac{2}{n}[\mathrm{tr}(T)]^2\right\}. \tag{7.20}$$

Both these results apply for any value of n.

Example. For I, $T = W$ and $\mathrm{tr}(T) = \mathrm{tr}(W) = 0$, so that $E(I \mid H_0) = 0$. Likewise, $\mathrm{tr}[T(T+T')] = \sum_{(2)} w_{ij}(w_{ij} + w_{ji}) = S_1$, so that

$$\mathrm{var}(I \mid H_0) = \frac{S_1}{n(n+2)}. \tag{7.21}$$

If these results are compared with equations (1.66) and (1.67), we see that only the leading terms are retained when assumption (7.9) is made. However, as n increases, equations (1.66) and (1.67) approach (7.19) and (7.20), provided that the asymptotic distribution is normal. Similarly for c,

$T = \Omega - W$ and $\mathrm{tr}(T) = \mathrm{tr}(\Omega) - \mathrm{tr}(W)$, so that $\mathrm{tr}(T) = W - 0 = n$, since $W = n$. Thus

$$\mathrm{E}(c \mid \mathrm{H}_0) = 1 .$$

Likewise,

$$\mathrm{var}(c \mid \mathrm{H}_0) = \frac{S_1(1+\theta)}{n(n+2)} , \tag{7.22}$$

where

$$\theta = \frac{S_2 - 4n}{2S_1} .$$

Under the alternative hypothesis H_1 we cannot evaluate $\mathrm{E}(h \mid \mathrm{H}_1)$ directly. However, from equation (7.8) it can be seen that

$$\boldsymbol{x} = (\boldsymbol{I}_n - \rho \boldsymbol{D})^{-1} \boldsymbol{u} . \tag{7.23}$$

If we substitute (7.23) into (7.18), we obtain

$$h = \frac{\boldsymbol{x}'\boldsymbol{T}\boldsymbol{x}}{\boldsymbol{x}'\boldsymbol{x}} = \frac{\boldsymbol{u}'\boldsymbol{T}_*\boldsymbol{u}}{\boldsymbol{u}'\boldsymbol{V}\boldsymbol{u}} , \tag{7.24}$$

where $\boldsymbol{T}_* = (\boldsymbol{I}_n - \rho\boldsymbol{D})^{-1}\boldsymbol{T}(\boldsymbol{I}_n - \rho\boldsymbol{D}')^{-1}$ and $\boldsymbol{V}[= \boldsymbol{V}(\rho)]$ is defined by equation (7.11). Recalling that ρ is of order $n^{-1/2}$ in the evaluation of the efficacy, we can expand h as a series in terms of $n^{-1/2}$. Now

$$\boldsymbol{T}_* = \boldsymbol{T} = \rho(\boldsymbol{D}'\boldsymbol{T} + \boldsymbol{T}\boldsymbol{D}) + \mathrm{O}(\rho^2) ,$$

where $\mathrm{O}(\rho^2)$ means "terms of order two or higher in ρ", and

$$\boldsymbol{V} = \boldsymbol{I}_n + \rho(\boldsymbol{D} + \boldsymbol{D}') + \mathrm{O}(\rho^2) ,$$

so that

$$h = \frac{\boldsymbol{u}'\boldsymbol{T}\boldsymbol{u} + \rho\boldsymbol{u}'(\boldsymbol{D}'\boldsymbol{T} + \boldsymbol{T}\boldsymbol{D})\boldsymbol{u} + \mathrm{O}(\rho^2)}{\boldsymbol{u}'\boldsymbol{u} + \rho\boldsymbol{u}'(\boldsymbol{D} + \boldsymbol{D}')\boldsymbol{u} + \mathrm{O}(\rho^2)} .$$

If we remove the factor $\boldsymbol{u}'\boldsymbol{u}$ from the denominator of this expression for h, and expand h in terms of ρ, we obtain

$$h = \frac{\boldsymbol{u}'\boldsymbol{T}\boldsymbol{u}}{\boldsymbol{u}'\boldsymbol{u}} + \frac{\rho\boldsymbol{u}'(\boldsymbol{D}'\boldsymbol{T} + \boldsymbol{T}\boldsymbol{D})\boldsymbol{u}}{\boldsymbol{u}'\boldsymbol{u}} - \frac{\rho\boldsymbol{u}'\boldsymbol{T}\boldsymbol{u}}{\boldsymbol{u}'\boldsymbol{u}} \times \frac{\boldsymbol{u}'(\boldsymbol{D} + \boldsymbol{D}')\boldsymbol{u}}{\boldsymbol{u}'\boldsymbol{u}} + \mathrm{O}(\rho^2) . \tag{7.25}$$

The expectation of h under H_1 can now be evaluated from the series (7.25), using the methods of section 2.3.1. The result is

$$\mathrm{E}(h \mid \mathrm{H}_1) = \frac{1}{n}\mathrm{tr}(\boldsymbol{T}) + \frac{\rho}{n}\mathrm{tr}(\boldsymbol{D}'\boldsymbol{T} + \boldsymbol{T}\boldsymbol{D}) - \frac{\rho}{n(n+2)}\mathrm{tr}(\boldsymbol{D}'\boldsymbol{T} + \boldsymbol{T}\boldsymbol{D}) + \mathrm{O}(\rho^2) . \tag{7.26}$$

The efficacy, defined in equation (7.4), is then

$$\mathrm{F}(h) = \frac{(n+1)^2}{n(n+2)} \frac{[\mathrm{tr}(\boldsymbol{D}'\boldsymbol{T} + \boldsymbol{T}\boldsymbol{D})]^2}{\left\{\mathrm{tr}[\boldsymbol{T}(\boldsymbol{T} + \boldsymbol{T}')] - \dfrac{2}{n}[\mathrm{tr}(\boldsymbol{T})]^2\right\}} . \tag{7.27}$$

7.3.3 Comparison of the I and c statistics

The efficacy computed in the previous section is not of interest in itself, but it permits us to compute ARE's between pairs of statistics. First we consider the effect of two different weighting matrices, $\boldsymbol{W}_1$ and $\boldsymbol{W}_2$, upon the ARE of the I statistic. Suppose that I_1 has the weighting matrix $\boldsymbol{T}_1 = \boldsymbol{W}_1 = \boldsymbol{D}$, and that I_2 has the weighting matrix $\boldsymbol{T}_2 = \boldsymbol{W}_2 \neq \boldsymbol{D}$. From equation (7.27), the efficacy for I_1 is

$$\mathrm{F}(I_1) = \frac{(n+1)^2}{n(n+2)} \frac{[\mathrm{tr}(\boldsymbol{DD}'+\boldsymbol{D}^2)]^2}{\mathrm{tr}(\boldsymbol{DD}'+\boldsymbol{D}^2)}\,, \tag{7.28}$$

while for I_2, the efficacy is

$$\mathrm{F}(I_2) = \frac{(n+1)^2}{n(n+2)} \frac{[\mathrm{tr}(\boldsymbol{D}'\boldsymbol{W}_2+\boldsymbol{W}_2\boldsymbol{D})]^2}{\mathrm{tr}(\boldsymbol{W}_2\boldsymbol{W}_2'+\boldsymbol{W}_2^2)}\,.$$

Thus, the ARE is given by:

$$\begin{aligned}\mathrm{ARE}(I_1, I_2) &= \frac{F(I_1)}{F(I_2)} \\ &= \frac{\mathrm{tr}(\boldsymbol{DD}'+\boldsymbol{D}^2)\,\mathrm{tr}(\boldsymbol{W}_2\boldsymbol{W}_2'+\boldsymbol{W}_2^2)}{\mathrm{tr}(\boldsymbol{D}'\boldsymbol{W}_2+\boldsymbol{W}_2\boldsymbol{D})}\,. \end{aligned} \tag{7.29}$$

This is equivalent to

$$\frac{\sum_{(2)}[w_{ij}(1)]^2 \sum_{(2)}[w_{ij}(2)]^2}{\sum_{(2)} w_{ij}(1)\, w_{ij}(2)}\,, \tag{7.30}$$

where $w_{ij}(k)$ is the (i,j)th element of $\boldsymbol{W}_k$ $(k = 1, 2)$. By the Cauchy–Schwartz inequality, expression (7.29) cannot be less than one, that is,

$$\mathrm{ARE}(I_1, I_2) \geqslant 1. \tag{7.31}$$

We conclude, therefore, that the best I statistic uses the weighting matrix $\boldsymbol{W} = \boldsymbol{D}$ to test H_0 against the alternative hypothesis specified by equation (7.7). Thus *the investigator should choose, a priori,* $\boldsymbol{W}$ *to represent the autocorrelation pattern he hypothesises under* H_1 *(that is, so that* $\boldsymbol{W} = \boldsymbol{D}$*).* Result (7.29) measures the penalty paid if some other $\boldsymbol{W}$ matrix is specified. Exactly the same argument holds for the c statistic.

Example. If we return to the example given at the beginning of section 7.3, an appropriate choice of weights was $w_{ij}(1) = d_{ij} = \frac{1}{2}$, if county j was a due north or south neighbour of county i, and $w_{ij}(1) = d_{ij} = 0$, otherwise. However, suppose that the researcher decided to use the weights

$$w_{ij}(2) = \begin{cases} \frac{1}{2}(1-\alpha), & \text{if county } j \text{ is a due north or south neighbour of } i, \\ \frac{1}{2}\alpha, & \text{if county } j \text{ is a due east or west neighbour of } i, \\ 0 & \text{otherwise.} \end{cases}$$

Then the ARE of a test based on I using the second set of weights, compared to a test based on the first set is

$$\mathrm{ARE}(I_2, I_1) = \frac{1}{\mathrm{ARE}(I_1, I_2)}$$

$$= \frac{(1-\alpha)^2}{(1-\alpha)^2+\alpha^2},$$

since $\sum_{(2)}[w_{ij}(1)]^2 = \frac{1}{2}n, \sum_{(2)}[w_{ij}(2)]^2 = \frac{1}{2}n[(1-\alpha)^2+\alpha^2]$, and $\sum_{(2)}w_{ij}(1)w_{ij}(2) = \frac{1}{2}n(1-\alpha)$. Clearly $\mathrm{ARE}(I_2, I_1)$ has a maximum value of one when $\alpha = 0$, and falls from one to zero as α increases from zero to one. If the rook's case ($\alpha = \frac{1}{2}$) is used, then ARE $= \frac{1}{2}$. In this case the pattern of weights appears 'half-correct' and the ARE result is intuitively reasonable.

By the same approach it can be shown that, for any lattice, the efficacy for the c statistic with $\boldsymbol{W} = \boldsymbol{D}$ is given by:

$$\mathrm{F}(c) = \frac{(n+1)^2}{n(n+2)} \frac{[\mathrm{tr}(\boldsymbol{DD}'+\boldsymbol{D}^2)]^2}{\mathrm{tr}(\boldsymbol{DD}'+\boldsymbol{D}^2)+2\mathrm{tr}(\boldsymbol{\Omega}^2)-2n}, \tag{7.32}$$

where $\boldsymbol{\Omega}$ is defined as the diagonal matrix with elements $\boldsymbol{\Omega}_{ii} = \frac{1}{2}\sum_j(w_{ij}+w_{ji})$. Thus

$$\mathrm{tr}(\boldsymbol{\Omega}^2) = \tfrac{1}{4}\sum(w_{i.}+w_{.i})^2 = \tfrac{1}{4}S_2 .$$

From equations (7.28) and (7.32) it follows that

$$\mathrm{ARE}(c, I) = \frac{1}{1+\theta}, \tag{7.33}$$

where

$$\theta = \frac{S_2 - 4n}{2S_1}. \tag{7.34}$$

It is easily shown that $S_2 \geqslant 4n$, with equality only when $w_{i.} = w_{.i} = 1$, for all $i = 1, \ldots, n$. Therefore, for regular lattices (including time series), θ is near to or equal to zero for all n, and always converges to zero as n increases. However, this need not happen for a lattice with irregular weights. (In this context, a regular lattice is one which has the same pattern of weights for *every* county, except possibly at the boundary.)

Examples.

1. Consider a lattice broken up into blocks of size three as in figure 7.2.

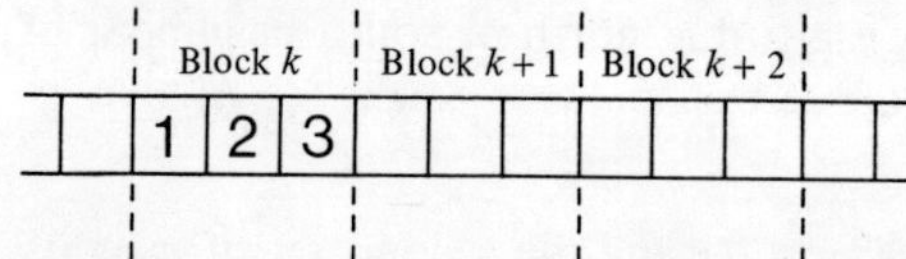

Figure 7.2. Lattice used for example in section 7.3.3.

In each block of three define the weights $w_{12} = 1$, $w_{21} = w_{23} = \frac{1}{2}$, $w_{32} = 1$, and $w_{ij} = 0$ for all other pairs. If there are m $(= \frac{1}{3}n)$ blocks, it follows that $W = 3m$, $S_1 = 4{\cdot}5m$, and $S_2 = 13{\cdot}5m$. Therefore $\vartheta = \frac{1}{6}$ and $\text{ARE}(c, I) = \frac{6}{7}$ for any m.
2. For the Eire county system shown in figure 3.1 the reader can demonstrate that similar calculations yield $\text{ARE}(c,I) = 0{\cdot}897$.

While such comparisons can only be justified for $n \to \infty$, the following conclusion appears reasonable on the basis of the ARE results: *that the I test is generally better than the c test, although the margin of advantage may be slight.*

7.3.4 The join count statistics

Instead of using the I or c statistics we could, of course, use one of the join counts. Three major questions arise.
(1) What is the best choice of weights?
(2) What is the best choice of p, where p = prob(county coded black)?
(3) Should the BB or BW test be used?
We assume first that p is known, and so the free sampling model is appropriate. The moments under the null hypothesis H_0 are given in equations (1.54–1.57), so to calculate the efficacy we need the expected values under H_1. Let us suppose that X_i and X_j are normally distributed with zero means, unit variances, and correlation ρ_{ij}. Let county i be coded B if $X_i \geqslant a$, and W otherwise $(i = 1, 2, \dots, n)$. Then the probability that both X_i and X_j are coded B is

$$P(X_i \geqslant a,\ X_j \geqslant a) = \int_a^\infty \int_a^\infty (2\pi)^{-1}(1-\rho_{ij}^2)^{-\frac{1}{2}} \exp\{-[2(1-\rho_{ij}^2)]^{-1} \times (x_i^2 + x_j^2 - 2\rho_{ij}x_i x_j)\} \mathrm{d}x_i \, \mathrm{d}x_j \,. \tag{7.35}$$

For small ρ_{ij}, this reduces to

$$\int_a^\infty \int_a^\infty (2\pi)^{-1} \exp[-\tfrac{1}{2}(x_i^2 + x_j^2)][1 + \rho_{ij}x_i x_j + \mathrm{O}(\rho_{ij}^2)] \,. \tag{7.36}$$

If

$$p = P(X_i \geqslant a) = \int_a^\infty (2\pi)^{-\frac{1}{2}} \exp(-\tfrac{1}{2}x_i^2)\mathrm{d}x_i \qquad (i = 1, \dots, n),$$

it follows that

$$P(X_i \geqslant a,\ X_j \geqslant a) = p^2 + \rho_{ij}[\mathrm{f}(a)]^2 + \mathrm{O}(\rho_{ij}^2) \,, \tag{7.37}$$

where $\mathrm{f}(a) = (2\pi)^{-\frac{1}{2}}\exp(-\frac{1}{2}a^2)$. Let us consider $BB = \frac{1}{2}\sum_{(2)} w_{ij}u_i u_j$, where

$$u_i \begin{cases} = 1, \text{ if } x_i \geqslant a \\ = 0, \text{ otherwise} \end{cases} \tag{7.38}$$

By using equation (7.37), and ignoring terms in ρ_{ij}^2 and higher powers, the expected value under H_1 is

$$\mathrm{E}(BB\,|\,\mathrm{H}_1) = \tfrac{1}{2}Wp^2 + \tfrac{1}{2}[\mathrm{f}(a)]^2 \textstyle\sum_{(2)} w_{ij}\rho_{ij}$$
$$= \tfrac{1}{2}Wp^2 + \tfrac{1}{2}\rho[\mathrm{f}(a)]^2 \textstyle\sum_{(2)} w_{ij}(d_{ij}+d_{ji}), \qquad (7.39)$$

since $\rho_{ij} = \rho(d_{ij}+d_{ji}) + \mathrm{O}(\rho^2)$ from equation (7.7). Likewise, for BW

$$\mathrm{E}(BW\,|\,\mathrm{H}_1) = Wpq - \rho[\mathrm{f}(a)]^2 \textstyle\sum_{(2)} w_{ij}(d_{ij}+d_{ji}). \qquad (7.40)$$

From equations (7.39), (7.40), and the variances (1.55) and (1.57), the efficacies are

$$\mathrm{F}(BB) = \frac{\{[\mathrm{f}(a)]^2 \sum_{(2)} w_{ij}(d_{ij}+d_{ji})\}^2}{S_1p^2q^2 + S_2p^3q}, \qquad (7.41)$$

and

$$\mathrm{F}(BW) = \frac{\{[\mathrm{f}(a)]^2 \sum_{(2)} w_{ij}(d_{ij}+d_{ji})\}^2}{S_1p^2q^2 + S_2pq(\frac{1}{4}-pq)}. \qquad (7.42)$$

Following the argument of section 7.3.3, we can establish that the best choice of weights in the test statistic is $w_{ij} = d_{ij}$ [or $w_{ij} = \frac{1}{2}(d_{ij}+d_{ji})$]. Then, maximising $\mathrm{F}(BW)$ with respect to p, we find that the best value for p is 0·5, for any lattice. For BB the results are more involved, as the best value of p varies with $\tau = S_2/4S_1$. At the minimum value of τ, $\tau = 1$ as for a circular time series, $p \sim 0{\cdot}25$ is best, and this slowly falls to $p \sim 0{\cdot}20$ at $\tau = 4$ (queen's case mapped onto a torus). As $1 \leqslant \tau \leqslant 4$ for almost all lattices of practical interest, $p = 0{\cdot}20$ or $0{\cdot}25$ is recommended as a simple choice.

When $w_{ij} = d_{ij}$, result (7.41) reduces to

$$\mathrm{F}(BB) = \frac{[\mathrm{f}(a)]^4 S_1}{p^2q(q+4\tau p)}, \qquad (7.43)$$

from which the best value for p can be found, given τ. Likewise when $w_{ij} = d_{ij}$, and $p = 0{\cdot}5$, since $\mathrm{f}(0) = (2\pi)^{-1/2}$ we have

$$\mathrm{F}(BW) = \frac{4S_1}{\pi^2}. \qquad (7.44)$$

Thus,

$$\mathrm{ARE}(BB,BW) = \frac{\mathrm{F}(BB)}{\mathrm{F}(BW)} \qquad (7.45)$$

can be computed from results (7.43) and (7.44). Since the maximum value of this ARE, for any p and all $\tau \geqslant 1$ is only 0·307, the BW test is clearly much superior to the BB test.

However, when the nonfree sampling situation is considered, a quite different picture emerges. Using the approach given already for free sampling, we now find that $p = 0{\cdot}5$ is the best value for both the BW

and the BB tests, and that $\mathrm{F}(BW) = 4S_1/\pi^2$ as before, while

$$\mathrm{F}(BB) = \frac{4S_1}{\pi^2(1+2\theta)}, \tag{7.46}$$

where θ is defined as in equation (7.34). Thus, for nonfree sampling,

$$\mathrm{ARE}(BB, BW) = \frac{1}{1+2\theta}, \tag{7.47}$$

which is equal to one for regular lattices, but is less than one for irregular lattices. Thus *we recommend that BW be used in preference to BB*, although the margin of advantage may be slight.

Finally we note that, from equations (7.28) and (7.44),

$$\mathrm{ARE}(BW, I) = \frac{4}{\pi^2}, \tag{7.48}$$

representing the loss of power when the BW test is used for interval scaled data. This compares with an ARE figure of $2/\pi$ for the sign test against Student's t, when testing for a difference between population means. We now show why expression (7.48) is lower than the ARE for the test of means.

7.3.5 An alternative derivation of the join count results

Let $\{x_i\}$ denote the original observations drawn from a normal population, and let $\{x_i'\}$ denote the coded values (0 or 1 for example). Daniels (1944) has shown that a test for correlation based on $\{x_i', y_i'\}$ instead of $\{x_i, y_i\}$, where y_i' is the coded value for y_i, has ARE equal to $[\rho(x,x')\rho(y,y')]^2$, where ρ denotes the correlation between the two sets of values. In the case of tests for autocorrelation, it can be shown that the ARE reduces to

$$\mathrm{ARE} = [\rho(x,x')]^4. \tag{7.49}$$

For two colour coding, $\rho(x,x') = (2/\pi)^{1/2}$ and so

$$\mathrm{ARE}(BW, I) = (2/\pi)^2, \tag{7.50}$$

as given in equation (7.48). For the sign test comparison with Student's t, the ARE is $[\rho(x,x')]^2$, giving the value $2/\pi$ already noted. The BB and c tests represent less efficient variants of BW and I respectively, and are not covered by result (7.50).

Geary (1954) observed that using three classes (0, 1, and 2, say) rather than two, improved the efficiency of the test procedure. The logical conclusion of such an increase in the number of classes is to use the ranks, $\{x' = 1, 2, \ldots, n\}$. It is known that $\rho(x,x') = (3/\pi)^{1/2}$ for the ranks, and so the use of ranks in I yields an ARE of $(3/\pi)^2 \approx 0{\cdot}91$. Thus the use of a test based on ranks appears to provide a nonparametric procedure of high asymptotic efficiency, although a study of non-normal populations would be required to confirm this result. The first two moments, under H_0, for the I statistic using rank data are

$$E(I) = -\frac{1}{n-1}, \tag{7.51}$$

and

$$E(I^2) = \frac{1}{5W^2(n-1)^2(n+1)}[n(n-1)(5n+6)S_1-(5n+7)(nS_2-3W^2)]. \tag{7.52}$$

7.3.6 Analysis of regression residuals

If the $\{x_i\}$ are not independent observations drawn from a normal population, but regression residuals, $\{e_i\}$ say, derived from a least squares regression (LS) with k regressor variables, we could consider a test based on the $(n-k)$ BLUS residuals,

$$\boldsymbol{z} = \boldsymbol{Be} = \boldsymbol{BMy}, \tag{7.53}$$

where $\boldsymbol{B}$ is an $(n-k) \times n$ matrix such that $\boldsymbol{BMB}' = \boldsymbol{I}_{n-k}$. For the notation used in this section, see section 5.5. In particular, the test statistic given in equation (5.51) may be expressed in matrix notation as

$$I = \frac{\boldsymbol{z}'\boldsymbol{W}_0\boldsymbol{z}}{\boldsymbol{z}'\boldsymbol{z}}. \tag{7.54}$$

Under the alternative hypothesis H_1 the population residuals obey relationship (5.19), that is

$$\boldsymbol{\epsilon} = \rho\boldsymbol{D\epsilon}+\boldsymbol{u},$$

or

$$\boldsymbol{\epsilon} = (\boldsymbol{I}-\rho\boldsymbol{D})^{-1}\boldsymbol{u}. \tag{7.55}$$

Since $\boldsymbol{e} = \boldsymbol{My}$ from equation (5.42), and this further reduces to $\boldsymbol{e} = \boldsymbol{M\epsilon}$, it follows that

$$\boldsymbol{e} = \boldsymbol{M}(\boldsymbol{I}-\rho\boldsymbol{D})^{-1}\boldsymbol{u},$$

and from equation (7.53) that

$$\begin{aligned}\boldsymbol{z} &= \boldsymbol{BM}(\boldsymbol{I}-\rho\boldsymbol{D})^{-1}\boldsymbol{u}\\ &= \boldsymbol{BM}(\boldsymbol{I}-\rho\boldsymbol{D})^{-1}\boldsymbol{MB}'\boldsymbol{v},\end{aligned} \tag{7.56}$$

where $\boldsymbol{v}$ is the $(n-k)$ vector defined by $\boldsymbol{v} = \boldsymbol{BMu}$ or $\boldsymbol{u} = \boldsymbol{B}'\boldsymbol{v}$. Then, from equation (7.56), expanding the right hand side as a series in ρ yields

$$\boldsymbol{z} = \boldsymbol{v}+\rho\boldsymbol{BMDB}'\boldsymbol{v}+O(\rho^2),$$

which is, to the same order in ρ,

$$\boldsymbol{z} = \rho\boldsymbol{BMDB}'\boldsymbol{z}+\boldsymbol{v}+O(\rho^2), \tag{7.57}$$

Equation (7.57) is in the same form as equation (7.8), and so it follows from the work of section 7.3.3 that $\boldsymbol{W}_0$ in the numerator of (7.54) should be

$$W_0 = BMDB'. \tag{7.58}$$

Now $z'W_0z = e'B'W_0Be$, so that a test based on the residuals e should have the weighting matrix

$$W_1 = B'W_0B.$$

Premultiplying by BM and postmultiplying by MB', we have that

$$BMW_1MB' = BMB'W_0BMB' = W_0, \tag{7.59}$$

which is *consistent with* $W_1 = DM$ or $W_1 = D$, since $Me = e$. Thus the optimal choice of weights for testing residuals is to use $W_1 = D$ with the LS residuals. Construction of the BLUS residuals corresponding to these is determined up to an arbitrary orthogonal transformation, and therefore W_0 is determined only up to the same arbitrary transformation.

The ARE of other sets of weights can be derived in the same way as in section 7.3.3. Extensive Monte Carlo results comparing the Durbin–Watson statistic with the BLUS form [using an $(n-k)$ square submatrix of W_1] are reported in Abrahamse and Koerts (1969). These results indicate that the exact Durbin–Watson test is the more efficient, in accord with the large sample result given by equation (7.59). Of course, in practical testing situations, the BLUS procedure with a submatrix of W_1 leads to an easily tabulated statistic for the time series case, the Von Neumann ratio, and this benefit may outweigh the gains in efficiency. From the viewpoint of choosing a weighting matrix for the BLUS test as a submatrix of W_1, the intuitively appealing procedure of discarding the least connected counties works well in ARE terms; that is, discard the k counties with the smallest values of $\sum_j w_{ji}$.

7.4 Combinations of tests

Given the variety of different tests used in this monograph, it is of interest to ask whether or not some combination of tests would be more efficient than a single test. Since the I statistic is derived from the ratio of the likelihoods (albeit as a local, asymptotic, test), the ARE of any procedure combined with I will not yield an improvement, although finite sampling results might show that possible gains in power exist. For the join count statistics, however, the possibilities of gain through a combined procedure seem more tangible. To explore this, we evaluate the correlation between the *BB* and *BW* statistics, and then compare the best combined test with *BW*.

7.4.1 The correlation between the *BB* and *BW* join count statistics

From equations (1.41) and (1.42), the *BB* and *BW* statistics are defined as

$$BB = \tfrac{1}{2}\textstyle\sum_{(2)} w_{ij}x_ix_j\,,$$

and

$$BW = \tfrac{1}{2}\textstyle\sum_{(2)} w_{ij}(x_i - x_j)^2 ,$$

where $x_i = 1$, if county i is coded black, and $x_i = 0$, otherwise. The correlation between BB and BW is given by the standard formula

$$\rho(BB, BW) = \frac{\mathrm{E}(BB\,BW) - \mathrm{E}(BB)\mathrm{E}(BW)}{\sigma(BB)\sigma(BW)} . \tag{7.60}$$

Since the means and variances are given in section 1.4.3, we need only to compute the cross product term. We have

$$\begin{aligned}\mathrm{E}(BB\,BW) &= \mathrm{E}\{(\tfrac{1}{2}\textstyle\sum_{(2)} w_{ij}x_ix_j)[\tfrac{1}{2}\sum_{(2)} w_{ij}(x_i - x_j)^2]\} \\ &= -\,2\mathrm{E}[(\tfrac{1}{2}\textstyle\sum_{(2)} w_{ij}x_ix_j)^2] + \tfrac{1}{4}\mathrm{E}[\sum_{(2)} w_{ij}x_ix_j \sum_{(2)} w_{ij}(x_i^2 + x_j^2)] \\ &= -\,2\mathrm{E}[(BB)^2] + \tfrac{1}{4}\mathrm{E}(A), \qquad \text{say.}\end{aligned} \tag{7.61}$$

$\mathrm{E}[(BB)^2]$ is known, so we need only $\mathrm{E}(A)$ to evaluate (7.61). To obtain this expectation, we expand A and determine the expectations and frequencies of each type of term. This gives the following table (in which n_1 denotes the number of counties coded B).

Term	Expectation		Total weight
	free	nonfree	
$x_i^3x_j$	p^2	$\dfrac{n_1^{(2)}}{n^{(2)}}$	S_2
$x_i^2x_jx_k$	p^3	$\dfrac{n_1^{(3)}}{n^{(3)}}$	$2W^2 - S_2$

Substituting these terms into equation (7.61), we find, after some simplification, that the expectations are:
free sampling

$$\mathrm{E}(BB\,BW) = \tfrac{1}{4}p^2q[S_2(1-2p) - 2S_1q + 2W^2p] ; \tag{7.62}$$

nonfree sampling

$$\mathrm{E}(BB\,BW) = \frac{(n-n_1)n_1^{(2)}}{4n^{(4)}}[S_2(n-2n_1+1) - 2S_1(n-n_1-1) + 2W^2(n_1-2)]. \tag{7.63}$$

7.4.2 Relative efficiency of combined tests

Using the results given in equations (7.62) and (7.63), we find that the variance of the combined statistic,

$$u = \alpha BB + (1-\alpha)BW ,$$

where α is an arbitrary constant, is given by

$$\text{var}(u) = \alpha^2\sigma^2(BB) + (1-\alpha)^2\sigma^2(BW) + 2\alpha(1-\alpha)\sigma(BB)\sigma(BW)\rho(BB,BW). \tag{7.64}$$

When $p = \frac{1}{2}$, for the free sampling models, we find that the efficacy of u is

$$F(u) = \frac{4S_1(2-3\alpha)^2}{\pi^2[(2-3\alpha)^2 + 4\alpha^2\tau]}, \tag{7.65}$$

so that $\alpha = 0$ is the best choice and corresponds to the use of BW test alone. For the nonfree sampling case, with $p = \frac{1}{2}$,

$$F(u) = \frac{4S_1(2-3\alpha)^2}{\pi^2[(2-3\alpha)^2 + 2\alpha^2\theta]}. \tag{7.66}$$

Thus, for $\theta > 0$, the best choice is again $\alpha = 0$ (the BW test alone). For $\theta = 0$, any linear combination of the two tests is equally efficient. Therefore *we cannot improve upon the use of the BW test alone*. If the BB test is used with a value of p different from that used for the BW test, a gain in efficiency would result. This is only to be expected, since more information has been used.

7.5 Comparisons between tests using real data

In section 6.3, the data of Taaffe *et al.* (1963) were analysed using both the I and join count statistics. Certain comparisons between the tests were made and we shall now explore these results further, bearing in mind, however, that caution is needed in their evaluation since the data used were regression residuals and not original observations.

The Spearman rank correlation between the standard deviates for I and for each of the join count statistics was evaluated, which gave

$$\rho(I, BB_F) = 0\cdot22 \qquad \rho(I, BW_F) = -0\cdot39$$

$$\rho(I, BB_{NF}) = 0\cdot22 \qquad \rho(I, BW_{NF}) = -0\cdot70$$

where the subscripts F and NF denote free and nonfree sampling respectively; the negative signs for BW are expected because low BW scores should coincide with high I scores for positive spatial autocorrelation. The better performance of the BW statistic is apparent, particularly under the NF assumption. However, this analysis does not take account of the relative magnitudes of the coefficients, and so the results have been analysed using 2 x 2 tables with dichotomies corresponding to $z \geqslant 1\cdot6449$ (significant) or $z < 1\cdot6449$ (not significant). The results are presented in table 7.1, and from this analysis we conclude that the performance of BW is much better than that of BB, while the choice of sampling model does not appear to make much difference. It is arguable that the free sampling model should be used with $p = \frac{1}{2}$, given the assumption of normally distributed errors with zero means, but as noted in section 5.3.1, neither model is strictly valid.

The analysis in this section is of limited generality because only two distinct data sets have been used, but the results suggest that BW is much better than BB, confirming the asymptotic results (especially for free sampling) given earlier. We believe that further analyses of real data would support these tentative conclusions.

Table 7.1. Comparison of standard deviates for I and join count test statistics.

		BB_F		BW_F	
		significant	not significant	significant	not significant
I	significant	1	4	5	0
	not significant	1	5	1	5
		BB_{NF}		BW_{NF}	
		significant	not significant	significant	not significant
I	significant	0	5	5	0
	not significant	1	5	1	5

7.6 Monte Carlo studies

In this section we use Monte Carlo methods to construct the power curves of the BB, BW, I, and c statistics for several small lattices. We assume under H_1 that the dependence between the $\{x_i\}$ values in a county system is specified by a spatial Markov process of the type given in equation (7.7). That is

$$x_i = \rho \sum_j d_{ij} x_j + u_i\,, \qquad i = 1, 2, ..., n\,, \tag{7.67}$$

or, in matrix notation

$$\boldsymbol{x} = \rho \boldsymbol{D} \boldsymbol{x} + \boldsymbol{u}\,. \tag{7.68}$$

See also appendix 1.

In these equations the weights matrix $\boldsymbol{D}$ specifies the extent to which each county is related to every other one in the county system. ρ measures the overall degree of spatial autocorrelation, $\boldsymbol{D}$ being given, between the values of the variate X in the related counties of the system. Finally, $\boldsymbol{u}$ is a vector of independent identically distributed disturbance terms. For the Monte Carlo studies described below, each u_i was taken to be normally distributed with zero mean and variance σ^2 [that is u_i is $N(0, \sigma^2)$].

7.6.1 The simulation experiment(7)

The simulation experiment had the following steps.

(7) The authors wish to thank Mr. E. Sheppard, an undergraduate in the Department of Geography at Bristol, for computing many of the results in this section.

Step 1: choose a lattice and specify $\boldsymbol{D}^*$ for that lattice, where the $\{d_{ij}\}$ are obtained from $\{d^*_{ij}\}$ by the scaling

$$d_{ij} = \frac{d^*_{ij}}{\sum_j d^*_{ij}},$$

so that, in all cases

$$\sum_j d_{ij} = 1. \tag{7.69}$$

We examined the following lattices.

Lattice	Value of A/n	$\boldsymbol{D}^*$
4 x 3	1·42	rook's case
25 cell circle	1·00	$d^*_{ij} = 1$, if counties i and j had a common boundary, and $d^*_{ij} = 0$ otherwise
5 x 5	1·6	rook's case
5 x 5	2·88	queen's case
5 x 5	4·0	queen's case mapped onto a torus
Eire (excluding County Dublin)	2·2	$d^*_{ij} = 1$, if counties i and j had a common boundary, and $d^*_{ij} = 0$ otherwise
7 x 7	1·71	rook's case

Thus, in all cases, we have assumed that the value of X in county i is affected only by contiguous counties.

For each lattice:

Step 2: specify a value for ρ. We took $\rho = 0{\cdot}0\ (0{\cdot}1)\ 0{\cdot}9$;

Step 3: from equation (7.68) it is evident that

$$\boldsymbol{x} = (\boldsymbol{I} - \rho\boldsymbol{D})^{-1}\boldsymbol{u}. \tag{7.70}$$

Compute $(\boldsymbol{I} - \rho\boldsymbol{D})^{-1}$;

Step 4: generate the vector $\boldsymbol{u}$ by random sampling from an N(0, 1) population, and then compute $\boldsymbol{x}$ from equation (7.70);

Step 5: calculate I and c;

Step 6: code the counties with the n_1 largest x values in the n county system 1 ($\equiv B$) and the remainder 0 ($\equiv W$). For $n = 12, 25, 49$, we took $n_1 = 6, 12, 24$ respectively.

Step 7: calculate BB and BW. (The results obtained are, because of step 6, for nonfree sampling.)

Step 8: repeat steps 4 to 7 t times for each value of ρ. We took $t = 200$. Note that when $\rho = 0$. the sample relates to the test statistic (given H_0).

Step 9: having obtained t (= 200) values of the I, c, BB, and BW statistics for $\rho = 0{\cdot}0\ (0{\cdot}1)\ 0{\cdot}9$ in each lattice, we took the results for $\rho = 0{\cdot}0$

and determined the $\alpha = 0 \cdot 05$ cutoff point for a one-tailed test of positive spatial autocorrelation in each set. In the case of I and c, this cutoff point was given by the tenth largest (I) or smallest (c) generated value. For BB and BW, determination of the $\alpha = 0 \cdot 05$ cutoff point was made more complicated by the lumpy nature of the probability distributions (see chapter 2). So in the 5×5 rook's case, for example, we observed the following frequencies of joins:

BB	11	12	13
frequency	12	4	2

The decision rule was
reject H_0 with probability 1 if $BB \geqslant 12$,
with probability $\frac{4}{15}$ if $BB = 11$,
with probability 0 if $BB \leqslant 10$.
This randomised decision rule gives $\alpha = 0 \cdot 05$ for the size of the test, based on the distribution function for BB under H_0 estimated from the 200 generated values of BB.

The procedure is used so that a value of $\alpha = 0 \cdot 05$ can be achieved, and is not recommended as a practical testing method;

Step 10: recall that, for I and BB, positive spatial autocorrelation corresponds to the positive tails of the probability distributions for these statistics, while for c and BW, positive spatial autocorrelation corresponds to the negative tails. For each value of ρ [$= 0 \cdot 1\ (0 \cdot 1)\ 0 \cdot 9$] and for each lattice, count the number of generated values of each statistic which are more extreme than, or equal to, the $0 \cdot 05$ cutoff value. The frequencies obtained, when expressed as a fraction of 200, represent the estimated power of the test statistic for that value of ρ.

The same random number streams were used for each lattice (2 separate runs of length 100) so that the power curves are directly comparable for
(a) different statistics (same lattice, same ρ);
(b) different statistics, different values of ρ (same lattice);
(c) different statistics, different value of ρ, different lattices of the same size.

7.6.2 Interpretation of results

1 In table 7.2, we give the results obtained for I and c with each value of ρ for the two separate runs of length 100 in the 4×3 rook's case lattice. Steps 9 and 10 of section 7.6.1 were carried out for each set of 100, and for the combined set of 200, to obtain some idea of the different results one gets because of sampling variation in the Monte Carlo procedure. For the sets of 100, the $\alpha = 0 \cdot 05$ cutoff points for I and c were computed separately, using the fifth most extreme value when $\rho = 0$. The sampling variation is quite considerable for this lattice, but it was much less for the larger lattices and when the cutoff point was found from all 200 values.

In retrospect we should have taken a larger value of t at $\rho = 0$ (600 say) to determine the cutoff point more accurately. However, we have no reason to believe that the sampling variations have materially affected our conclusions. As the lattice size increases, the power curves are smoother and more stable.

2 Figure 7.3 gives the power curves for the I, c, BB, and BW statistics in the various $n = 25$ lattices. It shows the effect of shape, as measured by A/n, upon the power curves. (For nonbinary weights the ratio n/S_1 may be interpreted in the same way; $n/S_1 = 1$ for the circle lattice, but 4 for the queen's torus. If the weights are not scaled so that $W = n$, the ratio W^2/nS_1 should be used.) Figure 7.4 gives the power curves for the various test lattices with the lattice structure fixed (square lattice, rook's case), but n is allowed to vary.

From figure 7.3 it is evident that the power of each of the statistics decreases as A/n increases. For a given test statistic and value of ρ, power is highest in the 25 cell circle (equivalent to a circular time series) and decreases monotonically, as A/n increases, to the queen's case on a torus. It can be shown that, in a totally connected lattice with $d_{ij}^* = 1$ for all $i \neq j$, the power of all the spatial autocorrelation test statistics is equal to α (= 0·05 in this case) for all ρ. In other words power is inversely related to the degree of connectedness of the lattice.

There is clearly a conflict between a choice of d_{ij}^* which (a) maximises power and (b) increases the 'coverage' of possible patterns of spatial autocorrelation. For example, on count (a) the rook's case might be preferred, but on count (b) the queen's case. *The researcher must think carefully about the choice of weights.*

Table 7.2. Power curves[a] for I and c in the 4 x 3 rook's case, $\alpha = 0{\cdot}05$ (one-tailed test).

ρ	1st hundred		2nd hundred		All two hundred	
	I	c	I	c	I	c
0·0	5	5	5	5	5	5
0·1	7	6	3	5	4	7
0·2	9	8	11	11	9·5	9
0·3	12	6	8	12	10·5	12·5
0·4	16	11	15	17	15·5	16·5
0·5	24	16	16	22	21·5	24·0
0·6	29	24	32	34	31	32·5
0·7	36	24	32	45	36	37·5
0·8	57	48	51	56	55·5	57·5
0·9	56	52	58	65	57·5	62

[a] Power is expressed in percentage terms.

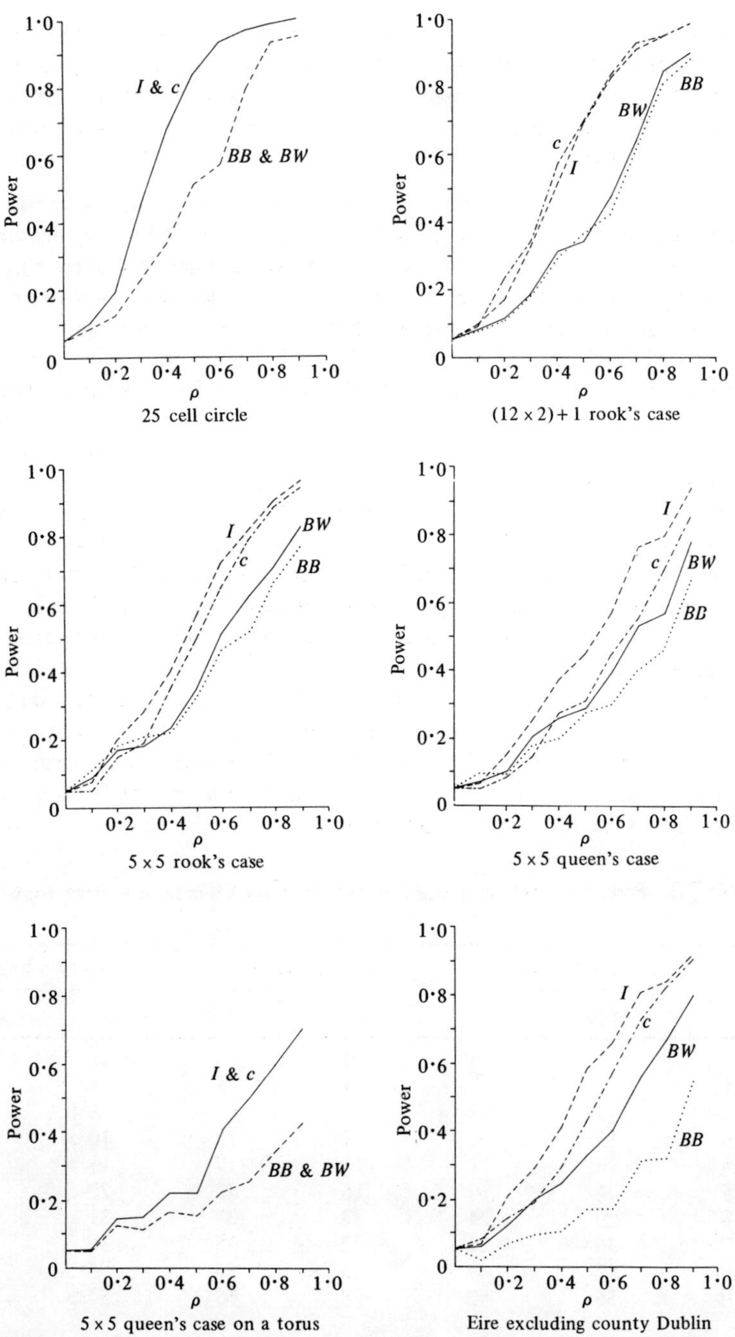

Figure 7.3. Power curves for BB, BW, I, and c for various $n = 25$ lattices.

3 From figure 7.4 we note, as would be expected, that power increases as n increases.

4 Using figures 7.3 and 7.4 together, we find that I and c, and BW and BB, have identical power curves when L_i is the same for each county. See, for example, the 25 cell circle and the 5 × 5 queen's case mapped onto a torus. This confirms the ARE results given in equations (7.33) and (7.47), and the discussion following those equations. In the case of the (12 × 2)+ 1 rook's case, where 22 of the 25 counties each have links to three other counties, I and c, and BB and BW differ only slightly. When we split the t (= 200) values into the two separate hundreds for this lattice, we found that I was more powerful than c for one set, and c more powerful than I for the other. Similar results were obtained for BB and BW.

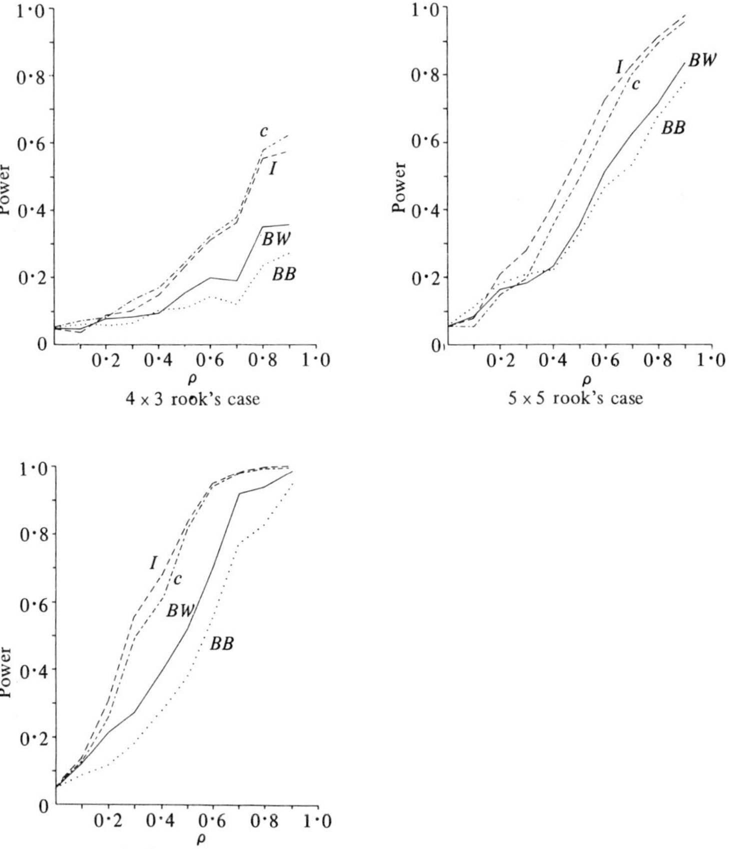

Figure 7.4. Power curves for BB, BW, I, and c for three lattices with fixed W but varying n.

When most counties do not have the same L_i value, we generally find, in confirmation of results (7.33), (7.47), and (7.48), that

$$\text{power } (I) > \text{power } (c) > \text{power } (BW) > \text{power } (BB). \tag{7.71}$$

The use of the same random number stream precludes our testing the differences between the power curves because of the dependence between the results, but comparison of the separate hundreds for each statistic and between statistics allows us to assess the sampling variation in the results. We feel that statement (7.71) is, in general, supported by the results, given differences between the L_i.

5 From figures 7.3 and 7.4 it is evident that, when ρ is small, there is little to choose between the various coefficients, and the relationship (7.71) is sometimes not satisfied by the sample results.

6 In figure 7.5 we have constructed the power curves of I in the 5 x 5 rook's case for various values of α and β, the probabilities of type I and type II errors. The method described in steps 9 and 10 of section 7.6.1 was used. It is evident that the risk of a type II error is high when ρ is low, whatever the value of α. The graph demonstrates well the severe risk of a type II error when extreme values of α are used, and argues for the use of less stringent significance levels in inferential work. Finally, if we look at the position of the 'break-even' line, $\alpha = \beta$, it is clear that a considerable amount of spatial autocorrelation must be present in the county system before we can hope to detect it without undue risk of either a type I or a type II error. For lattices with the same value of n,

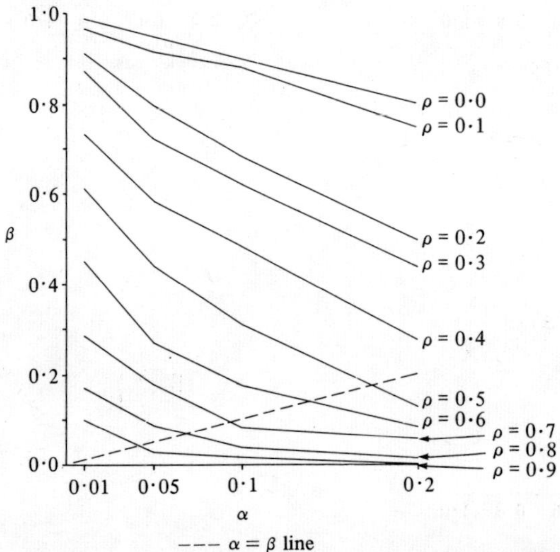

Figure 7.5. Comparison of probabilities of Type I and Type II errors for I in 5 x 5 rook's case lattice.

but higher A/n (or W^2/nS_1) values, diagrams like figure 7.5 give an even bleaker impression. Fortunately, in empirical work, when spatial autocorrelation is present, it is usually marked (that is, ρ is high).

7.7 Conclusions

In this section we attempt to draw together the conclusions which arise from the three approaches used in this chapter to examine the various tests of spatial autocorrelation. These conclusions are as follows:

(1) Given interval scaled data, use I in preference to c or the join count statistics. This conclusion has been validated only for normal data, but the shape of the lattice seems to be more important than the type of data (sections 7.3.3, 7.5, and 7.6.2).

(2) For rank data, use the rank version of I (section 7.3.5).

(3) For regression residuals, use the original weights together with the LS residuals, or the BLUS procedure corresponding to it (section 7.3.6).

(4) Given binary data, use BW in preference to BB or any combination of BW and BB, particularly if the free sampling model is assumed (sections 7.3.4, 7.4, 7.5, and 7.6.2). Code the counties so that p (county coloured B) is as near as possible to one half in both free and nonfree sampling.

(5) The weights used in the test statistic should correspond to the weights postulated in the alternative hypothesis (sections 7.3.1, 7.3.3).

(6) The choice of weights will depend upon the tradeoff between power and 'coverage' of possible patterns of spatial autocorrelation (section 7.6.2).

(7) Small values for α can lead to high probabilities of type II error (section 7.6.2).

Analysis using partial correlations

8.1 Introduction

In chapters 5 and 6 of this monograph we have analysed relationships between variables by regression methods, but we may also use correlation analysis. In section 2 of this chapter we review and extend the concepts of partial correlation, and then go on to apply these methods in section 3 to some data of O'Sullivan (1969), already considered in sections 6.2 and 6.6.

8.2 Partial correlations and autocorrelations

We define the sample correlation for observations x_{1i}, x_{2i} $(i = 1, 2, ..., n)$ on the random variables X_1 and X_2 as

$$r_{12} = \text{corr}(x_1, x_2) = \frac{\sum x_{1i}x_{2i} - n\bar{x}_1\bar{x}_2}{(\sum x_{1i}^2 - n\bar{x}_1^2)^{1/2}(\sum x_{2i}^2 - n\bar{x}_2^2)^{1/2}} \quad . \tag{8.1}$$

Its population analogue is

$$\rho_{12} = \frac{\mathrm{E}(X_1X_2) - \mathrm{E}(X_1)\mathrm{E}(X_2)}{[\mathrm{E}(X_1^2) - \mathrm{E}^2(X_1)]^{1/2}[\mathrm{E}(X_2^2) - \mathrm{E}^2(X_2)]^{1/2}} \,, \tag{8.2}$$

where E is the expectation operator. In the remainder of this section we define the sample statistics, but the population parameters can always be found on replacing r_{ij} by ρ_{ij}.

The sample partial correlation between X_1 and X_2, after allowing for the effect of X_3, is denoted by $r_{12.3}$, and is defined as

$$r_{12.3} = \frac{r_{12} - r_{13}r_{23}}{(1 - r_{13}^2)^{1/2}(1 - r_{23}^2)^{1/2}} \quad . \tag{8.3}$$

Higher order partial correlations are defined in terms of (partial) correlations of the next lowest order. Thus $r_{12.34}$ is defined as

$$r_{12.34} = \frac{r_{12.4} - r_{13.4}r_{23.4}}{(1 - r_{13.4}^2)^{1/2}(1 - r_{23.4}^2)^{1/2}} \,, \tag{8.4}$$

or by a similar form with the subscripts 3 and 4 interchanged throughout on the right hand side. Note that equation (8.4) is of the same structure as (8.3), except that the r_{ij} have been replaced throughout by $r_{ij.4}$.

The sample coefficient of multiple correlation for X_1 on X_2, X_3, and X_4, is $R_{1.234}^2$. It is defined in terms of the partial correlations by

$$1 - R_{1.234}^2 = (1 - r_{12}^2)(1 - r_{13.2}^2)(1 - r_{14.23}) \,, \tag{8.5}$$

or any alternative permutation of the subscripts 2, 3, and 4. These results are standard and so no derivations are given. For a fuller discussion, consult Kendall and Stuart (1967, chapter 27).

To incorporate autocorrelations into this framework, we must cast the autocorrelation statistics into the mould of equations (8.1) and (8.2). This can be done without difficulty but, of course, the distributions of such statistics are quite different from those of ordinary correlation statistics. Recall from equation (5.65) that the spatially lagged value for county i is Lx_i, defined as

$$Lx_i = \sum_j w_{ij} x_j, \qquad \sum_j w_{ij} = 1. \tag{8.6}$$

The sample correlation between X and LX is obtained from equation (8.1) by writing $X_1 = X$ and $X_2 = LX$. This yields

$$r(1) = \mathrm{corr}(x, Lx) = \frac{\sum x_i(Lx_i) - n\bar{x}(\overline{Lx})}{(\sum x_i^2 - n\bar{x}^2)^{1/2}[\sum (Lx_i)^2 - n(\overline{Lx})^2]^{1/2}}, \tag{8.7}$$

where

$$(\overline{Lx}) = \frac{1}{n}\sum_{i=1}^{n} Lx_i.^{(8)}$$

If we define $z_i = x_i - \bar{x}$, the sample spatial autocorrelation for X is

$$I \equiv I(1) = \frac{\sum w_{ij} z_i z_j}{\sum z_i^2} = \frac{\sum z_i(Lz_i)}{\sum z_i^2}, \tag{8.8}$$

and equation (8.7) can be written in terms of z_i as

$$r(1) = \frac{\sum w_{ij} z_i z_j}{(\sum z_i^2)^{1/2}[\sum (Lz_i)^2 - n(\overline{Lz})^2]^{1/2}} \tag{8.9}$$

where $Lz_i = L(x_i - \bar{x}) = Lx_i - \bar{x}$, and $(\overline{Lz}) = (\overline{Lx}) - \bar{x}$. Note that $(\overline{Lz}) \neq 0$ unless $\sum_i w_{ij} = 1$ for all $i = 1, 2, \ldots, n$. We now define $I^*(1)$, by interchanging z_i and Lz_i in equation (8.8), as

$$I^*(1) = \frac{\sum (Lz_i) z_i}{\sum (Lz_i)^2 - n(\overline{Lz})^2}, \tag{8.10}$$

so that

$$r(1) = [I(1) I^*(1)]^{1/2}. \tag{8.11}$$

We should note that $I^*(1)$ is equivalent to $\tilde{\rho}$ used in sections 5.8 and 6.6. While no formal limits exist for $I(1)$ and $I^*(1)$, $r(1)$ must lie in the range $[-1,1]$, like any other correlation coefficient. Partial correlations may be calculated using terms like $r(1)$ in equations (8.3) and (8.4).

(8) A correct derivation of partial autocorrelations would proceed using the methods of section 6.6 when Lx_i is lagged only in space, the methods of this section are incorrect for the same reasons that the least squares estimators are invalid in section 6.6. However, the present approach is much simpler computationally, while it still provides useful insights in a preliminary analysis of the data. Also, the methods *are* formally correct whenever Lx_i is lagged in time as well as in space.

Finally, we wish to consider higher order autocorrelations and higher order partial autocorrelations. A kth order autocorrelation may be defined as

$$I(k) = \frac{\sum z_i (\mathrm{L}^k z_i)}{\sum z_i^2} , \tag{8.12}$$

where $\mathrm{L}^k z_i$ denotes the kth lagged value of z_i. Then, defining $I^*(k)$ by analogy with equation (8.10), we have the kth order spatial autocorrelation coefficient

$$r(k) = [I(k) I^*(k)] . \tag{8.13}$$

For time series data the kth lagged value is simply $\mathrm{L}^k z_i = z_{i-k}$, but the definition of spatial lags is more involved. At first sight it may seem plausible to use $\mathrm{L}^2 \boldsymbol{z} = \boldsymbol{W}^2 \boldsymbol{z}$, since $\mathrm{L}\boldsymbol{z} = \boldsymbol{W}\boldsymbol{z}$. Unfortunately, this definition includes circular routes $i \rightarrow j \rightarrow i$ in the county system, which are not genuine second order effects. To remove these effects, we must use

$$\begin{aligned} \mathrm{L}^2 \boldsymbol{z} &= (\boldsymbol{W}^2 - \boldsymbol{\Delta}_2) \boldsymbol{S}_2 \boldsymbol{z} \\ &= \boldsymbol{C}_2 \boldsymbol{z}, \qquad \text{say.} \end{aligned} \tag{8.14}$$

In equation (8.14), $\boldsymbol{\Delta}_2$ is the diagonal matrix with elements δ_{2i} corresponding to the leading diagonal of $\boldsymbol{W}^2$. $\boldsymbol{S}_2$ is a diagonal scaling matrix which ensures that each row of $\boldsymbol{C}_2$ sums to one, if the row has at least one nonzero off-diagonal element. If there are no such elements, the entry on the diagonal of $\boldsymbol{S}_2$ should be unity. If all the rows of $\boldsymbol{W}^2$ have nonzero off-diagonal elements, $\boldsymbol{S}_2 = (\boldsymbol{I} - \boldsymbol{\Delta}_2)^{-1}$; that is the ith element on the leading diagonal of $\boldsymbol{S}_2$ is $(1-\delta_{2i})^{-1}$. In table 8.1 we give y_i, $\mathrm{L}y_i$, $\mathrm{L}^2 y_i$, and δ_i for the variable Y set equal to the percentage of own agricultural produce consumed by a county of Eire, where $\mathrm{L}^2 y_i$ is computed from formula (8.14). In these calculations $\boldsymbol{W}$ is of form '3' in section 6.2 (that is, the set of standardised weights given in appendix 2). Y is the dependent variable in regression (2) of section 6.2. These results show clearly the smoothing effect of computing the lags, and the consequent reduction in variance of the lagged values. The definition of higher order lags is more involved, and the reader is referred to Haggett and Chorley (1969, pp.38–47), and Ross and Harary (1952) for a discussion on the powering of connection (binary weighting) matrices, and the elimination of redundancies. Here, we record that, for the third order lags, $\mathrm{L}^3 \boldsymbol{z} = \boldsymbol{C}_3 \boldsymbol{z}$, where

$$\boldsymbol{C}_3 = (\boldsymbol{W}^3 - \boldsymbol{\Delta}_2 \boldsymbol{W} - \boldsymbol{W} \boldsymbol{\Delta}_2 - \boldsymbol{\Delta}_3 + \boldsymbol{G}_3) \boldsymbol{S}_3 . \tag{8.15}$$

In equation (8.15) $\boldsymbol{\Delta}_3$ and $\boldsymbol{S}_3$ are defined by analogy with $\boldsymbol{\Delta}_2$ and $\boldsymbol{S}_2$, while $\boldsymbol{G}_3$ is a matrix with elements $g_{ij} = w_{ij} w_{ji} w_{ij}$; that is, $\boldsymbol{G}_3 = \boldsymbol{W} \boxtimes \boldsymbol{W}' \boxtimes \boldsymbol{W}$, where the operation $\boxtimes$ represents the multiplication of matrices element by element.

Example
Consider

$$W = \begin{pmatrix} 0 & 1 & 0 \\ \frac{1}{2} & 0 & \frac{1}{2} \\ 0 & 1 & 0 \end{pmatrix}$$

Then the first order lag yields

$$\mathrm{L}z = Wz = \begin{pmatrix} z_2 \\ \frac{1}{2}(z_1 + z_3) \\ z_2 \end{pmatrix}$$

Table 8.1. Lagged values of own produce consumption patterns in Eire.

County code letter	Percentage of own agricultural produce consumed			Adjustment factors
	original data Y	lagged once $\mathrm{L}Y$	lagged twice L^2Y	δ_{2i}
A	8·6	8·99	9·46	0·2946
B	15·0	15·71	15·76	0·3780
C	19·0	16·56	16·39	0·2758
D	9·0	13·74	12·81	0·4805
E	27·0	23·10	19·55	0·0229
F	9·4	9·12	11·39	0·1519
G	21·9	22·45	17·86	0·3582
H	17·0	10·33	11·71	0·3908
I	9·0	10·46	10·87	0·1967
J	8·0	9·00	10·63	0·2428
K	10·3	11·17	11·03	0·2462
L	23·1	19·72	19·82	0·2516
M	11·4	12·69	12·68	0·3032
N	19·0	18·34	16·99	0·2936
O	10·1	9·96	13·41	0·2290
P	30·0	22·16	21·19	0·2977
Q	8·7	12·30	14·61	0·3641
R	13·0	13·49	14·62	0·2887
S	14·3	12·05	12·34	0·2951
T	23·0	22·12	20·67	0·2394
U	22·0	25·92	21·17	0·2665
V	9·0	11·40	12·71	0·2714
W	8·0	8·72	11·60	0·1620
X	16·0	15·55	15·08	0·3288
Y	8·6	8·87	9·02	0·1922
Z	10·2	8·88	9·18	0·2638
Variance	41·32	27·29	14·17	

However, W^2z yields

$$\begin{pmatrix} \frac{1}{2}(z_1+z_3) \\ z_2 \\ \frac{1}{2}(z_1+z_3) \end{pmatrix} .$$

If this vector was used as the second order spatial lag, then even when there is no spatial autocorrelation in the data, the population correlation $\rho(2) = (2/3)^{1/2} \approx 0{\cdot}82$. This high spurious correlation is caused by the appearance of nonzero elements on the leading diagonal of

$$W^2 = \begin{pmatrix} \frac{1}{2} & 0 & \frac{1}{2} \\ 0 & 1 & 0 \\ \frac{1}{2} & 0 & \frac{1}{2} \end{pmatrix} .$$

To avoid this we use C_2 defined in equation (8.14) above. We obtain

$$\Delta_2 = \begin{pmatrix} \frac{1}{2} & 0 & 0 \\ 0 & 1 & 0 \\ 0 & 0 & \frac{1}{2} \end{pmatrix}$$

and then use

$$S_2 = \begin{pmatrix} 2 & 0 & 0 \\ 0 & 1 & 0 \\ 0 & 0 & 2 \end{pmatrix}$$

to yield

$$C_2 = \begin{pmatrix} 0 & 0 & 1 \\ 0 & 0 & 0 \\ 1 & 0 & 0 \end{pmatrix} .$$

For the third lag,

$$W^3 = \begin{pmatrix} 0 & 1 & 0 \\ \frac{1}{2} & 0 & \frac{1}{2} \\ 0 & 1 & 0 \end{pmatrix} , \ \Delta_3 = \mathbf{0}, \text{ and } G = \begin{pmatrix} 0 & \frac{1}{2} & 0 \\ \frac{1}{4} & 0 & \frac{1}{4} \\ 0 & \frac{1}{2} & 0 \end{pmatrix} ,$$

leading to $C_3 = \mathbf{0}$. This is as we should expect, since the first order effects, $z_1 - z_2$, $z_2 - z_3$, and the second order effect, $z_1 - z_2 - z_3$, exhaust the set of possible autocorrelation patterns for this lattice.

Returning to definition (8.13), we can use $r(k)$ to define the sample partial correlation between X and L^2X, given LX, as

$$r(2.1) = \frac{r(2)-r(1)\tilde{r}(1)}{[1-r^2(1)]^{1/2}[1-\tilde{r}^2(1)]^{1/2}}, \tag{8.16}$$

where

$$\tilde{r}(1) = \text{corr}(Lx_i, L^2x_i).$$

In time series, the simple nature of the temporal lag ensures that $\tilde{r}(1) \approx r(1)$. In fact,

$$\frac{\tilde{r}(1)}{r(1)} = \sum_{t=3}^{n} z_t^2 \Big/ \sum_{t=1}^{n-2} z_t^2 \tag{8.17}$$

which approaches one as n increases. However, no such guarantee is available for the more general spatial lag, and $\text{var}(L^k x_i)$ falls with increasing j. Extension of equation (8.16) to higher orders is straightforward, even if notationally trying.

Coefficients (8.13) may be used for a spatial correlogram analysis, as is done in time series statistics, while equation (8.16) and its extensions allow the investigator to explore whether a first order scheme is adequate, or whether higher orders are needed. Because of the need to specify the weighting matrix, it is arguable that the existence of second order partial autocorrelation is as much as indication of the wrong choice of weights as of the need for a higher order autocorrelative scheme.

It is clear from equation (8.5) that if the regression of X_1 on X_2 and X_3 were computed, a selection of potential X_4 variables could be scanned to see which gave the greatest increase in R^2 (that is, the one with the largest $r_{14.23}^2$). This is the basis of stepwise regression procedures (cf. Draper and Smith, 1966, chapter 6; 1969). Element analysis, developed by Newton and Spurrell (1967a, 1967b), takes this further by examining the contribution of each variable singly and its joint contribution with one or more other variables. Our purpose in including this chapter is, therefore, to indicate how a researcher might deepen his understanding of a process by examining the correlation structure.

8.3 Reexamination of O'Sullivan's data

One of the purposes of the analysis in sections 6.2 and 6.6 was to develop a model which accounted for variations in the dependent variable Y, the percentage of an area's agricultural produce consumed *in situ* (the area, in this example, being the counties of Eire), in terms of various explanatory variables X_i. In table 8.2 we give the correlations between Y and X_i, and the partial correlations for Y and X_i after allowing for X_1 = ARA (arterial road accessibility index) and LY, the lagged value of Y.

The results presented in table 8.2 show the importance of the degree of subsistence farming (variables X_6 and X_7) in determining the patterns of own produce consumption. The contribution of the other accessibility indices (variables X_2–X_5) is less marked. The correlation between Y and L^2Y is very high, but $r(2.1)$, computed from equation (8.16), is equal to 0·266, showing that most of the explanatory power of the lagged values can be accounted for using the first order lag only. In fact, the best two variable relation (in terms of R^2), is Y on LY and X_1, which achieves a level of $R^2 = 0{\cdot}868$, just short of the value $R^2 = 0{\cdot}882$ for Y on LY, X_1 and LX_1 obtained in section 6.6.

The positive value of $r(2.1)$ would seem to suggest that the spatial dependence between counties falls off rather more slowly than the weights used would indicate. The use of weights that reduce more gradually with distance between county centres might give a better description of the autocorrelation pattern. This raises the important general question as to whether we can estimate the whole matrix of weights, not just the parameter ρ. However, this topic is beyond the scope of the present study.

In conclusion, while the researcher may often prefer a stepwise regression analysis to an examination of the entrails via partial (auto) correlations, we feel that the latter exercise can often give deeper insight into the structure of both model and data.

Table 8.2. Correlation analysis for own produce consumption patterns in Eire.

Variable name[a]	Letter	Correlation with Y	Partial correlation with Y		R^2-with other variable and	
			given X_1	given LY	X_1	LY
Y lagged once	LY	0·902	0·744	–	0·868	–
Y lagged twice	L^2Y	0·895	0·741	0·266	0·864	0·827
ARA	X_1	0·835	–	0·538	–	0·868
Rail accessibility, (i)	X_2	0·292	−0·452	0·143	0·759	0·818
Through-freight service, (ii)	X_3	−0·599	−0·279	−0·148	0·720	0·818
Rail cost-accessibility, (iii)	X_4	0·312	−0·382	0·215	0·741	0·823
Port accessibility, (iv)	X_5	0·289	0·476	0·288	0·765	0·829
Large agricultural holdings, (v)	X_6	−0·725	−0·545	−0·251	0·787	0·826
Family agricultural labour, (vi)	X_7	0·757	0·574	0·310	0·796	0·832

[a] For full definitions of the variables and numbers, see section 6.2.

Models for spatial autocorrelation

To examine possible models for spatial autocorrelation, we start with an autocorrelation-free, or white noise, process. Let $X(t,s)$ denote a zero-mean white noise process on a Cartesian scale at the point (t,s); that is,

$$\mathrm{E}[X(t,s)] = 0, \qquad \text{for all } t,s, \tag{A.1}$$

and

$$\begin{aligned}\mathrm{E}[X(t,s)X(t',s')] &= 0, \qquad \text{for all } t \neq t',\ s \neq s' \\ &= \sigma_X^2, \qquad \text{when } t = t' \text{ and } s = s'.\end{aligned} \tag{A.2}$$

The process is passed through a filter to yield the spatially autocorrelated function $Y(t,s)$ as

$$Y(t,s) = \iint_{R_2} g(x,y)X(t+x,\ s+y)\,\mathrm{d}x\,\mathrm{d}y\,. \tag{A.3}$$

Here, R_2 denotes the two dimensional space of all possible values of x and y; $g(x,y)$ is the filter function denoting the weight placed on the white noise process at a distance $(x^2+y^2)^{1/2}$ from the origin (t,s). Taking expectations in function (A.3), we see from expressions (A.1) and (A.2) that

$$\mathrm{E}[Y(t,s)] = 0, \qquad \text{for all } t,s\,, \tag{A.4}$$

and

$$\mathrm{E}[Y(t,s)Y(t',s')] = \sigma_X^2 \iint_{R_2} g(x,y)g(x+T,\ y+S)\,\mathrm{d}x\,\mathrm{d}y\,, \tag{A.5}$$

where $T = t-t'$ and $S = s-s'$. Thus, when $T = S = 0$, we have

$$\mathrm{var}[Y(t,s)] = \sigma_X^2 \iint_{R_2} g^2(x,y)\,\mathrm{d}x\,\mathrm{d}y\,. \tag{A.6}$$

The filter used is spatially stationary since it depends only on the *relative* location of points in the plane.

To make progress analytically we assume directional, or circular, symmetry, so that the filter is a function of distance only; that is,

$$g(x,y) = \mathrm{h}[(x^2+y^2)^{1/2}] = \mathrm{h}(r)\,, \tag{A.7}$$

where $r^2 = x^2+y^2$. Immediately below we give the form of the correlation function for three sorts of filter; in addition to the notation already used, we define $d^2 = T^2+S^2$.

$h(r)$	$\text{corr}[Y(t,s),\ Y(t+T,\ s+S)]$
$\exp(-\alpha r^2)$	$\exp(-\alpha d^2)$
$\exp(-\alpha r)$	$\exp(-\alpha d)$
$(2\pi\alpha)^{-1},\quad r \leqslant \alpha$	$2/\pi[\cos^{-1}u - u(1-u^2)^{1/2}],\quad 0 \leqslant u \leqslant 1,$
$0,\quad r > \alpha$	$0,\quad u > 1,$ where $u = d/2\alpha$.

For a sample of n data recording *points*, such as well-borings or meteorological stations, the spatial autocorrelation between points may be specified by a function such as the above. Thus, for example, we might hypothesise an n-variate normal distribution with a spatial autocorrelation structure given by one of these forms and dependent on the single parameter α. However, with data collected for, or aggregated over, an *area* (most census data, for example), a further stage must be inserted. If unit j is defined for $(t,s) \in A_j$, we create the new variable Z_j given by

$$Z_j = \iint_{A_j} X(t,s)\,\mathrm{d}t\,\mathrm{d}s\,, \tag{A.8}$$

where $A_j \cap A_k = \phi$, $j \neq k$, and $\bigcup_{j=1}^{n} A_j = R_2$. Clearly $\mathrm{E}(Z_j) = 0$. If the weighting function $g(x,y)$ is then used as before, we obtain

$$\mathrm{E}(Z_j Z_k) = \sigma_X^2 \iint_{R_2}\iint_{A_j}\iint_{A_k} g(x,y)g(x+T,\ y+S)\,\mathrm{d}x\,\mathrm{d}y\,\mathrm{d}t\,\mathrm{d}s\,\mathrm{d}t'\mathrm{d}s'\,. \tag{A.9}$$

Even for simple circular symmetric weighting functions this approach is virtually intractable for predefined A_j. As a consequence a simpler approach has been adopted in the main text of this monograph. The variables Z_j are defined as in (A.8), but these variables are then passed through a linear filter which relates to the aggregate variables and not to the point process. That is, we define the spatially autocorrelated process as

$$Y_j^* = \sum_{k=1}^{n} g_{jk} Z_k\,. \tag{A.10}$$

or in matrix notation

$$\boldsymbol{Y}^* = \boldsymbol{G}\boldsymbol{Z}\,, \tag{A.11}$$

where $\boldsymbol{Y}^*$ and $\boldsymbol{Z}$ are $(n \times 1)$ vectors and $\boldsymbol{G}$ is a square matrix of order n. In particular we use the form

$$\boldsymbol{G} = (\boldsymbol{I}_n - \rho\boldsymbol{W})^{-1} \tag{A.12}$$

in sections (5.2.3), (7.3), and (7.6), where ρ is the single unknown parameter. This is a first order spatial Markov process.

APPENDIX 2

Table A1. Unstandardised weighting matrix for the 26 counties of Eire.

County	Contiguous counties and weights						
A	I, 0·0039	J, 0·0142	K,0·0031	Y,0·0112	Z,0·0119		
B	L,0·0099	N,0·0061	Q,0·0089	R,0·0113	X,0·0006		
C	G,0·0134	H,0·0018	M,0·0103	V,0·0028			
D	H,0·0125	M,0·0084	V,0·0008	W,0·0030			
E	L,0·0186						
F	I, 0·0101	Q,0·0246	Z,0·0105				
G	C,0·0087	P,0·0068	S,0·0010	T,0·0079	V,0·0013		
H	C,0·0021	D,0·0175	M,0·0046				
I	A,0·0028	F,0·0038	K,0·0062	Q,0·0059	S,0·0059	Z,0·0090	
J	A,0·0111	K,0·0088	V,0·0086	W,0·0051	Y,0·0044		
K	A,0·0025	I, 0·0074	J, 0·0090	S,0·0185	V,0·0033		
L	B,0·0106	E,0·0008	N,0·0055	T,0·0079	U,0·0098		
M	C,0·0080	D,0·0077	H,0·0030	V,0·0095			
N	B,0·0079	L,0·0067	T,0·0105	X,0·0202			
O	Q,0·0324	R,0·0134					
P	G,0·0094	T,0·0049	U,0·0100				
Q	B,0·0066	F,0·0051	I, 0·0046	O,0·0071	R,0·0005	S,0·0005	X,0·0071
R	B,0·0319	O,0·0109	Q,0·0023				
S	G,0·0012	I, 0·0044	K,0·0134	Q,0·0006	R,0·0010	V,0·0062	X,0·0088
T	G,0·0088	L,0·0049	N,0·0054	P,0·0039	S,0·0009	U,0·0054	X,0·0015
U	L,0·0100	P,0·0133	T,0·0089				
V	C,0·0016	O,0·0006	G,0·0012	J, 0·0047	K,0·0018	M,0·0071	S,0·0046
	W,0·0055						
W	D,0·0051	J, 0·0071	V,0·0140	Y,0·0023			
X	B,0·0006	N,0·0179	Q,0·0092	S,0·0120	T,0·0022		
Y	A,0·0165	J, 0·0083	W,0·0032	Z,0·0108			
Z	A,0·0116	F,0·0076	I, 0·0119	Y,0·0072			

In some examples we excluded county F (Dublin) from the analysis. If this is done the weights of counties contiguous to Dublin are changed, and the revised weights for these counties are as follows.

I	A,0·0034	K,0·0081	Q,0·0063	S,0·0068	Z,0·0110	
Q	B,0·0083	I, 0·0052	O,0·0087	R,0·0008	S,0·0008	X,0·0086
Z	A,0·0139	I, 0·0146	Y,0·0086			

Table A2. Standardised weighting matrix for the 26 counties of Eire.

County	Contiguous counties and weights						
A	I, 0·0874	J, 0·3207	K,0·0699	Y,0·2540	Z,0·2680		
B	L,0·2690	N,0·1658	Q,0·2426	R,0·3073	X,0·0153		
C	G,0·4808	H,0·0617	M,0·3590	V,0·0985			
D	H,0·5056	M,0·3411	V,0·0327	W,0·1206			
E	L,1·0000						
F	I, 0·2226	Q,0·5442	Z,0·2332				
G	C,0·3392	P,0·2639	S,0·0394	T,0·3076	V,0·0499		
H	C,0·0866	D,0·7218	M,0·1916				
I	A,0·0820	F,0·1123	K,0·1839	Q,0·1760	S,0·1761	Z,0·2697	
J	A,0·2919	K,0·2312	V,0·2259	W,0·1345	Y,0·1166		
K	A,0·0610	I, 0·1808	J, 0·2217	S,0·4558	V,0·0807		
L	B,0·3057	E,0·0229	N,0·1604	T,0·2277	U,0·2833		
M	C,0·2827	D,0·2732	H,0·1075	V,0·3365			
N	B,0·1628	L,0·1387	T,0·2169	X,0·4816			
O	Q,0·7080	R,0·2920					
P	G,0·3881	T,0·2000	U,0·4119				
Q	B,0·2109	F,0·1604	I, 0·1465	O,0·2239	R,0·0167	S,0·0161	X,0·2254
R	B,0·7075	O,0·2416	Q,0·0508				
S	G,0·0348	I, 0·1245	K,0·3742	Q,0·0177	T,0·0289	V,0·1748	X,0·2451
T	G,0·2871	L,0·1586	N,0·1748	P,0·1269	S,0·0306	U,0·1749	X,0·0471
U	L,0·3114	P,0·4126	T,0·2760				
V	C,0·0602	D,0·0203	G,0·0432	J, 0·1743	K,0·0649	M,0·2611	S,0·1713
	W,0·2045						
W	D,0·1797	J, 0·2488	V,0·4901	Y,0·0814			
X	B,0·0134	N,0·4288	Q,0·2196	S,0·2861	T,0·0521		
Y	A,0·4254	J, 0·2146	W,0·0810	Z,0·2791			
Z	A,0·3036	F.0·1985	I, 0·3099	Y,0·1880			

In some examples we excluded county F (Dublin) from the analysis. If this is done the weights of counties contiguous to Dublin are changed, and the revised weights for these counties are as follows.

I	A,0·0959	K,0·2274	Q,0·1766	S,0·1907	Z,0·3095	
Q	B,0·2560	I, 0·1624	O,0·2685	R,0·0233	S,0·0249	X,0·2649
Z	A,0·3740	I, 0·3935	Y,0·2325			

Calculation of maximum likelihood estimator for the autoregressive model
In section 5.7 we stated that the ML solution to the estimation of β in the model

$$y_t = \alpha + \beta \mathrm{L} y_t + \epsilon_t \tag{5.63}$$

was that value of β which minimised

$$|\boldsymbol{I}_n - \beta \boldsymbol{W}|^{-2/n} \sum [y_t - \bar{y} - \beta(\mathrm{L}y_t - \bar{y}_\mathrm{L})]^2 . \tag{5.67}$$

If the eigenvalues of $\boldsymbol{W}$ are $\lambda_1, \ldots, \lambda_n$, it is known that

$$|\lambda \boldsymbol{I}_n - \boldsymbol{W}| = \prod_{i=1}^{n} (\lambda - \lambda_i) .$$

Therefore, putting $\beta = 1/\lambda$, we have that

$$|\boldsymbol{I}_n - \beta \boldsymbol{W}| = \prod_{i=1}^{n} (1 - \beta\lambda_i) .$$

Thus equation (5.67) may be rewritten as

$$\left[\prod_{i=1}^{n} (1 - \beta\lambda_i)\right]^{-2/n} \sum [y_t - \bar{y} - \beta(\mathrm{L}y_t - \bar{y}_\mathrm{L})]^2 ,$$

or

$$\left[\prod_{i=1}^{n} (1 - \beta\lambda_i)\right]^{-2/n} [S(y, y) - 2\beta S(y, \mathrm{L}y) + \beta^2 S(\mathrm{L}y, \mathrm{L}y)] , \tag{5.67*}$$

where

$$S(x, y) = \sum_{t=1}^{n} (x_t - \bar{x})(y_t - \bar{y}) .$$

If $w_{i.} = 1$ for all i, the λ_i have modulus less than one except for one root $\lambda_{\max} = 1$ (since $\boldsymbol{W}$ could then be considered a stochastic matrix). Further, it may be shown that these roots are real and lie in the range $|\lambda_i| \leqslant 1$ (see Ord, 1973 for details).

The equation (5.67*) can be evaluated very quickly given the λ_i and a value for β. The above argument indicates that the search for a minimum should extend over the range $\beta \leqslant \lambda_{\max}^{-1}$. The inconsistent OLS estimator for β will give a starting value provided that it lies inside the range. A direct search procedure for β is recommended.

The eigenvalues of the standardised weighting matrix for the 26 counties of Eire are (in descending order, correct to 4 decimal places): 1·0000, 0·8850, 0·8589, 0·7273, 0·5703, 0·4853, 0·4547, 0·3426, 0·2460, 0·2011, 0·0559, −0·0052, −0·0644, −0·1078, −0·1808, −0·2066, −0·3021, −0·3356, −0·3868, −0·4361, −0·4888, −0·5106, −0·6121, −0·6471, −0·7439, −0·7992.

Glossary of notation

(a) Mathematical

$\propto$	is proportional to
$j \in J$	the set of j counties contiguous to county i
$n^{(j)}$	$n(n-1) \ldots (n-j+1)$
$\sum_{(2)}$	$\sum_{i=1}^{n} \sum_{\substack{j=1 \\ i \neq j}}^{n}$
$\sum_{(3)}$	$\sum_{i=1}^{n} \sum_{j=1}^{n} \sum_{\substack{k=1 \\ i \neq j \neq k}}^{n}$
$\sum_{(4)}$	$\sum_{i=1}^{n} \sum_{j=1}^{n} \sum_{k=1}^{n} \sum_{\substack{l=1 \\ i \neq j \neq k \neq l}}^{n}$
5(1)10	the set of numbers 5, 6, 7, 8, 9, 10
5(2)9	the set of numbers 5, 7, 9
$\rightarrow$	approaches, goes to
O( )	of the same order as the term in brackets
o( )	of smaller order than the term in brackets

(b) Terms used

$A = \frac{1}{2}\sum_{i=1}^{n} L_i$	the total number of joins in the county system
$A(i,N)$	the accessibility of the ith vertex in the Nth road network
ARA	arterial road accessibility, defined by equation (6.1)
ARE	asymptotic relative efficiency—see section 7.2
b_1	the sample coefficient of skewness, m_3^2/m_2^3
b_2	the sample coefficient of kurtosis, m_4/m_2^2
BB	the number of black–black joins in a county system
β	the beta distribution
$\beta_{i(j)}$	the proportion of the perimeter of county i

Bishop's case	in a regular lattice with binary weights, $\delta_{ij} = 1$ if the ith and jth cells have a common vertex, and $\delta_{ij} = 0$ otherwise
BLUS estimators	the best linear unbiased estimators of the $(n-k)$ regression residuals which have a scalar covariance matrix
BW	the number of black–white joins in a county system
c	the test statistic defined in equation (1.45)
Column-only case	in a regular lattice with binary weights, $\delta_{ij} = 1$ if the ith and jth cells have an edge in common on a column of the lattice, and $\delta_{ij} = 0$ otherwise
$\mathrm{corr}(x_1, x_2)$	the sample correlation between the observations x_{1i}, x_{2i} $(i = 1, 2, \ldots, n)$ on the random variables X_1 and X_2
$D = \frac{1}{2}\sum_{i=1}^{n} L_i(L_i - 1)$	the total number of joins of the form o——o——o in the county system
Di	the index of dispersion given by m_2/m_1
δ_{ij}	the special form of binary $\{w_{ij}\}$; that is $w_{ij} = 1$ or $w_{ij} = 0$
Density function	an expression giving the frequency of a variate value x as a function of x; or, for continuous variates, the frequency in an elemental range dx. Unless the contrary is specified, the total frequency is taken to be unity, so that the frequency function represents the proportion of variate values x
d_{ij}	the 'distance' between the ith and jth counties
Eigenvalue	for any matrix $\boldsymbol{A}$ the eigenvalues are the solution to the determinantal equation $\lvert \boldsymbol{A} - \lambda \boldsymbol{I} \rvert = 0$. Thus if $\boldsymbol{A} = \begin{bmatrix} 2 & 1 \\ 1 & 2 \end{bmatrix}$, $\lvert \boldsymbol{A} - \lambda \boldsymbol{I} \rvert = \begin{vmatrix} 2-\lambda & 1 \\ 1 & 2-\lambda \end{vmatrix} = (2-\lambda)^2 - 1$, and $(2-\lambda)^2 - 1 = 0$ has roots $\lambda = 1$ and $\lambda = 3$. The corresponding row vectors $\boldsymbol{u}$ or column vectors $\boldsymbol{v}$, for which $\boldsymbol{uA} = \lambda \boldsymbol{u}$ or

Eigenvalue (continued)	$\boldsymbol{Av} = \lambda\boldsymbol{v}$, are called the eigenvectors of $\boldsymbol{A}$. The eigenvectors are determined up to an arbitrary scaling constant. Thus for the example, when $\lambda = 3$, $\boldsymbol{v} = c_1\begin{pmatrix}1\\1\end{pmatrix}$, and when $\lambda = 1$, $\boldsymbol{v} = c_2\begin{pmatrix}1\\-1\end{pmatrix}$, c_1, and c_2 any constants. When $\boldsymbol{A}$ is symmetric, $\boldsymbol{u} = \boldsymbol{v}'$ for each value of λ
Eigenvector	see eigenvalue
E(X)	the expected, average or mean value of X, the first moment of X
F	Snedecor's F distribution
F as a subscript	refers to the free sampling assumption defined on page 5
F(h)	the asymptotic relative efficacy of a test based on h. See section 7.2
$g(X)$	some function, g, of X
$h(X)$	some function, h, of X
$\boldsymbol{I}$ or $\boldsymbol{I}_n$	the unit matrix (of order n)
I	the test statistic defined in equation (1.44)
I'	a weighted spatial autocorrelation test statistic proposed by Dacey (1965). See equation (1.40)
$I(k)$	the kth order spatial autocorrelation using the test statistic I. See chapter 8
Idempotent	a matrix $\boldsymbol{A}$ is said to be idempotent if $\boldsymbol{A}^2 = \boldsymbol{A}$
κ_j	the jth cumulant. Cumulants are constants of a frequency distribution defined in terms of the moments by the identity in t, $$\exp\left(\sum_{r=0}^{\infty}\frac{\kappa_r t^r}{r!}\right) = \sum_{r=0}^{\infty}\frac{\mu_r' t^r}{r!} .$$ They are thus given by the coefficients in the expansion of a power series formed from the logarithm of the characteristic function of a variable, if such an expansion exists

L	a spatial or temporal lag operator. See section 5.7
$L_i = \sum_{j=1}^{n} \delta_{ij}$	the number of counties joined to county i
Likelihood ratio test	a test of a hypothesis H_0 against an alternative H_1 based on the ratio of two likelihood functions, one derived from each of H_0 and H_1
Markovian scheme	a stochastic process such that the conditional probability distribution for the state at any future instant, given the present state, is unaffected by any additional knowledge of the past history of the system
$\mu'_1(X)$ or μ'_1 or μ	the expected, average or mean value of X, the first moment of X
$\mu_2(X)$ or μ_2	the variance of X, the second moment of X
$\mu_j(X)$ or μ_j	the jth moment of X about the mean
$\mu'_j(X)$ or μ'_j	the jth moment of X about the origin
m_j, m'_j	sample moments corresponding to μ_j and μ'_j respectively
Moment generating function	defined as $E(e^{tX})$ or $\sum_{j=0}^{\infty} t^j \mu'_j/j!$; exists only if all moments exist
N	the normal distribution
N as a subscript	refers to assumption N defined on page 8
n	the total number of counties in the study area
n_1	the number of black cells in a two colour lattice
n_2	the number of white cells in a two colour lattice
n_r	the number of cells of colour r in a k colour lattice
NF as a subscript	refers to the nonfree sampling assumption defined on page 5
OLS	ordinary least squares

p	probability that a cell is coloured black in a two colour lattice
$\hat{p}$	an estimate of p from the data, for example by n_1/n
p_r	probability that a cell is of colour r in a k colour lattice
Positive definite	if the matrix $\boldsymbol{A}$ is positive definite, all the eigenvalues of $\boldsymbol{A}$ will be positive
Power of a test	$1-$prob(type II error), the probability of rejecting H_0 when H_1 is true (cf. size of a test)
$P(h, \psi)$	power of a test based on the test statistic h when the parameter has the value ψ under H_1
prob$(X_i = 1)$ or $p(X_i = 1)$	probability that $X_i = 1$
$q = 1-p$	probability that a cell is coloured white in a two colour lattice
Queen's case	in a regular lattice with binary weights, $\delta_{ij} = 1$ if the ith and jth cells have a common edge or vertex, and $\delta_{ij} = 0$ otherwise
R as a subscript	refers to assumption R defined on page 8
R^2	the coefficient of multiple correlation
r_{12}	the sample correlation between the observations x_{1i}, x_{2i} $(i = 1, 2, \ldots, n)$ on the random variables X_1 and X_2
ρ_{12}	the population analogue of r_{12}
$r_{12.3}$	the sample partial correlation between the observations x_{1i}, x_{2i} $(i = 1, 2, \ldots, n)$ on the random variables X_1 and X_2, after allowing for the effect of X_3
$r(k)$	the kth order correlation
Rook's case	in a regular lattice with binary weights, $\delta_{ij} = 1$ if the ith and jth cells have a common edge, and $\delta_{ij} = 0$ otherwise
Row-only case	in a regular lattice with binary weights, $\delta_{ij} = 1$ if the ith and jth cells have a common edge on a row of the lattice, and $\delta_{ij} = 0$ otherwise

σ^2	the variance of X, the second moment of X
S_1	$= \frac{1}{2}\sum_{(2)}(w_{ij}+w_{ji})^2 = 4A$ when $w_{ij} = \delta_{ij}$
S_2	$= \sum_{i=1}^{n}(w_{i.}+w_{.i})^2 = 8(A+D)$ when $w_{ij} = \delta_{ij}$
Size of a test	prob(type I error), the probability of rejecting H_0 when it is true (cf. power of a test)
t	Student's t statistic
torus	the three dimensional shape which results when the edges of a plane are joined together so that all end points (boundaries) are eliminated and the surface is continuous. The resulting object resembles a doughnut
tr($\boldsymbol{T}$)	the trace operator which sums elements on the leading diagonal of the matrix $\boldsymbol{T}$
Type I error	the error committed if, as the result of a statistical test, H_0 is rejected when it is true
Type II error	the error committed if, as the result of a statistical test, H_0 is not rejected when it is false
u	a test statistic based on both BB and BW (see pp.144–145)
var(X)	the variance of X, the second moment of X
$\hat{v}$ or vâr †	estimate of the variance of a statistic
v_i †	$= \sum_{i=1}^{n}(w_{ij}+w_{ji})x_j$
w_{ij}	the weight assigned to the link between counties i and j (assumed to be non-negative)
$w_{i.}$	$= \sum_{j=1}^{n} w_{ij}$
$w_{.j}$	$= \sum_{i=1}^{n} w_{ij}$
W	$= \sum_{(2)} w_{ij}$, the sum of the weights ($= 2A$ when $w_{ij} = \delta_{ij}$)

† This symbol is vee and should not be confused with the greek nu, ν.

W	the weighting matrix with elements w_{ij}
WW	the number of white–white joins in a county system
X or X_i	random variable
x or x_i	particular value taken on by X or X_i
$\overline{x}$	the average or mean value of the set of x values
χ^2	the chi-squared distribution
X^2	the test statistic, $X^2 = \sum_{i=1}^{n} \frac{(O_i - E_i)^2}{E_i}$, which is approximately distributed as χ^2. Here O_i is the observed frequency in the ith cell and E_i is the expected frequency in that cell under H_0
z_i	$= x_i - \overline{x}$

References and author index

The number(s) in square brackets at the end of each citation refer to the section(s) of the monograph in which the reference is used.

Abrahamse, A. P. J., Koerts, J., 1969, "A comparison between the power of the Durbin-Watson test and the power of the BLUS test", *Journal American Statistical Association,* **64**, 938-948. [7.3.6]

Anderson, T. W., 1948, "On the theory of testing serial correlation", *Skandinavisk Aktuarietidskrift,* **31**, 88-116. [7.3.1]

Attwood, E. A., Geary, R. C., 1963, "Irish County Incomes in 1960", Paper No.16, The Economic Research Institute, Dublin. [6.2]

Bartko, J. J., Greenhouse, S. W., Patlak, C. S., 1968, "On expectations of some functions of Poisson variates", *Biometrics,* **24**, 97-102. [3.3]

Bassett, K., Haggett, P., 1971, "Towards short-term forecasting for cyclic behaviour in a regional system of cities", *Regional Forecasting,* Ed. M. Chisholm, Proceedings of the 22nd Colston Symposium (Butterworths, London), 389-413. [preface]

Birch, B. P., 1967, "The measurement of dispersed patterns of settlement", *Tijdschrift voor Economische en Sociale Geografie,* **58**, 68-75. [3.3]

Brown, L. A., Moore, E. G., 1969, "Diffusion research in geography: a perspective", *Progress in Geography,* **1**, Eds. C. Board, R. J. Chorley, P. Haggett, D. R. Stoddart (Arnold, London), pp.119-157. [4.2.2]

Central Statistics Office, 1962, *Statistical Abstract of Ireland, 1961* (The Stationery Office, Dublin). [6.2]

Central Statistics Office, 1967, *Census of Population, 1966, Preliminary Report* (The Stationery Office, Dublin). [6.2]

Cliff, A. D., 1968, "The neighbourhood effect in the diffusion of innovations", *Transactions and Papers, Institute of British Geographers,* **44**, 75-84. [1.5.1]

Cliff, A. D., 1969, *Some Measures of Spatial Association in Areal Data,* unpublished Ph.D. Thesis, University of Bristol. [2.2.2]

Cliff, A. D., Ord, J. K., 1969, "The problem of spatial autocorrelation", *London Papers in Regional Science,* volume 1, *Studies in Regional Science,* Ed. A. J. Scott (Pion, London), pp.25-55. [1.3.3, 2.3.2, 2.5.2, 3.2, 3.2.1]

Cliff, A. D., Ord, J. K., 1971, "Evaluating the percentage points of a spatial autocorrelation coefficient", *Geographical Analysis,* **3**, 51-62. [2.5, 2.5.1, 2.5.2, 2.7]

Cliff, A. D., Ord, J. K., 1972, "Testing for spatial autocorrelation among regression residuals", *Geographical Analysis,* **4**, 267-284. [2.4, 5.6.1]

Cochrane, D., Orcutt, G. H., 1949, "Applications of least squares regressions to relationships containing autocorrelated error terms", *Journal American Statistical Association,* **44**, 32-61. [5.8]

Coras Iompair Eireann, 1966, *Scale of Charges by Merchandise Trains* (The Stationery Office, Dublin). [6.2]

Cox, K. R., 1969, "The voting decision in a spatial context", *Progress in Geography,* **1**, Eds. C. Board, R. J. Chorley, P. Haggett, D. R. Stoddart (Arnold, London), pp.81-117. [1.1]

Cruickshank, D. B., 1940, "A contribution towards the rational study of regional influences: Group formation under random conditions", *Papworth Research Bulletin,* **5**, 36-81. [1.1]

Cruickshank, D. B., 1947, "Regional influences in cancer", *British Journal of Cancer,* **1**, 109-128. [1.1]

Dacey, M. F., 1964, "Two dimensional random point patterns—a review and interpretation", Department of Geography, Northwestern University, Evanston, Illinois, mimeo. [3.3]

•Dacey, M. F., 1965, "A review on measures of contiguity for two and *k*-color maps", *Technical Report No.2, Spatial Diffusion Study,* Department of Geography, Northwestern University, Evanston, Illinois. [1.3.4, 2.2.2, glossary of notation]

Dacey, M. F., 1966a, "A county seat model for the areal pattern of an urban system", *Geographical Review,* **56**, 527-542. [3.3]

Dacey, M. F., 1966b, "A compound probability law for a pattern more dispersed than random with areal inhomogeneity", *Economic Geography,* **42**, 172-179. [3.3]

Dacey, M. F., 1968, "An empirical study of the areal distribution of houses in Puerto Rico", *Transactions and Papers, Institute of British Geographers,* **45**, 51-69. [3.3]

Dacey, M. F., 1969, "Similarities in the areal distributions of houses in Japan and Puerto Rico", *Area,* **3**, 35-37. [3.3]

Daniels, H. E., 1944, "The relation between measures of correlation in the universe of sample permutations", *Biometrika,* **33**, 129-135. [7.3.5]

Downs, R. M., 1970, "Geographical space perception: past approaches and future prospects", *Progress in Geography,* **2**, Eds. C. Board, R. J. Chorley, P. Haggett, D. R. Stoddart (Arnold, London), pp.65-108. [1.3.4, 1.4.2]

Draper, N. R., Smith, H., 1966, *Applied Regression Analysis* (John Wiley, New York). [8.2]

Draper, N. R., Smith, H., 1969, "Methods for selecting variables from a given set of variables for regression analysis", *Bulletin International Statistical Institute,* **43**, 7-15. [8.2]

Durbin, J., 1970, "Testing for serial correlation in least squares regression when some of the regressors are lagged dependent variables", *Econometrica,* **38**, 410-421. [5.7]

Durbin, J., Watson, G. S., 1950, "Testing for serial correlation in least squares regression I", *Biometrika,* **37**, 409-428. [2.4, 7.3.1]

Durbin, J., Watson, G. S., 1951, "Testing for serial correlation in least squares regression II", *Biometrika,* **38**, 159-178.

Durbin, J., Watson, G. S., 1971, "Testing for serial correlation in least squares regression III", *Biometrika,* **58**, 1-19. [5.6.1]

Gale, S., 1971, "A simple device for the recognition of geographic patterns", *Geographical Analysis,* **3**, 187-194. [4.2]

•Geary, R. C., 1954, "The contiguity ratio and statistical mapping", *The Incorporated Statistician,* **5**, 115-145. [1.3.2, 2.3.1, 2.5.2, 3.1, 3.2, 5.4.4, 7.3.5]

General Register Office, 1961, *England and Wales: Preliminary Census Report, 1961* (HMSO, London). [2.7]

Getis, A., 1964, "Temporal analysis of land use patterns with the use of nearest neighbor and quadrat methods", *Annals, Association of American Geographers,* **54**, 391-399. [3.3]

Ginsberg, N. S., 1958, *The Pattern of Asia* (Prentice-Hall, Englewood Cliffs, NJ). [3.3, 3.3.1]

Gould, P. R., 1970, "Is *Statistix Inferens* the geographical name for a wild goose?" *Economic Geography,* **46**, 439-448. [5.1]

Granger, C. W. J., 1969, "Spatial data and time series analysis", *London Papers in Regional Science,* volume 1, *Studies in Regional Science,* Ed. A. J. Scott (Pion, London), pp.1-24. [preface]

Greig-Smith, P., 1964, *Quantitative Plant Ecology* (Butterworths, London). [3.3]

Hägerstrand, T., 1953, "On Monte Carlo simulation of diffusion", reprinted in *Quantitative Geography, Part I: Economic and Cultural Topics,* Eds. W. L. Garrison, D. F. Marble (1967), Studies in Geography (Northwestern University Press, Evanston, Illinois), **13**, 1-32. [4.1, 4.2.2, 4.3.1, 4.3.2, 4.3.3]

Haggett, P., Chorley, R. J., 1969, *Network Analysis in Geography* (Arnold, London). [8.2]

Harvey, D. W., 1966, "Geographical processes and the analysis of point patterns: testing models of diffusion by quadrat sampling", *Transactions and Papers, Institute of British Geographers,* **40**, 81-95. [3.3]

Harvey, D. W., 1968, "Some methodological problems in the use of the Neyman type A and negative binomial probability distributions for the analysis of spatial point patterns", *Transactions and Papers, Institute of British Geographers,* **44**, 85-95. [3.3.1]

Hoeffding, W., 1952, "The large-sample power of tests based on permutations of observations", *Annals Mathematical Statistics,* **23**, 169-192.

Hope, A. C. A., 1968, "A simplified Monte Carlo significance test procedure", *Journal Royal Statistical Society, Series B,* **30**, 582-598. [2.7]

Hudson, J. C., 1967, *Theoretical Settlement Geography,* unpublished Ph.D. Thesis, University of Iowa. [3.3]

Johnston, J., 1972, *Econometric Methods* (Second edition, McGraw-Hill, London). [5.2.1, 5.2.2, 5.8]

•Kendall, M. G., 1939, "The geographical distribution of crop productivity in England", *Journal Royal Statistical Society,* **102**, 21-48. [6.1, 6.4]

Kendall, M. G., Stuart, A., 1967, *The Advanced Theory of Statistics,* volume 2 (Griffin, London). [5.3, 7.1, 7.2, 8.2]

Kershaw, K. A., 1964, *Quantitative and Dynamic Ecology* (Arnold, London). [3.3]

Koopmans, T. C., 1942, "Serial correlation and quadratic forms in normal variables", *Annals Mathematical Statistics,* **13**, 14-33. [2.3]

Krishna Iyer, P. V. A., 1949, "The first and second moments of some probability distributions arising from points on a lattice, and their applications", *Biometrika,* **36**, 135-141. [2.2.2]

McConnell, M., 1966, "Quadrat methods in map analysis", Department of Geography, University of Iowa, mimeo. [3.3]

Malm, R., Olsson, G., Warneryd, O., 1966, "Approaches to simulations of urban growth", *Geografiska Annaler, B,* **48**, 9-22. [3.3]

•Matsui, I., 1932, "Statistical study of the distribution of scattered villages in two regions of the Tonami Plain, Toyama Prefecture", *Japanese Journal Geology and Geography,* **9**, 251-266. [3.3, 3.3.1]

Mead, R., 1967, "A mathematical model for the estimation of inter-plant competition", *Biometrics,* **23**, 189-205. [5.7]

Moellering, H., Tobler, W., 1972, "Geographical variances", *Geographical Analysis,* **4**, 34-50. [3.3]

Moran, P. A. P., 1948, "The interpretation of statistical maps", *Journal Royal Statistical Society, Series B,* **10**, 243-251. [1.3.1, 2.2.2, 2.4]

Moran, P. A. P., 1950a, "Notes on continuous stochastic phenomena", *Biometrika,* **37**, 17-23. [1.3.2]

Moran, P. A. P., 1950b, "A test for serial independence of residuals", *Biometrika,* **37**, 178-181. [5.4.2]

Nerlove, M., Wallis, K. F., 1966, "Use of the Durbin-Watson statistic in inappropriate situations", *Econometrica,* **34**, 235-238. [5.7]

Newton, R. G., Spurrell, D. J., 1967a, "A development of multiple regression for the analysis of routine data", *Applied Statistics,* **16**, 51-64. [8.2]

Newton, R. G., Spurrell, D. J., 1967b, "Examples of the use of elements for clarifying regression analysis", *Applied Statistics,* **16**, 165-172. [8.2]

Noether, G. E., 1970, "A central limit theorem with non-parametric applications", *Annals Mathematical Statistics,* **41**, 1753-1755. [2.4]

Olsson, G., 1966, "Central place systems, spatial interaction, and stochastic processes", *Papers, Regional Science Association,* **18**, 13-45. [3.3]

Ord, J. K., 1972, *Families of Frequency Distributions* (Griffin, London). [2.6.3, 3.3]

Ord, J. K., 1973, *Methods of Estimation for Spatial Autoregressive Models*, unpublished manuscript. [5.7, 6.6, appendix 3]

O'Sullivan, P. M., 1968, "Accessibility and the spatial structure of the Irish economy", *Regional Studies*, 2, 195-206. [6.1, 6.2, 8.1]

O'Sullivan, P. M., 1969, *Transport Networks and the Irish Economy*, London School of Economics and Political Science Geographical Papers No.4 (Weidenfeld and Nicolson, London). [6.1, 6.2, 8.1]

Pierce, D. A., 1971a, "Distribution of residual autocorrelations in the regression model with autoregressive-moving average errors", *Journal Royal Statistical Society, Series B*, **33**, 140-146. [5.8]

Pierce, D. A., 1971b, "Least squares estimation in the regression model with autoregressive-moving average errors", *Biometrika*, **58**, 299-312. [5.8]

Pitman, E. J. G., 1937, "The 'closest estimates' of statistical parameters", *Proceedings, Cambridge Philosophical Society*, **33**, 212-222. [2.3]

Pitman, E. J. G., 1948, Lecture notes on non-parametric inference, Stanford University. Unpublished. [7.1]

Rayner, J. N., 1971, *An Introduction to Spectral Analysis* (Pion, London). [preface]

Rogers, A., 1965, "A stochastic analysis of the spatial clustering of retail establishments", *Journal American Statistical Association*, **60**, 1094-1103. [3.3]

Ross, I. C., Harary, F., 1952, "On the determination of redundancies in sociometric chains", *Psychometrika*, **17**, 195-208. [8.2]

Taaffe, E. J., Morrill, R. L., Gould, P. R., 1963, "Transport expansion in underdeveloped countries: A comparative analysis", *Geographical Review*, **53**, 503-529. [5.1, 6.1, 6.3, 7.5]

Theil, H., 1965, "The analysis of disturbances in regression residuals", *Journal American Statistical Association*, **60**, 1067-1079. [5.5, 5.5.1]

Tinline, R., 1971, "Linear operators in diffusion research", *Regional Forecasting*, Ed. M. Chisholm, Proceedings of 22nd Colston Symposium (Butterworths, London), pp.71-91. [4.3.3]

Tobler, W. R., 1965, "Computation of the correspondence of geographical patterns", *Papers, Regional Science Association*, **15**, 131-139. [4.2]

Whittle, P., 1954, "On stationary processes in the plane", *Biometrika*, **41**, 434-449. [1.2, 5.7]

Wickens, M. R., 1972, "A comparison of alternative tests for serial correlation in the disturbances of equations with lagged dependent variables", University of Bristol, mimeo. [5.7]

Yule, G. U., Kendall, M. G., 1958, *An Introduction to the Theory of Statistics* (Griffin, London), 14th edition. [6.1, 6.4]

Note: Articles marked • have been reprinted in *Spatial Analysis*, Eds. B. J. L. Berry, D. F. Marble (Prentice-Hall, Englewood Cliffs, NJ), 1968.

Subject index

DATE DUE FOR RETURN

Spatial autocorrelation

A.D.Cliff and J.K.Ord

Monographs in spatial and environmental systems analysis

Series editors R.J.Chorley and D.W.Harvey

1 **Entropy in urban and regional modelling** A.G.Wilson

2 **An introduction to spectral analysis** J.N.Rayner

3 **Perspectives on resource management** T.O'Riordan

4 **The mechanics of erosion** M.A.Carson

5 **Spatial autocorrelation** A.D.Cliff and J.K.Ord

Pion Limited, 207 Brondesbury Park, London NW2 5JN